Essential Maths 8 Higher

Homework Book

Elmwood Education

First published 2021 by
Elmwood Education Limited
Unit 5 Mallow Park
Watchmead
Welwyn Garden City
AL7 1GX
Tel. 01707 333232

ISBN 9781 906 622 817

Typeset and illustrated by Tech-Set Ltd., Gateshead, Tyne and Wear.

CONTENTS

UNIT 5

UNIT 6

UNIT 1

1.1 Rules of indices

HWK 1M — **Main Book page 2**

1 Answer ‘true’ or ‘false’.

a $7^2 \times 7^3 = 7^6$ **b** $5^{10} \div 5^3 = 5^7$ **c** $8 \times 8^5 = 64^5$

d $\frac{3^7}{3^4} = 3^3$ **e** $\frac{7^7 \times 7}{7^4} = 7^2$ **f** $3^2 \times 3^2 = 9^4$

2 Which gives the greater answer? Give reasons for your answer.
A $5^3 \times 5$ or B $\frac{5^8}{5^4}$

3 Work out and write each answer as a number in index form.

a $2^3 \times 2^5 \times 2^2$ **b** $5^{10} \div 5^5$ **c** $7^4 \times 7$

d $9 \times 9^4 \times 9$ **e** $\frac{11^6}{11^4}$ **f** $\frac{3^5 \times 3^4}{3^3}$

g $\frac{7^8 \times 7^4}{7^5 \times 7^2}$ **h** $\frac{5^4 \times 5^2 \times 5^2}{5^3 \times 5}$ **i** $\frac{6 \times 6^6 \times 6^3}{6^2 \times 6^2 \times 6^2}$

4

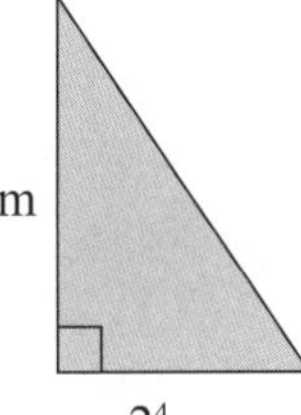

Work out the area of this triangle in index form.

5 Copy and complete

a $\square \times 3^6 = 3^8$ **b** $5^3 \times \square = 5^9$ **c** $2^8 \div \square = 2^5$

d $\frac{\square}{7^4} = 7$ **e** $\square \div 3^5 = 3^2$ **f** $\frac{9^4 \times \square}{9^3 \times 9^3} = 9^3$

6 In this question, give each answer as an ordinary number.
For example, $7^5 \div 7^3 = 7^2 = 7 \times 7 = 49$

a $2^4 \times 2^2$ **b** $7^8 \div 7^7$ **c** $\frac{3^4 \times 3^2}{3^3}$

d $\frac{5^6 \times 5^4}{5^5 \times 5^5}$ **e** $2^2 \times 2^3 \times 2^3$ **f** $\frac{10^5 \times 10^2 \times 10^4}{10^3 \times 10 \times 10^3}$

7 Which rectangle has the greater area and by how much? Give the answer as an ordinary number.

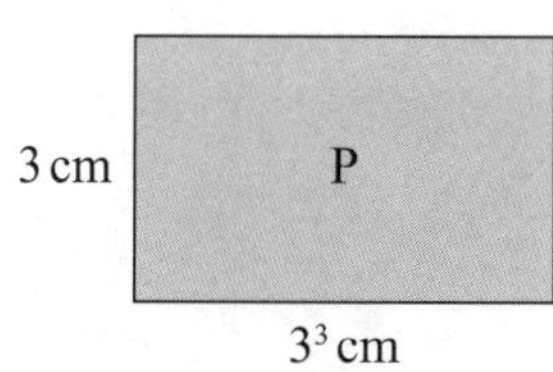

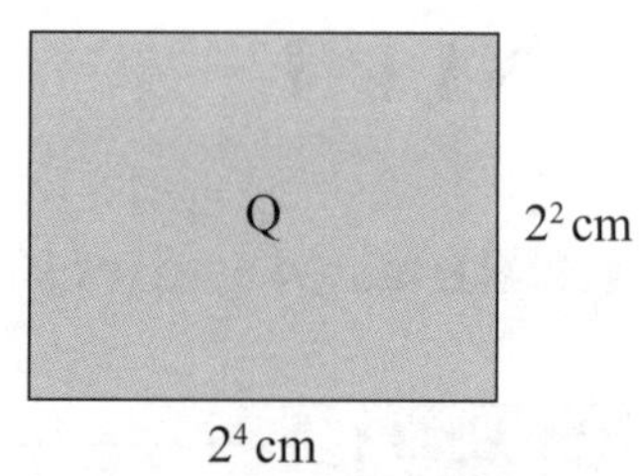

8 Use four numbers with indices to make a question that will give the answer 27

HWK 2M **Main Book page 3**

1 Which is greater and by how much: $(3^2)^2$ or $(2^2)^4$?

2 Work out and write each answer as a number in index form.

a $(5^3)^4$ **b** $(7^2)^8$ **c** $(3^3)^3 \times 3^4$

d $(6^4)^3 \div 6^9$ **e** $(2^4)^2 \times (2^5)^3$ **f** $(5^2)^5 \div (5^3)^3$

g $\dfrac{(9^2)^2 \times 9^5}{(9^2)^3}$ **h** $(6^4)^5 \times 6$ **i** $\dfrac{(7^4)^2 \times (7^5)^5}{(7^2)^6 \times (7^3)^4}$

3 Sketch a cube with a volume of $(3^2)^3$ cm³. Write on your sketch the length, width and height of the cube as ordinary numbers.

4 Which expression below gives the largest value?

$2^8 \div 2^3$	$(2^2)^3$	$2^3 \times 2^2$	$(2^2)^2 \times 2^3$	$(2^3)^2 \div 2$

5 Answer 'true' or 'false' for each statement below.

a $(7^3)^3 = 7^6$ **b** $(3^2)^2 < (2^3)^3$ **c** $3^2 \times 5^2 = 15^4$

d $(2^{-4})^2 = 2^{-8}$ **e** $\dfrac{(5^4)^2 \times 5}{(5^3)^2 \times 5^2} = 5$ **f** $\dfrac{7 \times (7^2)^3}{(7^2)^2 \times 7^0} = 7^2$

6 Jason says that 3^0 is equal to 0. Is Jason correct? Give a reason for your answer.

7 Write down the missing value in the box if: $\dfrac{(8^4)^2 \times (8^2)^{\square}}{(8^3)^5} = 8^3$

8

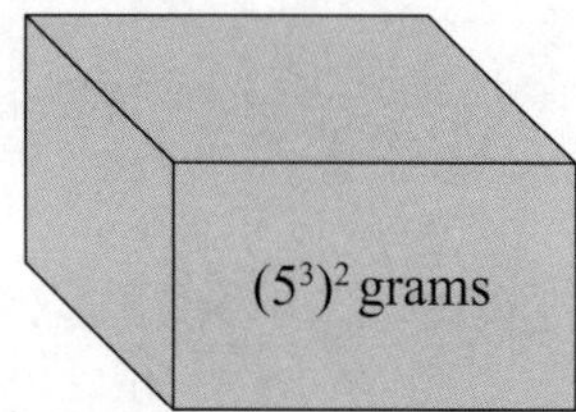

How many kilograms does this box weigh?

9 In this question, give each answer as an ordinary number.

a $(3^2)^4 \div 3^6$ **b** 5^0 **c** $(2^4 \times 2)^2$

d $7^2 \times 7^0$ **e** $(8^3)^3 \div 8^7$ **f** $(6^4)^5 \div (6^3)^6$

g $7^2 \times 7$ **h** $(2^4)^2 \times 2$ **i** $\dfrac{(7^3)^5 \times (7^2)^4}{(7^5)^4 \times 7^2}$

10 Work out the sum of $(4^2)^2$ and $(2^3)^3$

1.2 Prime factors, HCF and LCM

HWK 1M Main Book page 6

1 Find all the factors of

a 25 **b** 40 **c** 64

2 'The sum of all the prime numbers less than 8 is 17'. True or false?

3 **a** List all the factors of 30

b List all the factors of 48

c Write down the highest common factor of 30 and 48

4 Find the highest common factor (HCF) of 32 and 80

5 Which numbers below are prime?

6 Three factors of 20 add up to 16. Write down two different ways in which this can be done.

7 Why can a prime number not have 0 as its last digit?

8 **a** Write down the first six multiples of 15

b Write down the first six multiples of 20

c Write down the lowest common multiple (LCM) of 15 and 20

9 Find the LCM of

a 12 and 18 **b** 10 and 16 **c** 9 and 6

10 A baker delivers to a village every 5 days. A butcher delivers to the village every 7 days. How often will the baker and butcher deliver on the same day?

11 The number p is a multiple of 8 between 50 and 60. The number q is a multiple of 12 between 20 and 30. Work out $p - q$.

12 Answer 'true' or 'false':

'All square numbers have exactly three factors.'

Give a reason for your answer.

HWK 2M

Main Book page 8

1 Copy and complete this factor tree.

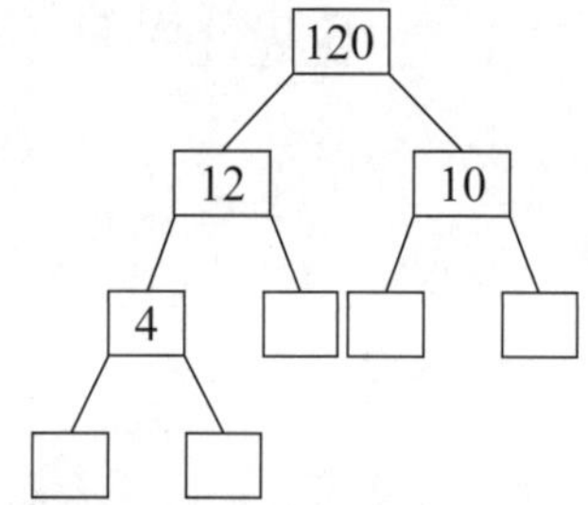

$120 = \square \times \square \times \square \times \square \times \square = \square^3 \times \square \times \square$

2 Draw factor trees then write each number below in prime index form.

a 50 **b** 240 **c** 420 **d** 1820 **e** 1617

3 **a** Given $196 = 2 \times 2 \times 7 \times 7$, find $\sqrt{196}$

b Given $9801 = 3 \times 3 \times 3 \times 3 \times 11 \times 11$, find $\sqrt{9801}$

4 Write 1764 as the product of its prime factors and then find $\sqrt{1764}$

5 **a** Given $3375 = 3 \times 3 \times 3 \times 5 \times 5 \times 5$, find $\sqrt[3]{3375}$

b Given $1\,331\,000 = 2 \times 2 \times 2 \times 5 \times 5 \times 5 \times 11 \times 11 \times 11$, find $\sqrt[3]{1\,331\,000}$

6 Write 2744 as the product of its prime factors and then find $\sqrt[3]{2744}$

7 Find a number between 500 and 600 which only has prime factors of 3, 5 and 13

8 Without using a calculator, find

a the square root of 3969 **b** the cube root of 17 576

HWK 3M — **Main Book page 9**

1 The prime factors for 42 and 910 are shown in the Venn diagram opposite.

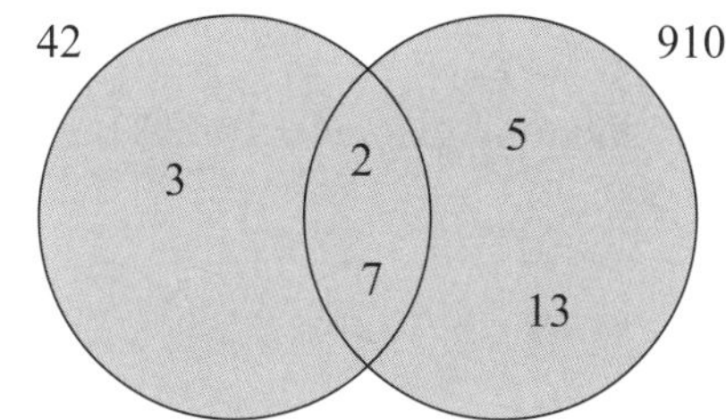

a Work out the HCF of 42 and 910

b Work out the LCM of 42 and 910

2 **a** If $210 = 2 \times 3 \times 5 \times 7$ and $525 = 3 \times 5 \times 5 \times 7$, draw a Venn diagram for the prime factors of 210 and 525

b Work out the HCF of 210 and 525

c Work out the LCM of 210 and 525

3 **a** Draw factor trees then a Venn diagram for 630 and 1560

b Find the HCF of 630 and 1560

c Find the LCM of 630 and 1560

4 Draw factor trees and Venn diagrams to find the HCF and LCM of each pair of numbers below.

a 105 and 110 **b** 231 and 273 **c** 770 and 1365

5

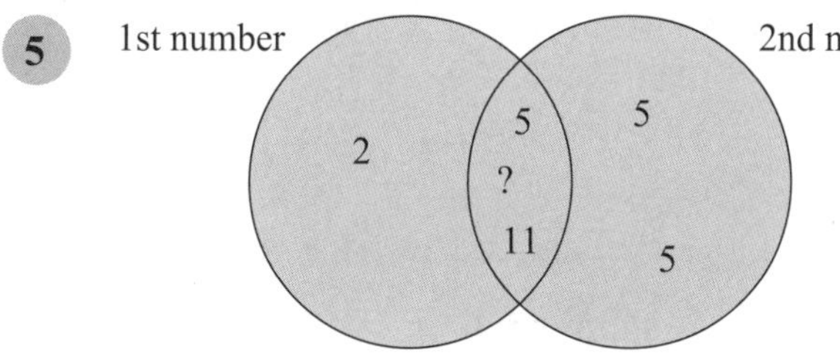

The Venn diagram shows the prime factors of two numbers. What are the two numbers if the HCF is 165?

6 A mobile library comes to a village every 28 days and a mobile bank comes to the village every 16 days. The library and the bank come to the village on 3rd March. After how many weeks do the library and bank both come to the village again on the same day?

1.3 Using algebra

HWK 1M — **Main Book page 14**

1 Find two matching pairs of expressions.

A $1 + 2m + 3$ B $2 + m + 4m - 1$ C $2 + 6m - 3m - 1$

D $7m + 1 - 2m$ E $5m + 4 - 3m$

2 Simplify

a $3m + 7 - 8m$ **b** $3y + 2x - y - 1$ **c** $6m + 3 - 5m - 2n + n$

3 Find an expression for the total distance from A to C.

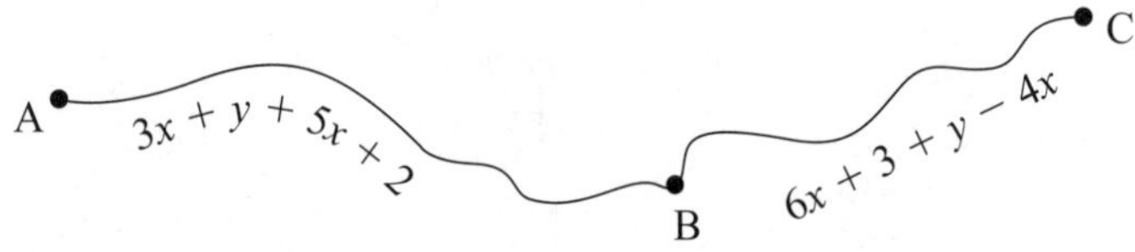

4 Multiply out the brackets.

a $4(m + 3)$ **b** $9(2p - 1)$ **c** $3(w + 3q)$ **d** $5(a - 3b)$

5 Copy and complete

a $4(\square + 1) = 8a + 4$ **b** $\square(2m - 3n) = 12m - \square$

6 Multiply out the brackets and simplify.

a $3(m + 2) + 5(m - 1)$ **b** $4(2n + 3) + 5(n - 2)$

c $5(3x + 4) + 2(4x + 3)$ **d** $7(m - 2) + 4(m + 6)$

e $4(m + n + 3) + 3(m - n + 2)$ **f** $6(a + 3b - 2c) + 4(2a - b + 4c)$

g $5(3x - 2y + 2) + 2(2x + y - 3)$ **h** $4(m - 3 + 2n) + 5(2 + m - n)$

7 Match each box to one of the words below.

$7m + 3n - 2$	$V = IR$	$6m$	$5n + 3 = 2$
equation	term	expression	formula

8 The perimeter of shape A is greater than the perimeter of shape B. Write down an expression for the difference between their perimeters.

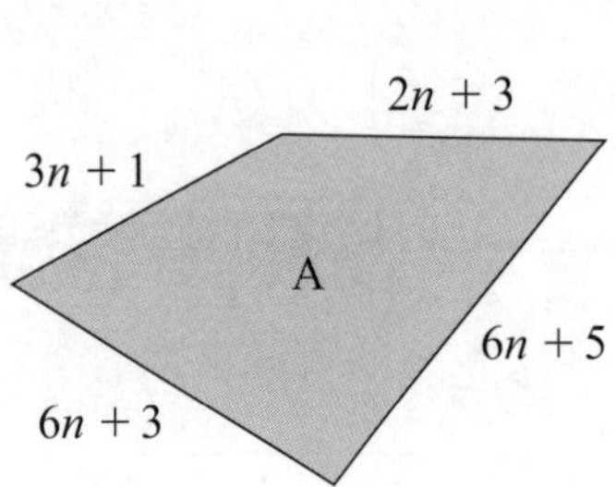

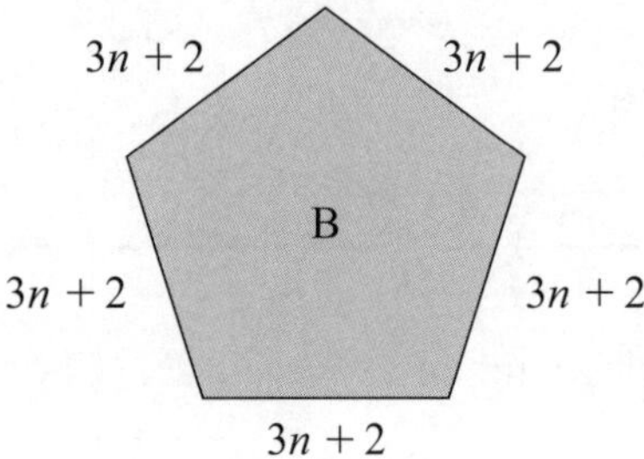

9 Write down any algebraic expression involving *a* and *b*.

HWK 2M — Main Book page 15

1 In number walls each brick is made by adding the two bricks underneath it.

$a + b$	
a	b

Draw the number walls below and fill in the missing expressions.

a

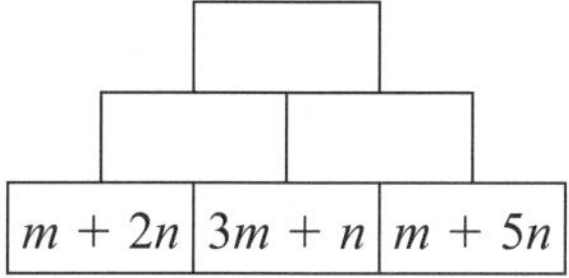

b

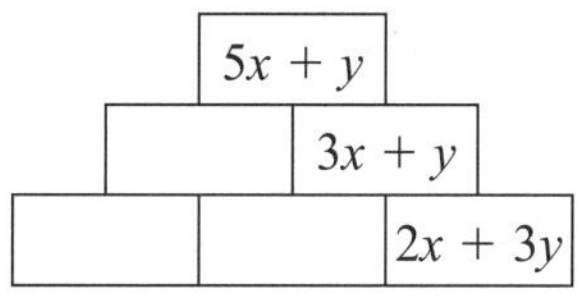

c

Top: $10a + b$; middle row: $5a + 4b$, (blank); bottom row: $2a + 3b$, (blank), (blank)

2 Answer 'true' or 'false'.

a $4 + m = 4m$ **b** $5p - p = 5$ **c** $m - n = n - m$

d $\frac{m + m + m}{m} = 3$ **e** $a + b = ab$ **f** $a \times a \times a = a^3$

g $m^2 + m^2 = m^4$ **h** $3a \times ba = 3a^2b$ **i** $a \times a \div b = \frac{2a}{b}$

3 Sonia says that $\frac{m}{n}$ can never equal $\frac{n}{m}$. Is she correct? Justify your answer.

4 Here are some cards.

$a + 3$ $5a$ a^2

$a - 1$ $a \div 2$ $a \times a$ $4a - a$

$2a + a + a$ $5 \div a$ $4a$

a Which card is the same as $a + a + a$?

b Which card is the same as $\frac{5}{a}$?

c The card $a \times a$ is the same as the card a^2.

Which other pair of cards are the same as each other?

d Which card is the same as $\frac{1}{2}a$?

e What is the difference in the value of the cards $a + 3$ and $a - 1$?

5 P

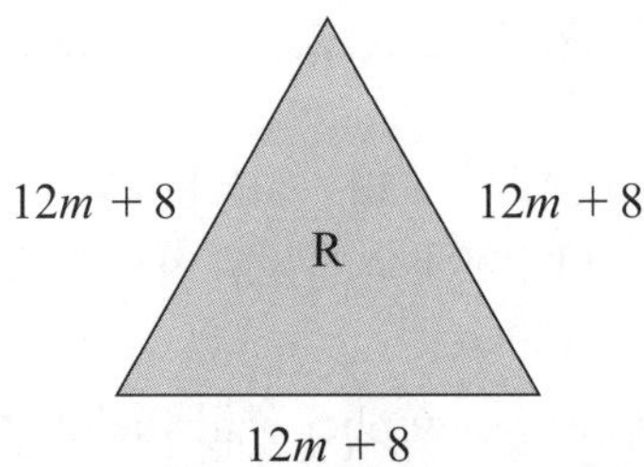

The perimeter of square Q is double the perimeter of triangle R. The length of rectangle P is treble the length of one side of square Q. Write down an expression for the length of rectangle P.

6 Draw these number walls like those in question **1** and fill in the missing expressions.

a

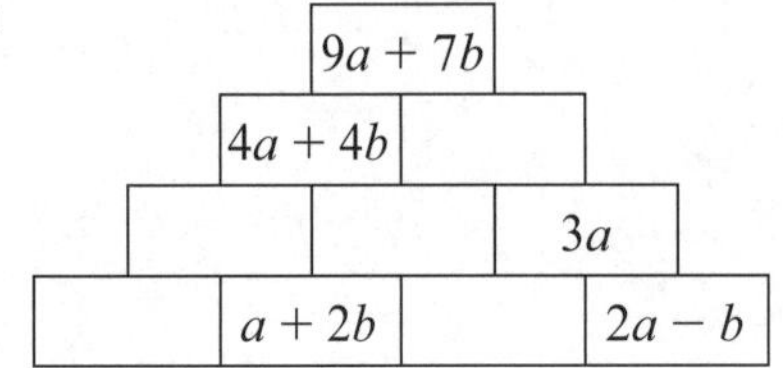

b

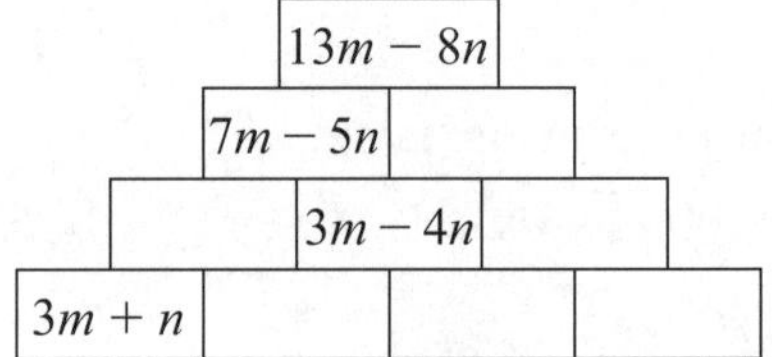

HWK 3M — Main Book page 17

Copy and complete

1 $5n + 25 = 5(n + \square)$

2 $6y - 3 = 3(2y - \square)$

3 $12m + 16 = 4(3m + \square)$

4 $24x + 18 = 6(\square + 3)$

5 $9a - 36 = 9(\square - 4)$

6 $16n - 28 = \square(4n - \square)$

7 $7 + 35p = 7(\square + \square)$

8 $10m - 75 = \square(\square - \square)$

9 7 cm

(? + ?) cm

The area of this rectangle is $(21m + 49)\,\text{cm}^2$. Write down an expression for the length of the rectangle.

Factorise

10 $8n + 48$

11 $6n + 48$

12 $30p - 12$

13 $5a + 15b$

14 $20y - 18$

15 $12x + 14y$

16 $28p - 16q$

17 $35m + 21n$

18 $60a - 56b$

19 $7m + 28p + 35q$

20 $4a - 10b + 8c$

21 $12c + 30d + 6e$

22 $18a - 45b - 36c$

23 $18f - 21g - 9h$

24 $12m + 54n - 42p$

HWK 4M — Main Book page 18

Factorise the following by removing common factors.

1. $a^2 + 5a$
2. $n^2 - 9n$
3. $a^2 - ab$
4. $xy - y^2$
5. $mn + m^2$
6. $mn + 3m^2$
7. $p^2 - 5pn$
8. $10a^2 + 6a$
9. $12n^2 - 10n$
10. $15b^2 + 10b$
11. $8m^2 + 18m$
12. $3n^2 + 6mn$
13. $8a^2 + 6ab$
14. $11y^2 + 33y$
15. $25n^2 + 15mn$
16. $18x^2 - 14xy$
17. $16m^2 + 12mn = 2m(8m + 6n)$ and $16m^2 + 12mn = 4m(4m + 3n)$.
Both the above statements are true but which answer is considered to be the best when factorising? Give a reason for your answer.
18. 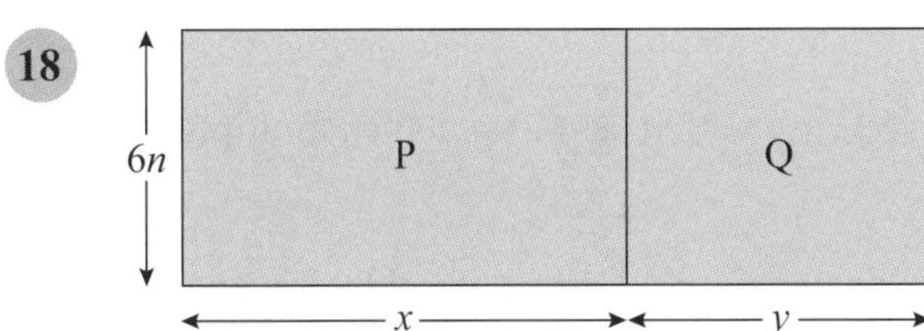

The area of rectangle P is $(12n^2 + 18n)\,\text{cm}^2$ and the area of rectangle Q is $(6n^2 + 30n)\,\text{cm}^2$. Write down an expression for the total length $x + y$.

Factorise

19. $6a^2 + 48abc$
20. $12mn + 9mp$
21. $18x^2 - 27xy$
22. $10m^2n - 8mnp$
23. $6a^2b + 15ab^2$
24. $15mn^2 - 35m^2n$
25. Factorise $14a^2bc^2 + 28ab^2c^2 - 21a^2b^2c^2$

HWK 5M — Main Book page 19

1. Here is a flow diagram for the expression $4(2n - 3)$ $n \rightarrow$ [×2] $\xrightarrow{2n}$ [−3] $\xrightarrow{2n-3}$ [×4] $\xrightarrow{4(2n-3)}$

Find the expression for each of the following flow charts.

a 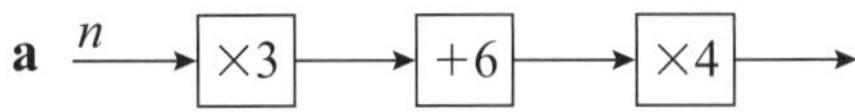

b $n \rightarrow$ [×5] $\rightarrow$ [−3] $\rightarrow$ [×8] $\rightarrow$

c $n \rightarrow$ [+4] $\rightarrow$ [×3] $\rightarrow$ [+1] $\rightarrow$

d 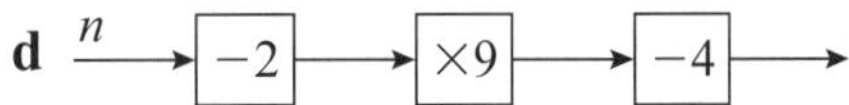

e $n \rightarrow$ [+5] $\rightarrow$ [square] $\rightarrow$ [×5] $\rightarrow$

f $n \rightarrow$ [square] $\rightarrow$ [+2] $\rightarrow$ [×7] $\rightarrow$

2 Draw a flow diagram for each of the following expressions.

a $6(4n + 1)$ **b** $4(5n - 8)$ **c** $5(n^2 + 4)$

d $\frac{3n - 6}{7}$ **e** $7(n - 4)^2$ **f** $8(n + 5)^2$

Simplify the expressions in the questions below.

3 $\frac{6m}{m}$ 4 $3m^2 - m^2$ 5 $n - 6 + 4n$ 6 $3ab + ba$

7 $\frac{n}{3} + \frac{n}{3} + \frac{n}{3}$ 8 $\frac{8x}{2}$ 9 $\frac{a \times a}{a}$ 10 $5p - 2 - p - 3$

11 $\frac{m^3}{m^4}$ 12 $\frac{n + n + n + n}{n}$ 13 $\frac{m \times m^2}{m}$ 14 $\frac{3a - a}{a}$

15 $\frac{m + m + m}{3}$ 16 $\frac{a^2 \times 5}{a}$ 17 $\frac{n}{5} + \frac{n}{5}$

18 Write down an expression for the result if you start with n, add $2y$ and then multiply everything by 4

19 Write down an expression for the result if you start with m, square it, subtract p and then multiply everything by 5

20 Write down an expression for the answer if you start with x, double it, add y and then square the result.

HWK 6M

Main Book page 21

1 Will is paid £7 per hour. How much does he earn if he works for y hours?

2 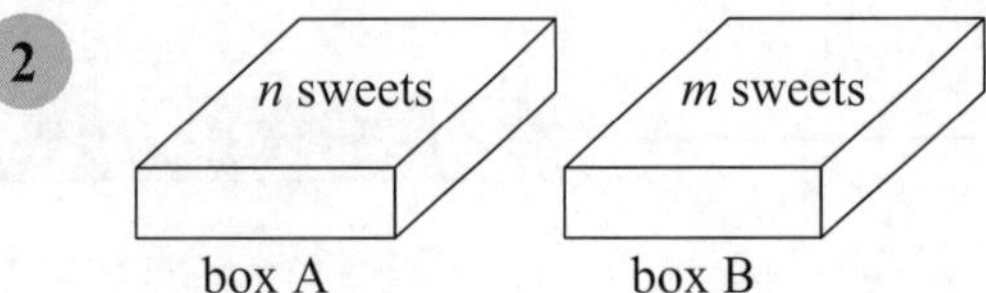

Ellie has two boxes of sweets, as shown.

Ellie takes five sweets out of box A and four sweets out of box B.

a How many sweets are left in box A?

b How many sweets are left in box B?

c What is the total number of sweets left in both boxes?

d Ellie now puts one sweet back into box B. How many sweets are now in box B?

3 Mark has £n. Marcus has three times as much money as Mark. Marcus spends £15. How much money does Marcus now have?

4 A bag of crisps costs m pence and a bottle of water costs n pence. Reena buys x bags of crisps and y bottles of water. How much change will she get if she hands over q pence?

5 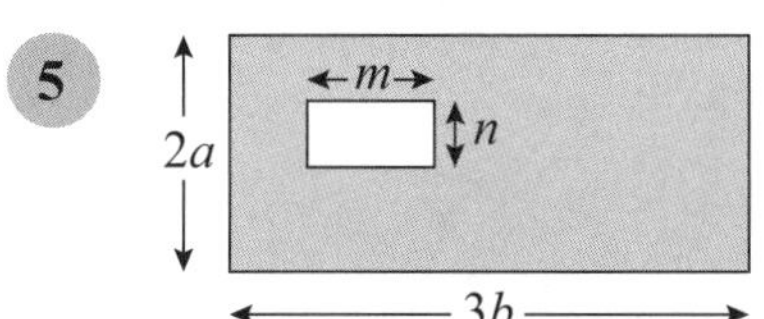

Write down an expression for the shaded area.

6 Felix has £$(9n + 23)$. He spends £$(3n + 9)$. He gives half of the remaining money to his sister. How much money does he have left?

7 Marie is selling plates at £m each. She reduces the price of each plate by £2 and sells 29 plates. How much money does she receive?

8 'Sunshine' cereal costs y pence per box. Fresco own brand of the same cereal costs x pence less per box.

How much will 3 'Sunshine' boxes and 5 Fresco boxes cost in total? Simplify your answer.

9 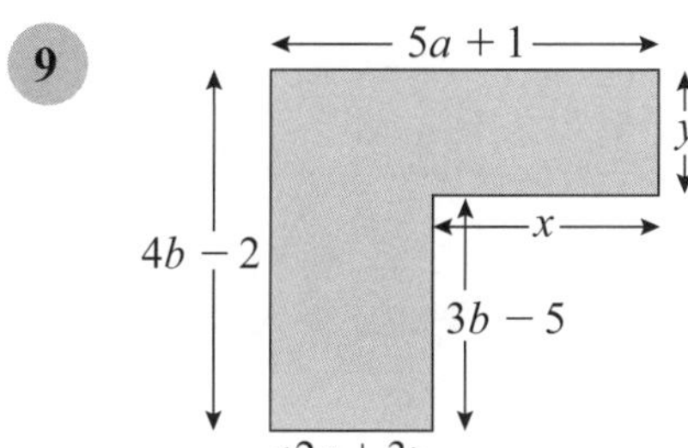

a Write down an expression for x in terms of a.

b Write down an expression for y in terms of b.

10 Here is a magic square in which the numbers in each row, column and diagonal add up to the same number; in this case 18

9	4	5
2	6	10
7	8	3

Copy and complete this magic square by first finding the value of n.

	7	$n + 7$	
	12	n	5
	1	15	
13	10	4	

1.4 Construction and locus

HWK 1M **Main Book page 30**

You need a ruler, protractor and pair of compasses.

1 Construct triangle ABC as shown.
Use a protractor to measure $A\hat{B}C$.

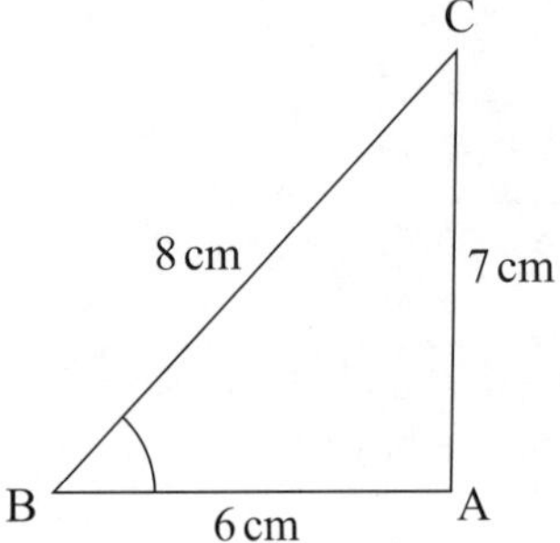

2 Construct each triangle and measure the side x.

a

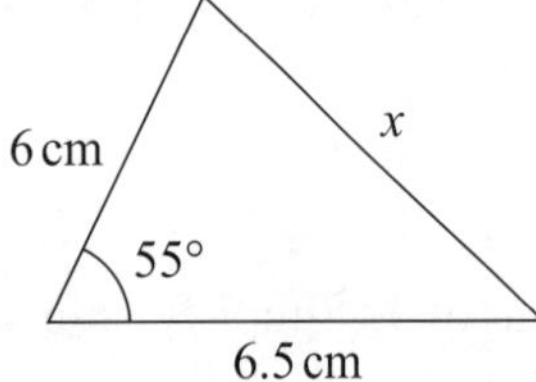

b

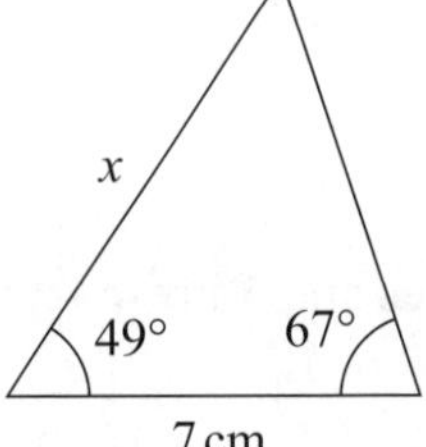

c

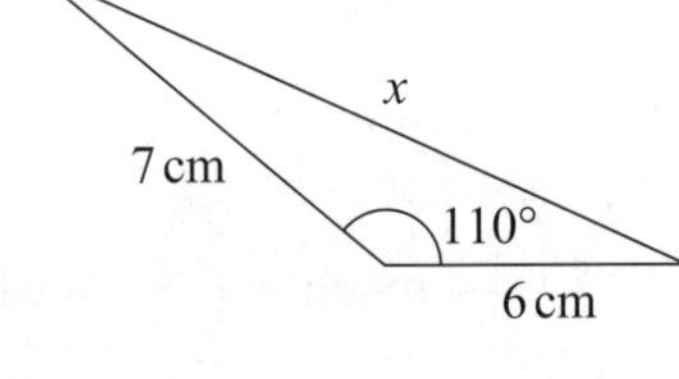

3 Construct rhombus PQRS as shown.
Use a protractor to measure $P\hat{Q}R$.

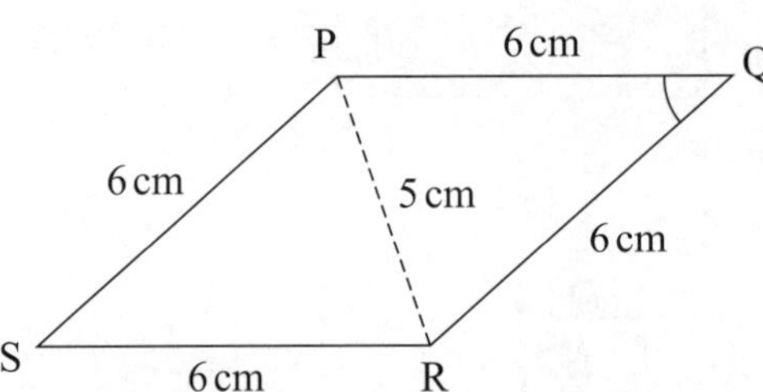

4

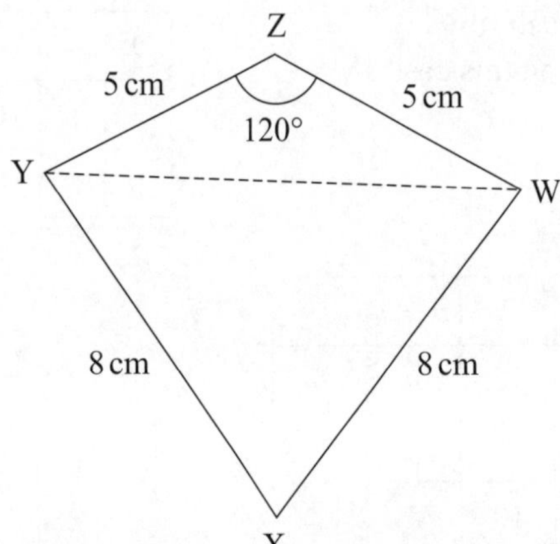

Construct the kite WXYZ. Use a protractor to measure $W\hat{X}Y$.

HWK 2M **Main Book page 31**

Remember: The *locus* of a point is the path traced out by the point as it moves.

1 Mark a point A with a cross. Hundreds of ants stand exactly 6 cm from the point A. Draw a diagram to show this.

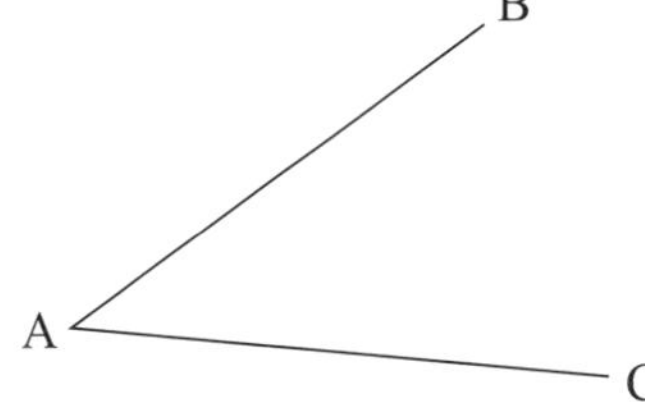

Copy this diagram. The ants now move so that each ant is exactly the same distance from line AB as line AC. Show this on your diagram.

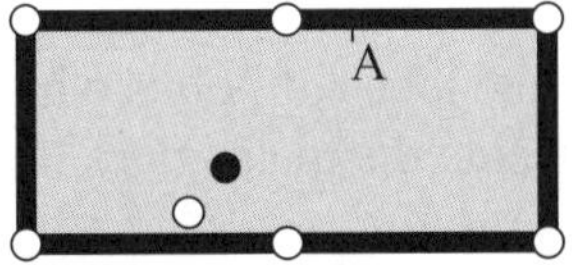

This diagram shows a white ball and a black ball on a snooker table. Copy the diagram. Darryl hits the white ball against the black ball. The black ball hits the side of the table at A then goes down the hole in the bottom right-hand corner. Darryl is very surprised. Show what happens to the black ball on your diagram.

4 Draw another copy of the snooker table with the black ball in the same starting position. If the black ball goes down a different hole, show what happens to the black ball on your diagram. *Describe* what happens to the black ball and which hole it goes down.

5 On a clock, the time goes from 10:00 to 10:20. Describe the *locus* of the tip of the minute hand.

6

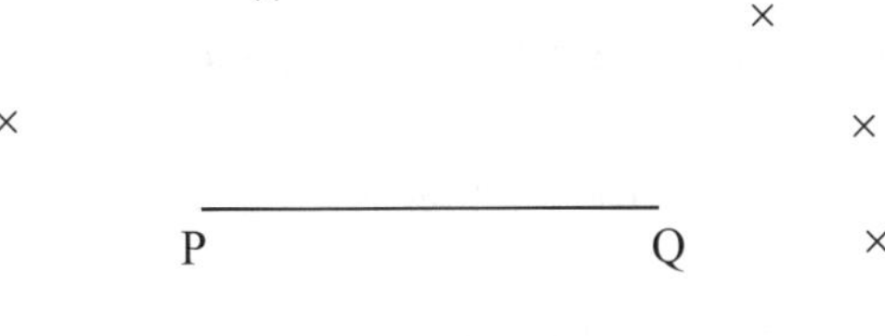

All the crosses shown above are 1.5 cm away from the line PQ. Copy the diagram and draw the locus of *all* the points 1.5 cm away from the line PQ.

7 Shade the locus of all the points which are less than or equal to 3 cm from a fixed point P.

8 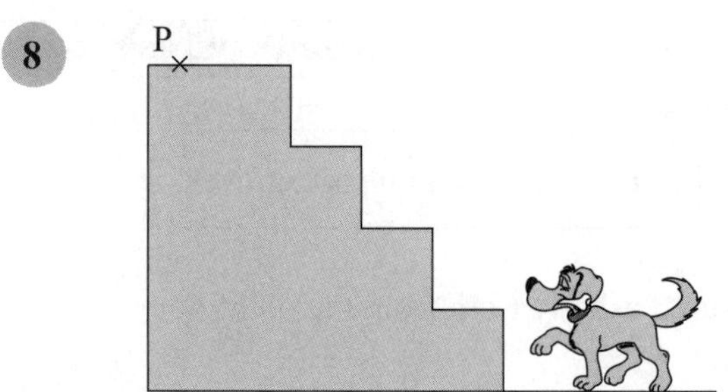

A dog with a bone in its mouth runs up these stairs and drops the bone on the point marked P. Copy the stairs and draw a rough sketch of the locus of the bone as it travels from the bottom of the stairs to the point P.

9 Mark two points P and Q which are 3 cm apart. Draw the locus of points which are an equal distance (equidistant) from P and Q.

• P

• Q

10 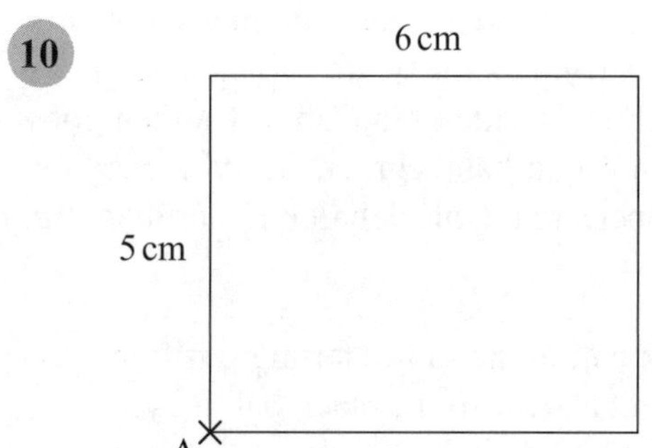

Copy this diagram. Draw the locus of points which are 4 cm from A and are inside the rectangle.

HWK 3M — Main Book page 33

You need a ruler, protractor and pair of compasses.

1 Draw a horizontal line PQ of length 7 cm. Construct the perpendicular bisector of PQ.

2 Draw a vertical line XY of length 6 cm. Construct the perpendicular bisector of XY.

3 Draw a line and a point Y on the line. Construct the perpendicular from the point Y.

4 • A

Copy this diagram and construct the line which passes through A and is perpendicular to the line.

5

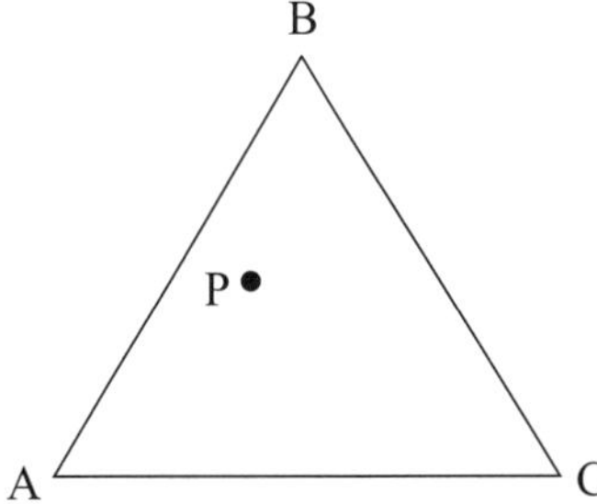

Copy this diagram. Construct three lines through P, one line being perpendicular to each of the three sides of the triangle.

HWK 4M

Main Book page 35

1 Draw an angle of about 50°. Construct the bisector of the angle.

2 **a** Construct the perpendicular bisector of a line AB, as shown. Label the bisector CD. Label the point Y, as shown.

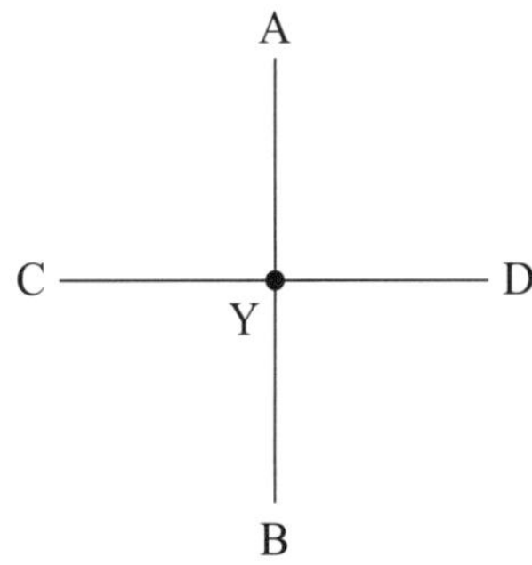

b Construct the bisector of $A\hat{Y}D$.

c Construct the bisector of $B\hat{Y}D$.

d Label the bisectors, as shown opposite.

e Use your protractor to measure $C\hat{Y}X$.

f Use your protractor to measure $A\hat{Y}Z$.

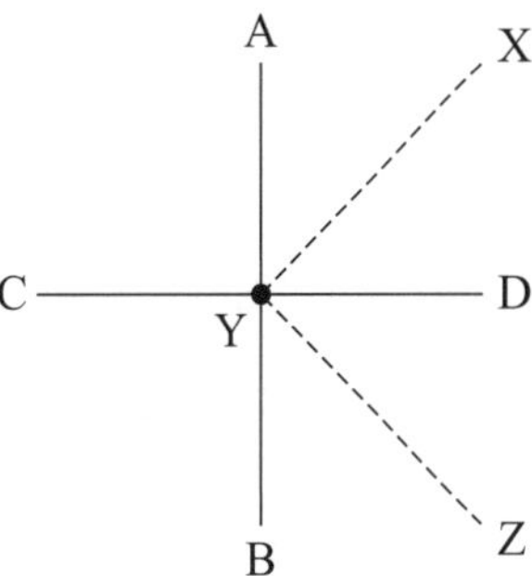

3 Use a ruler and compasses only to construct an angle of $22\frac{1}{2}°$

4 Using a ruler and compasses only, construct an angle of 60° (think about the angles in an equilateral triangle).

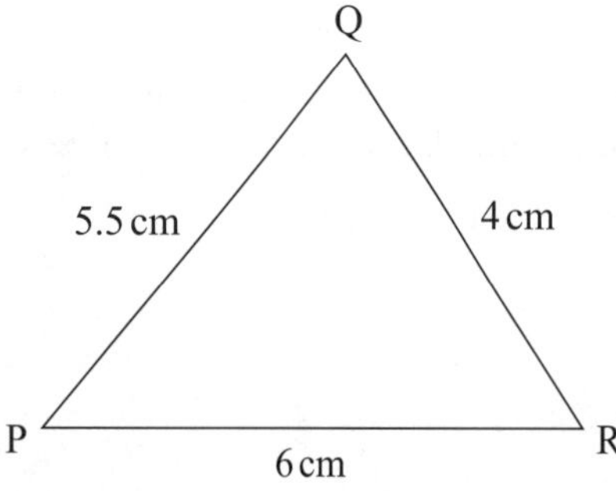

a Use a ruler and compasses only to construct triangle PQR as shown.

b Construct the angle bisector of $Q\hat{P}R$. Label this line PX.

c Construct the angle bisector of $P\hat{R}Q$. Label this line RY.

d Use your protractor to measure $Q\hat{P}X$ and $P\hat{R}Y$.

6 Denise does the constructions shown opposite.
AB = BC = AC = 5 cm

Explain clearly why $A\hat{C}Y = 30°$

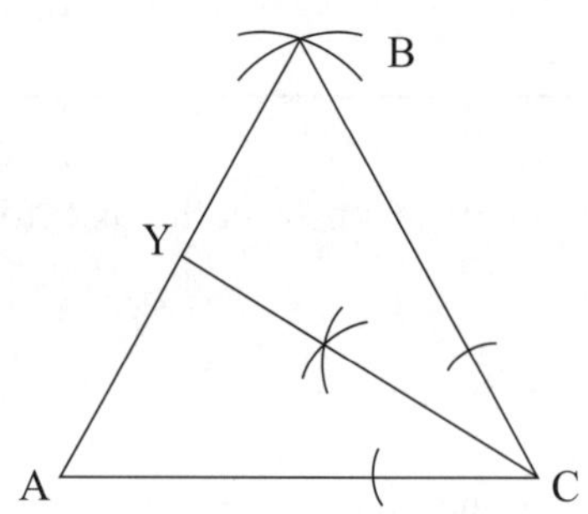

1.5 Angles, including polygons

HWK 1M — Main Book page 38

Find the angles marked with letters.

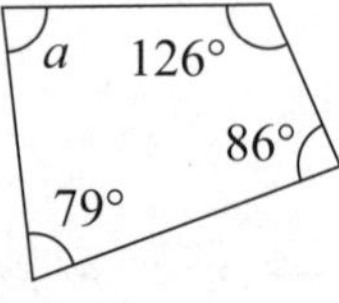

2

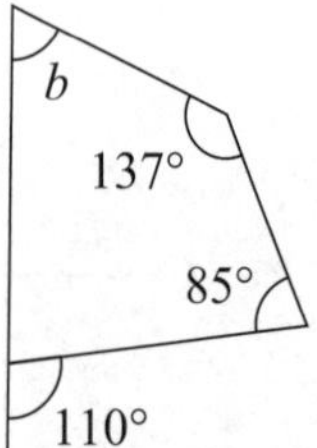

3

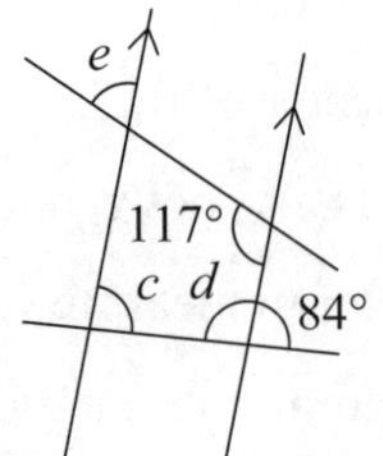

4

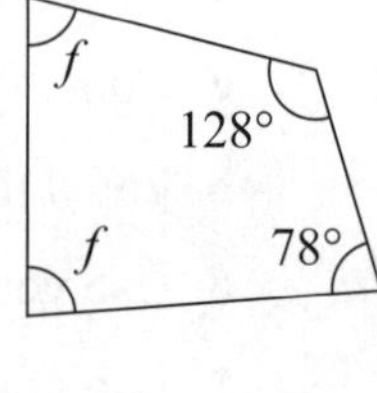

5

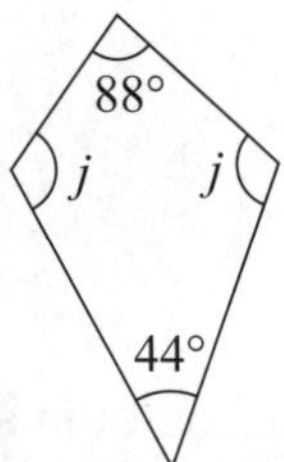

6

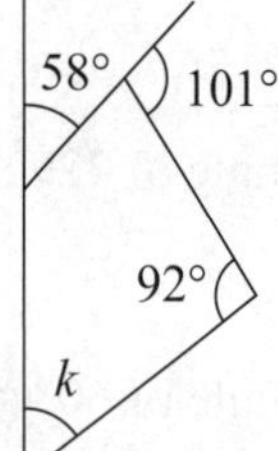

7

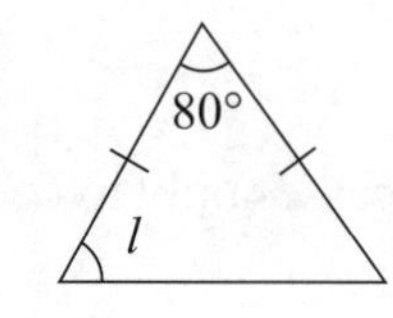

8

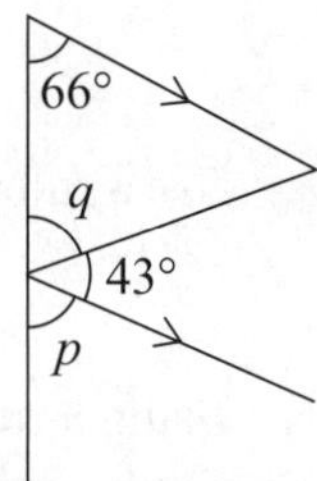

9 Find the values of

a $A\hat{B}C$ **b** $B\hat{C}D$ **c** $A\hat{D}C$ **d** $C\hat{D}Z$

Find the angles marked with letters. *Draw each diagram and show your working.*

10

11

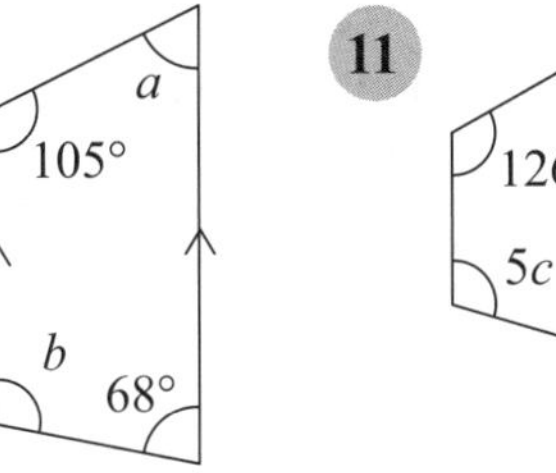

12

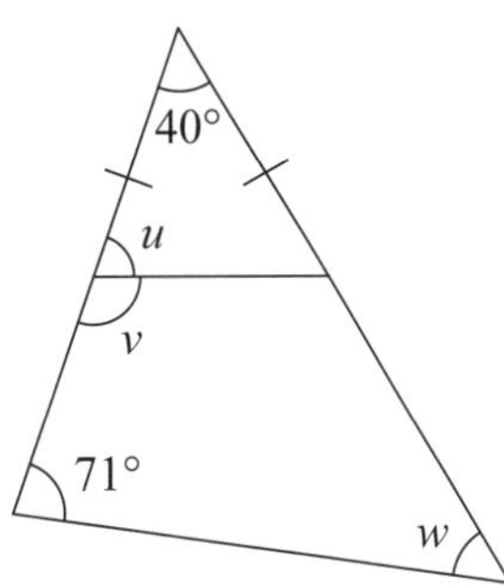

13

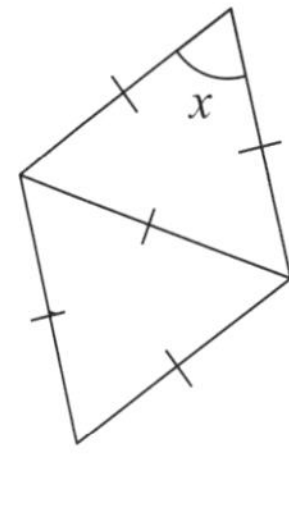

14 Find the value of $Q\hat{R}S$.

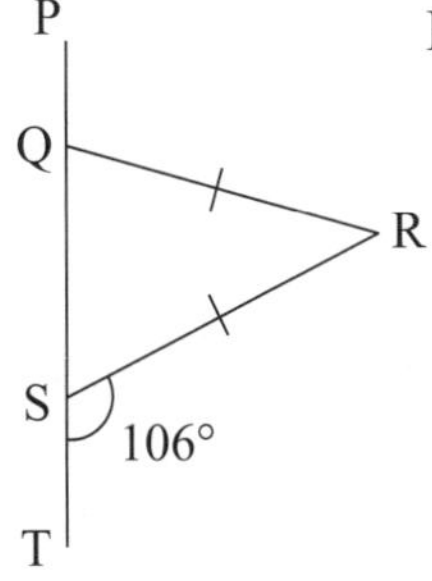

15 Find the value of $B\hat{E}C$.

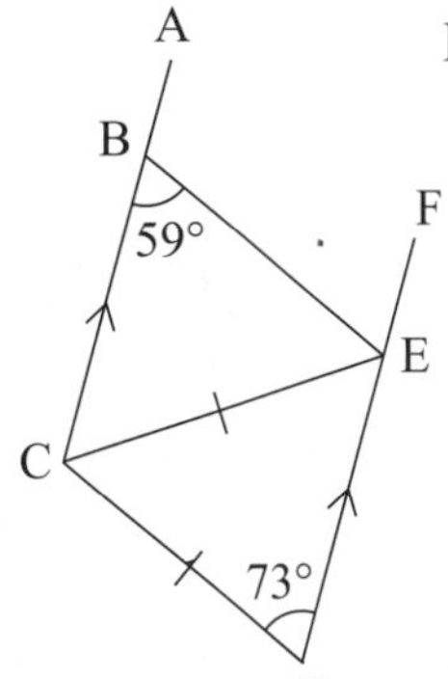

16

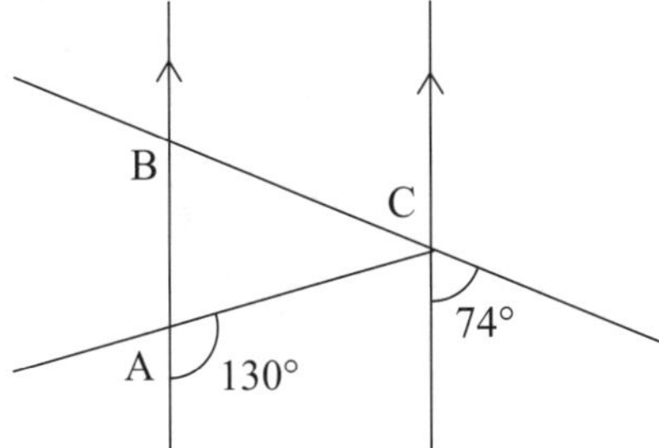

Find the value of $A\hat{B}C$.
Show your working.

17 ABCD is a square.
Find the value of $D\hat{E}F$.
Show your working.

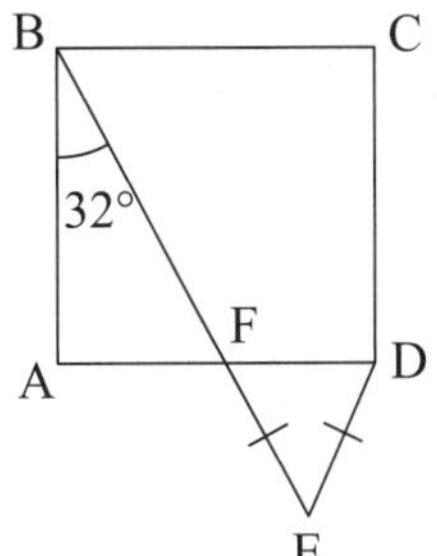

HWK 2M **Main Book page 40**

1

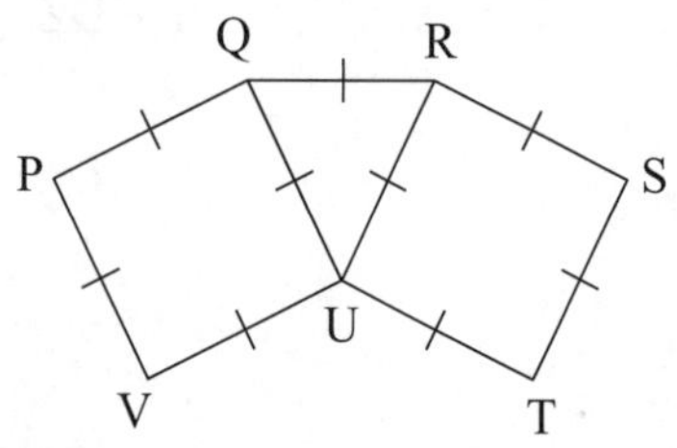

PQUV and RSTU are squares.
Find the value of $T\hat{U}V$.
Show your working.

2

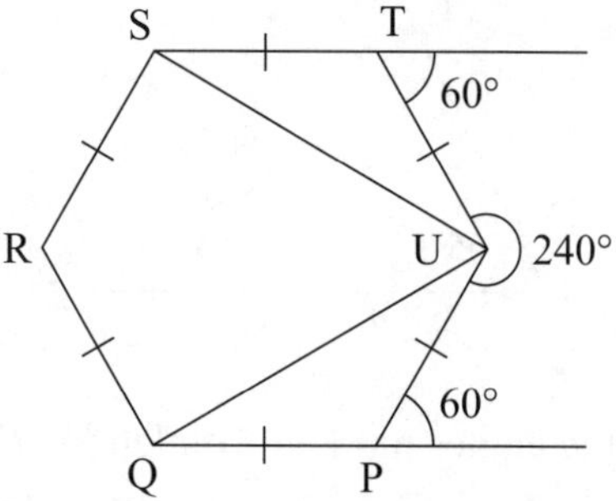

Find the value of $S\hat{U}Q$.

3 Calculate the value of angle n.

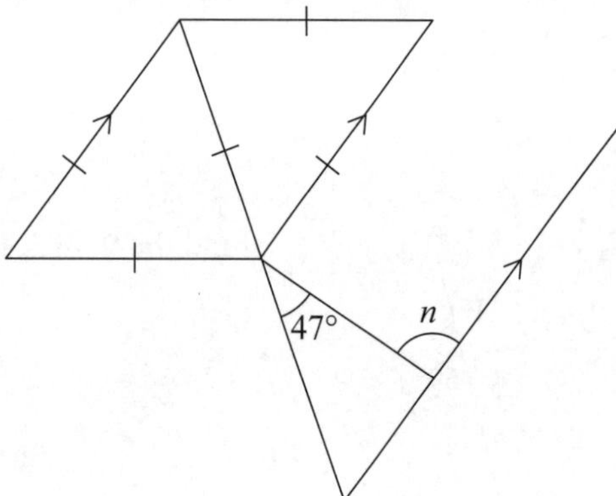

4 BDEA is a square.
$B\hat{C}A = 4 \times B\hat{A}C$.
Calculate the value of $C\hat{E}D$.

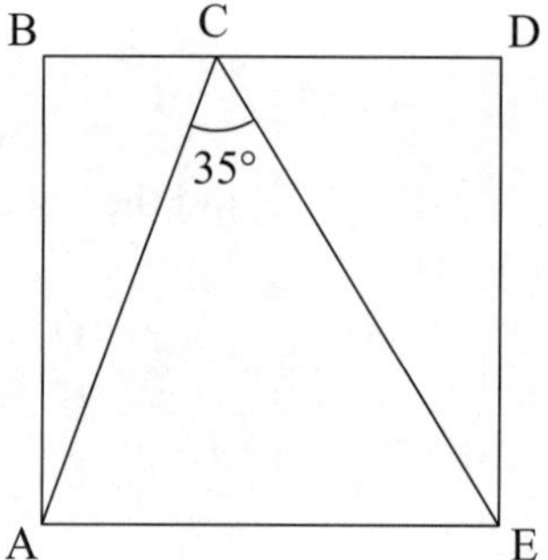

5 UVST is a square.
Calculate the value of $R\hat{S}V$.

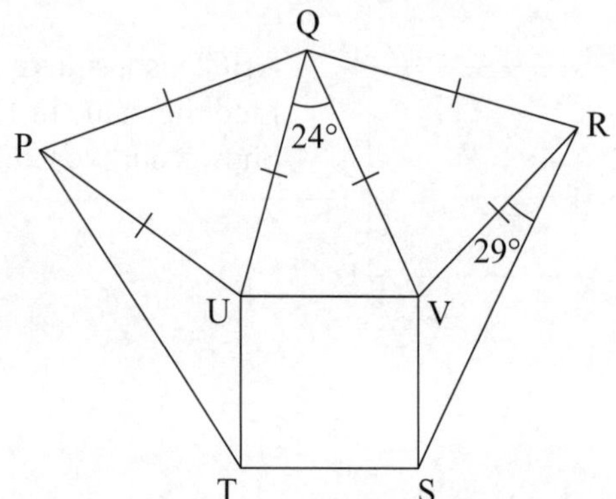

6 BD bisects $A\hat{B}C$.
Calculate the value of $A\hat{D}B$.

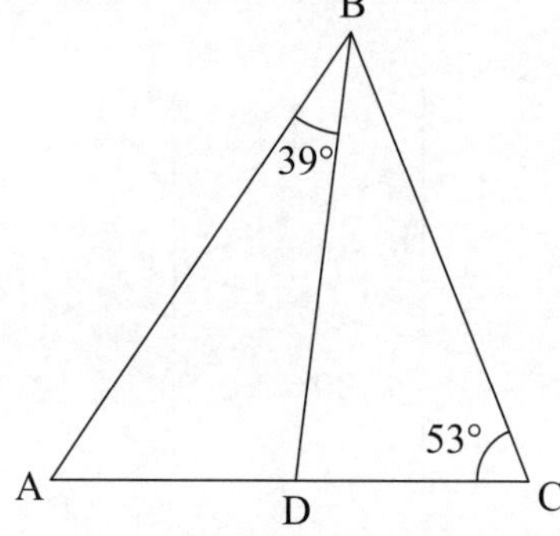

7 Draw a sketch of an isosceles triangle PQR with PQ = PR. Point Y lies on QR so that $P\hat{Y}Q = 85°$. If $P\hat{Q}R = 75°$, calculate the size of $R\hat{P}Y$.

8 Calculate the value of $E\hat{G}F$.

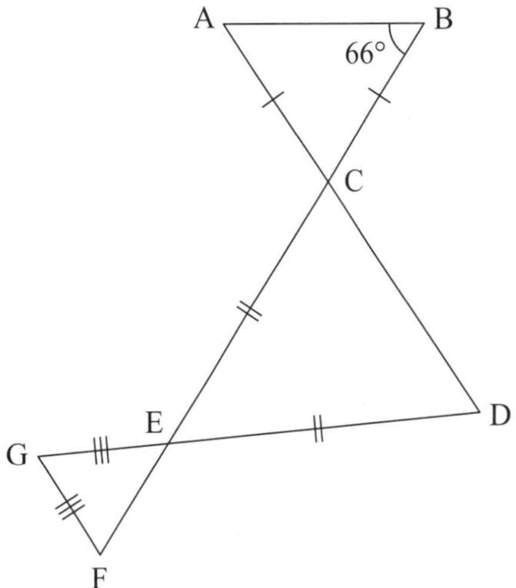

9 PQRT is a parallelogram.
SU bisects $P\hat{S}T$.
Calculate the value of $S\hat{U}T$.

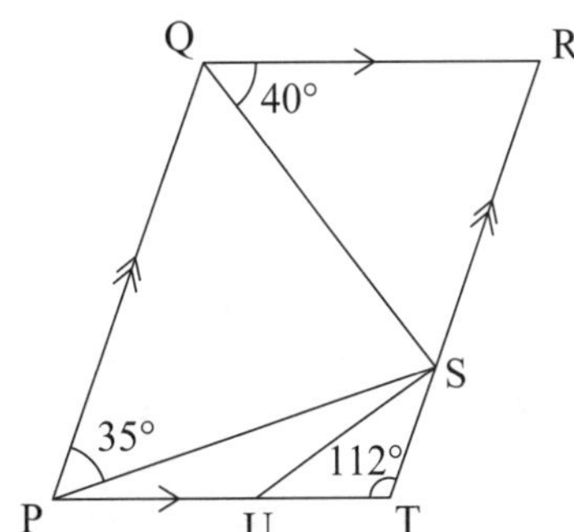

HWK 3M — **Main Book page 42**

1 Find the sum of the interior angles of a heptagon (7-sided polygon).

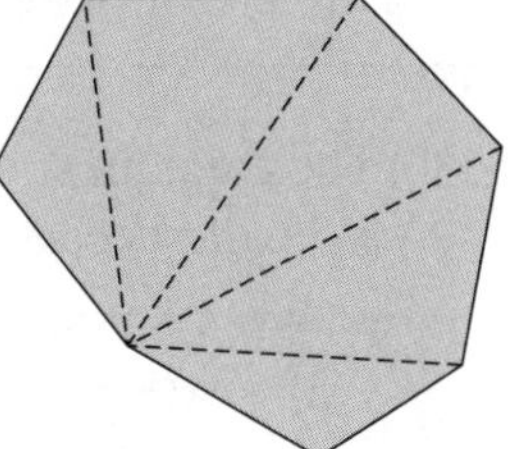

2 Find the sum of the interior angles of a decagon (10-sided polygon).

3 Work out the value of one interior angle in a regular hexagon.

4

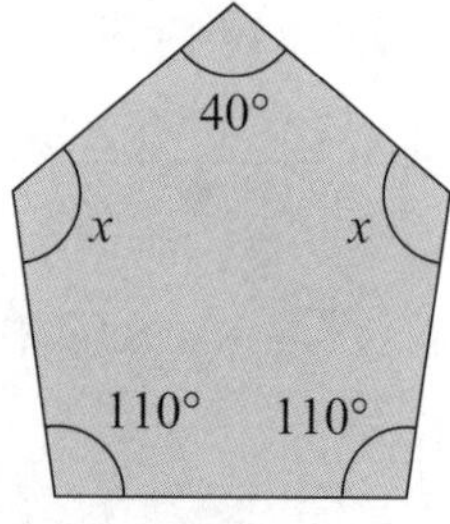

Work out the value of angle x.

5 The sum of the interior angles of a regular polygon is 1260°.
How many sides does this polygon have?

6 Find the sum of the interior angles of each polygon below, then work out the value of the angle marked with a letter.

a

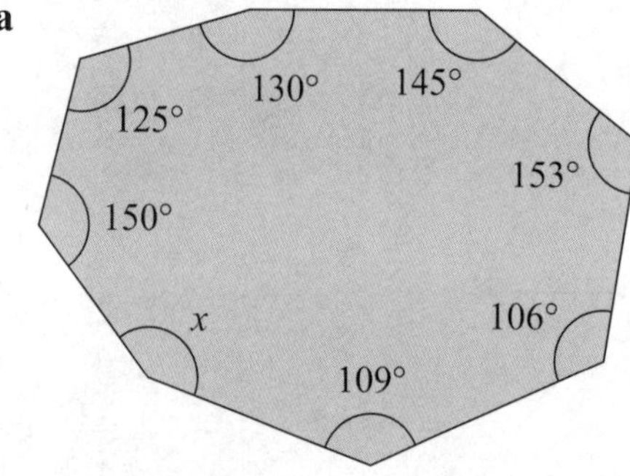

b

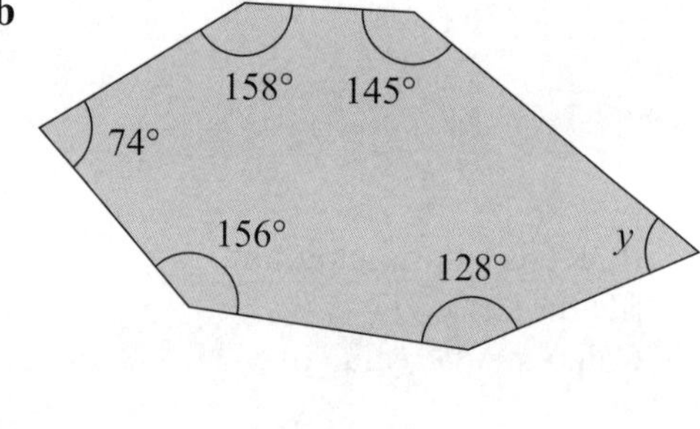

7 How much larger is the interior angle of a 20-sided regular polygon compared with the interior angle of an 18-sided regular polygon?

8 Write down an expression for the size of an interior angle in a regular n-sided polygon.

HWK 4M

Main Book page 43

Remember: The sum of the exterior angles of a polygon = 360°

1

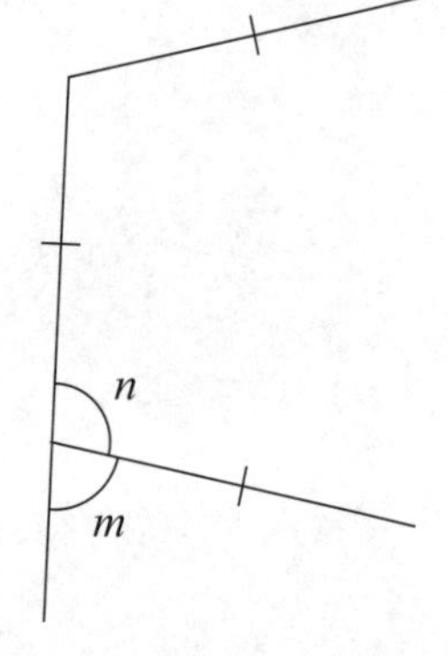

The diagram shows part of a regular decagon.

a Work out the value of the exterior angle m.

b Work out the value of the interior angle n.

2 Work out the size of an interior angle in a regular polygon with 30 sides.

3 A regular polygon has exterior angles each equal to 45°. How many sides has the polygon?

4 A regular polygon has exterior angles each equal to 18°

a How many sides has the polygon?

b Work out the sum of the interior angles of the polygon.

5 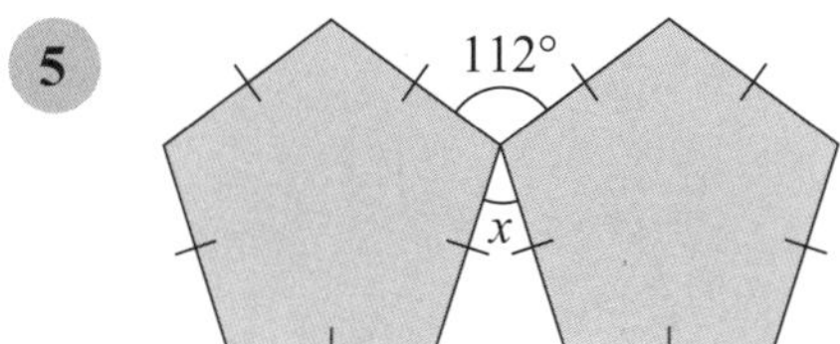

Work out the value of angle x.

6 A regular polygon has interior angles each equal to 156°. How many sides has the polygon?

7 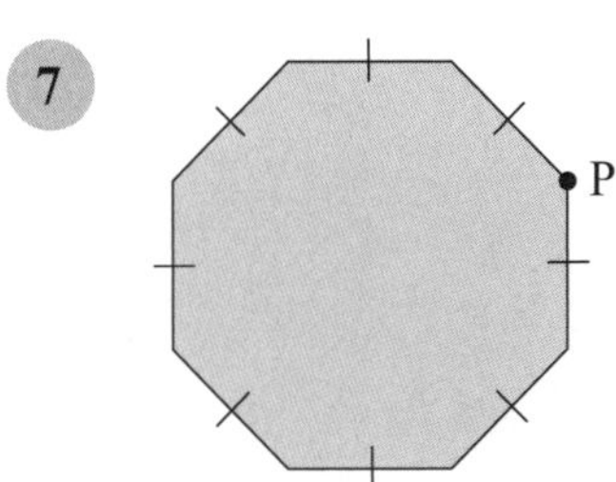

Three regular octagons each have a corner ‘P’ marked as shown. Explain clearly why the three octagons cannot be joined together without overlapping using each ‘P’ corner as the point of contact.

8 A regular polygon has n sides. Write down an expression for the size of

a an exterior angle **b** an interior angle.

9 The exterior angle of a regular polygon is $n°$ and the interior angle is $(3n + 20)°$. Find the value of n then write down how many sides the polygon has.

10 Part of a regular polygon is shaded and labelled P, as shown opposite. How many sides does this polygon have?

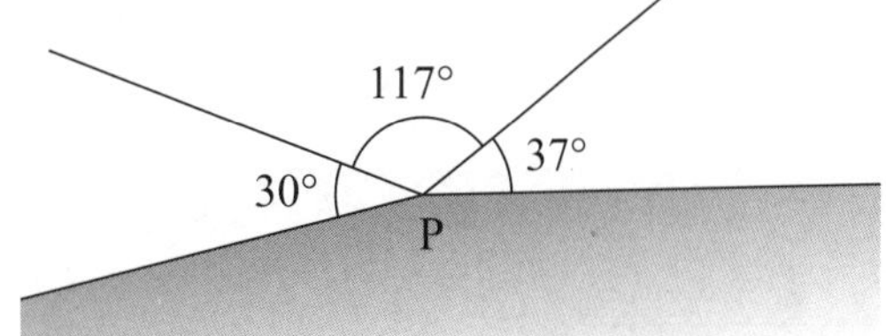

HWK 5M — Main Book page 45

1 Copy and complete this proof to show that $A\hat{D}C$ is equal to $A\hat{B}C$ in this kite.

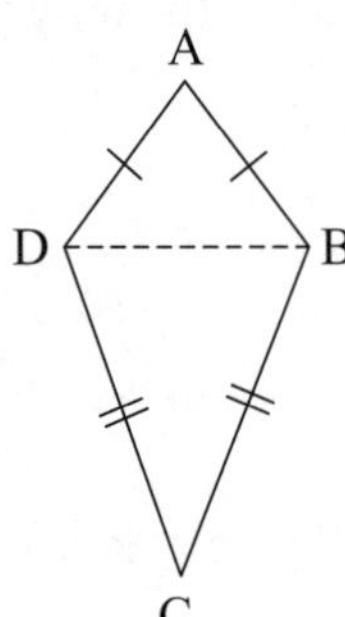

$A\hat{D}B = \square$ (angles in isosceles triangle ADB)

$B\hat{D}C = \square$ (angles in isosceles triangle BDC)

$A\hat{D}C = A\hat{D}B + B\hat{D}C$

$= \square + \square$

$= A\hat{B}C$

2 Prove that the angles in a right-angled isosceles triangle are 90°, 45° and 45°

3 Copy and complete this proof for the sum of the angles in a pentagon.

Draw any pentagon (5 sides) as shown.

$a + \square + c = 180°$ (angles in a △)

$d + e + f = \square$ (angles in a △)

$g + \square + \square = \square$ (angles in a △)

We must have

$a + \square + c + d + e + f + g + \square + \square = \square$

This shows that the sum of the angles in a pentagon is $\square$.

4

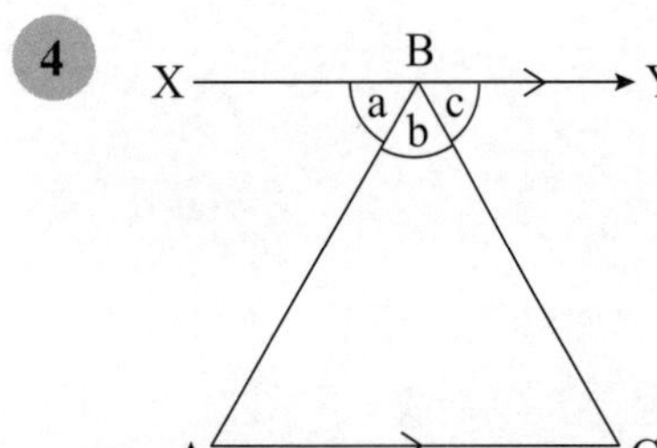

$a + b + c = 180°$ (angles on a straight line)

Prove that the sum of the angles in a triangle is 180°

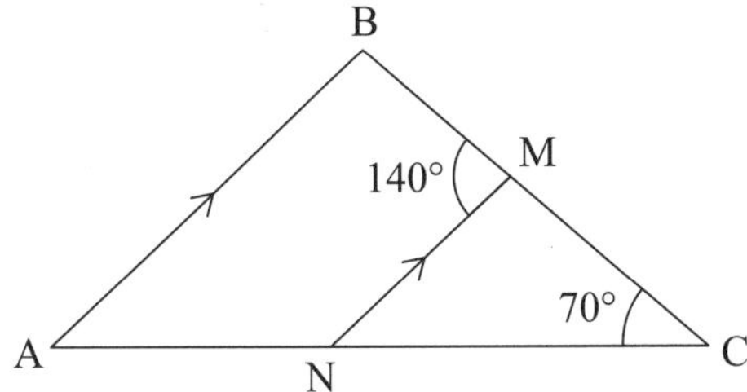

Prove that triangle ABC is isosceles.

1.6 Fractions

HWK 1M — **Main Book page 51**

1 Work out

a $\frac{3}{5} - \frac{1}{3}$ **b** $\frac{1}{4} + \frac{2}{3}$ **c** $\frac{2}{5} + \frac{3}{8}$ **d** $\frac{5}{7} - \frac{1}{8}$

e $\frac{1}{2} - \frac{3}{7}$ **f** $\frac{2}{9} + \frac{3}{10}$ **g** $\frac{7}{8} - \frac{2}{3}$ **h** $\frac{9}{10} - \frac{5}{7}$

2 Louise and Jake are sharing a pizza. Louise eats $\frac{2}{5}$ of the pizza and Jake eats $\frac{3}{7}$ of the pizza. What fraction of the pizza is left?

3 A test has four parts. This table shows what fraction of the test each part is.

Part A	Part B	Part C	Part D
$\frac{1}{3}$	$\frac{1}{5}$	$\frac{1}{4}$	?

a What fraction of the test is part D?

b Janice has completed parts A and B. What fraction of the test has she still got to do?

4 Ben carpets $\frac{5}{8}$ of his new house. He uses wood flooring for $\frac{1}{4}$ of the house. The remaining floor area in his house is tiled. What fraction of the floor area is tiled?

5 Work out, leaving each answer as a mixed number.

a $1\frac{1}{4} + 1\frac{1}{3}$ **b** $3\frac{1}{2} + 2\frac{1}{3}$ **c** $4\frac{3}{4} - 3\frac{1}{3}$ **d** $2\frac{1}{3} - \frac{5}{8}$ **e** $1\frac{1}{3} + 2\frac{5}{6}$ **f** $4\frac{1}{2} - 2\frac{7}{8}$

+	$\frac{1}{3}$			
$\frac{1}{4}$		$\frac{5}{8}$		
			$\frac{51}{70}$	
$\frac{2}{5}$				$\frac{28}{45}$
		$\frac{13}{24}$	$\frac{7}{15}$	

HWK 2M **Main Book page 53**

1 Which answer is the odd one out?

A $\frac{5}{8}$ of 56 B $\frac{4}{5}$ of 45 C $\frac{5}{6}$ of 42

2 Martin has to travel 16 km back to his village. He runs $\frac{3}{8}$ of the journey, then walks $\frac{3}{5}$ of the remaining distance. How far is he now from his village?

3 Copy and complete

a $\frac{\square}{3}$ of $15 = 10$ **b** $\frac{\square}{8}$ of $24 = 21$ **c** $\frac{5}{\square}$ of $18 = 15$

4 Work out

a $\frac{1}{8} \times \frac{4}{5}$ **b** $\frac{2}{3} \times \frac{6}{7}$ **c** $\frac{3}{10} \times \frac{5}{6}$ **d** $\frac{5}{7} \times \frac{1}{10}$

e $\frac{4}{7} \times \frac{7}{8}$ **f** $\frac{9}{10} \times \frac{5}{12}$ **g** $\frac{5}{9} \times \frac{6}{7}$ **h** $\frac{7}{12} \times \frac{6}{11}$

5 Rectangle A: $\frac{2}{3}$ m by $\frac{9}{10}$ m

Which rectangle has the larger area and by how much?

Rectangle B: $\frac{3}{4}$ m by $\frac{5}{6}$ m

6 Answer 'true' or 'false'.

a $\frac{3}{8} \times 4 = \frac{12}{32}$ **b** $\frac{2}{3} \times 6 = 4$ **c** $\frac{1}{6} \times 4 = \frac{2}{3}$ **d** $\frac{3}{4} \times 2 = \frac{6}{8}$

7 Work out $\left(\frac{1}{4} \times \frac{3}{7}\right) + \left(\frac{4}{7} \times \frac{1}{2}\right)$

8 Work out the difference between $\left(\frac{2}{3}\right)^2$ and $\left(\frac{3}{4}\right)^2$

9

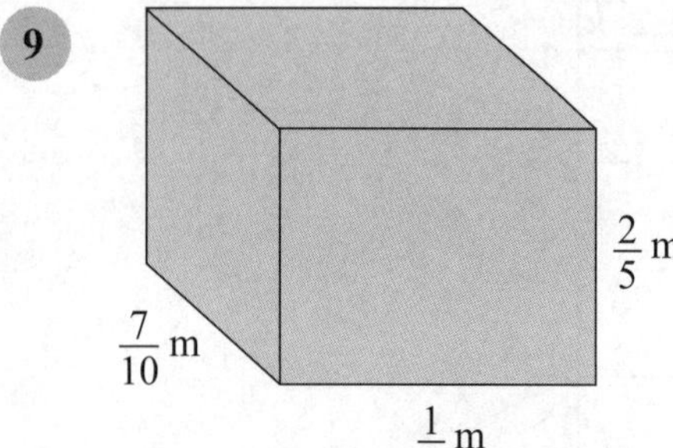

Work out the volume of this cuboid.

10 Sasha says that $\frac{5}{8} \times \frac{2}{15}$ is the same as $\frac{5}{6} \times \frac{1}{10}$

Show clearly whether Sasha is correct or not.

HWK 3M — Main Book page 55

1 Work out

a $\frac{5}{8} \times 20$ **b** $\frac{1}{6}$ of 15 **c** $\frac{5}{12}$ of 30 **d** $20 \times \frac{1}{12}$

e $16 \times \frac{5}{24}$ **f** $\frac{7}{20} \times 30$ **g** $\frac{5}{9}$ of 21 **h** $\frac{3}{7} \times 10$

2 Work out

a $2\frac{1}{3} \times \frac{1}{2}$ **b** $3\frac{1}{2} \times 1\frac{1}{4}$ **c** $2\frac{3}{4} \times 2\frac{3}{4}$ **d** $1\frac{2}{3} \times 1\frac{1}{2}$

3

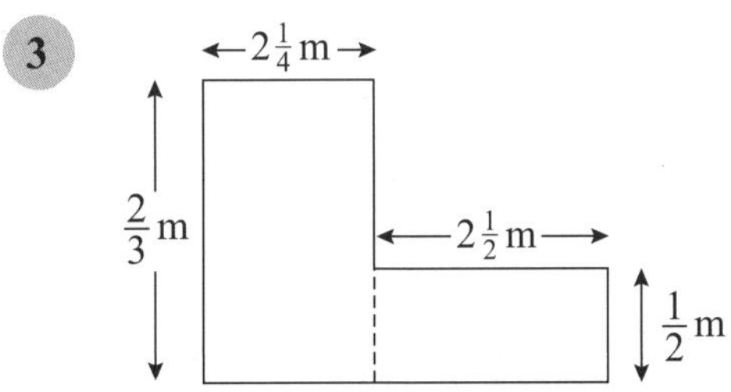

Work out the total area of this shape.

4 Find the missing fraction.

$\square\frac{\square}{\square} \div 2\frac{1}{2} = 1\frac{1}{3}$

5 Work out the area of this triangle.

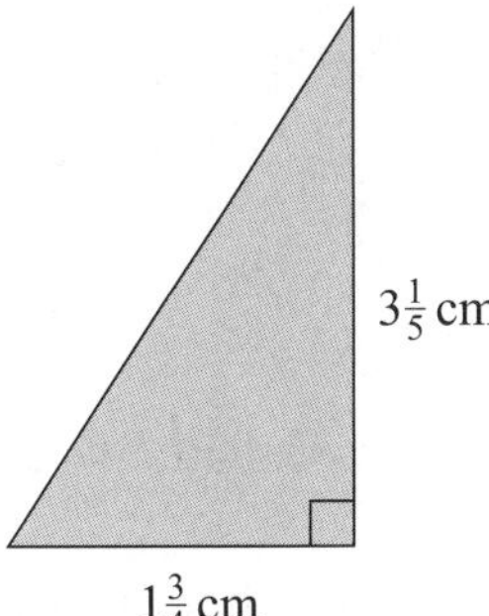

6 Work out $\left(2\frac{2}{3} \times \frac{1}{4}\right) + \left(1\frac{1}{2} \times 2\frac{1}{3}\right)$

HWK 4M

Main Book page 56

1 **a** How many fifths are there in 4?

b How many thirds are there in 7?

c How many sixths are there in 8?

2 Work out

a $6 \div \frac{1}{4}$ **b** $9 \div \frac{1}{7}$ **c** $3 \div \frac{1}{10}$ **d** $4 \div \frac{1}{9}$ **e** $10 \div \frac{1}{20}$ **f** $8 \div \frac{1}{50}$

3 Copy and complete

a $\square \div \frac{1}{8} = 32$ **b** $\square \div \frac{1}{6} = 54$ **c** $9 \div \frac{\square}{\square} = 45$

4 Copy and complete each number chain.

a $\square \xrightarrow{\div \frac{1}{3}} \boxed{24} \xrightarrow{\div \frac{1}{2}} \square$

b $\square \xrightarrow{\div \frac{1}{5}} \square \xrightarrow{\div \frac{1}{6}} \square \xrightarrow{\div \frac{1}{4}} \boxed{120}$

c $\square \xrightarrow{\times \frac{1}{6}} \square \xrightarrow{\div \frac{1}{5}} \square \xrightarrow{\times \frac{1}{10}} \boxed{4}$

5 Work out $3 \div \frac{1}{5} \div \frac{1}{3}$

HWK 5M

Main Book page 57

1 Work out

a $\frac{1}{4} \div \frac{1}{3}$ **b** $\frac{1}{2} \div \frac{3}{4}$ **c** $\frac{3}{8} \div \frac{1}{2}$ **d** $\frac{2}{5} \div \frac{7}{10}$

e $\frac{3}{5} \div \frac{7}{8}$ **f** $\frac{1}{9} \div \frac{2}{3}$ **g** $\frac{4}{7} \div \frac{7}{8}$ **h** $\frac{7}{12} \div \frac{3}{4}$

2 A strip of wood is $\frac{8}{9}$ m long. What is the total length of 12 strips of wood?

3 $\frac{1}{6}$ kg of flour is used to bake a cake. How much flour would be needed to bake 15 cakes?

4 Sam is watching his weight. He allows himself $\frac{3}{40}$ of a box of cereal for his breakfast, which he measures out carefully. How many breakfasts will he get from six boxes of cereal?

5 Work out

a $2\frac{1}{2} \div \frac{3}{7}$ **b** $1\frac{2}{3} \div \frac{5}{8}$ **c** $2\frac{1}{4} \div 3\frac{1}{2}$ **d** $3\frac{3}{4} \div 2\frac{2}{5}$

6 The area of this rectangle is $6\frac{5}{12}$ cm². Work out its length.

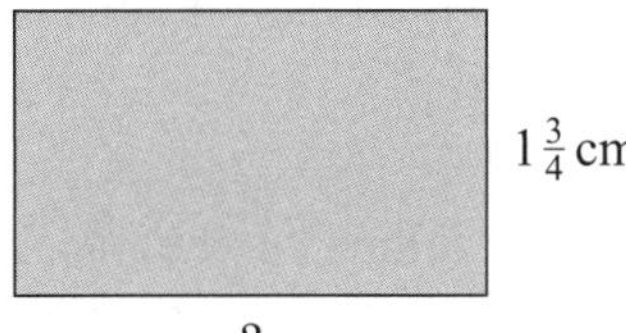

7

$\times$		$\frac{2}{5}$	
		$\frac{1}{20}$	
	$\frac{1}{2}$	$\frac{3}{5}$	
$\frac{7}{10}$			$2\frac{1}{3}$

Copy and complete this multiplication table.

8 Work out $\left(2\frac{2}{5} \div \frac{7}{10}\right) \div 2\frac{1}{7}$

1.7 Probability

HWK 1M **Main Book page 61**

1

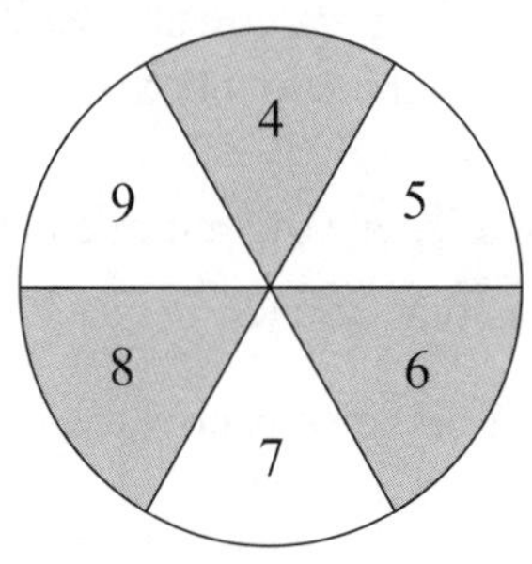

With this spinner find the probability of getting

a a 5 **b** a multiple of 4

c a prime number **d** not an even number.

2 The probability of Sid's dog barking sometime in the morning is 0.97. What is the probability of Sid's dog not barking sometime in the morning?

3 A dice is thrown. What is the probability of getting

a a 3 **b** a number less than 5 **c** a square number?

4 

One card is chosen from above at random. Find the probability of getting

a an 'S' **b** not a 'T' **c** a vowel.

5 47% of the children in Year 8 in Colne Community School are boys. When Year 8 walk into an assembly, what is the probability that the first child to arrive will be a girl?

6 

One digit is chosen at random from the digits shown above. What is the probability of selecting

a the digit '1' **b** a digit which is not a prime number?

7 Rosa is playing pool and pots 5 balls in a row. Colm says that Rosa will definitely pot the next ball. Is Colm correct? Justify your answer.

8 On a Saturday morning Mr Phelps always washes his car, gardens or cleans the house windows. The probability of him washing his car is 0.45 and the probability of him cleaning the house windows is 0.1. What is the probability that Mr Phelps will garden?

9 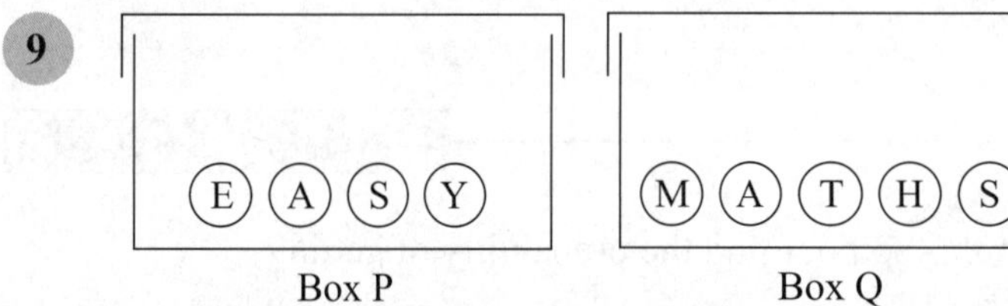

Two boxes contain discs as shown.

a One disc is removed from box P. What is the probability of selecting a vowel? The disc is placed back in box P.

b Four more discs, (V) (E) (R) (Y), are added to box P. If one disc is now removed from box P, what is the probability of selecting a vowel? The disc is placed back in box P.

c The disc (A) is now taken out of box Q and placed in box P. If one disc is now removed from box P, what is the probability of selecting a vowel?

10 **a** Colin has a bag with cherries and grapes inside it. If one piece of fruit is taken at random from the bag, the probability of picking a cherry is $\frac{5}{7}$. What is the probability of picking a grape?

b How many cherries could there be in the bag to start with?

c Write down another two possibilities for the number of cherries that might be in the bag to start with.

HWK 2M Main Book page 63

1 A bag contains yellow and red balls, as shown. One ball is selected at random from the bag and then replaced. This is done 420 times. How many times would you expect to select

a a red ball **b** a yellow ball?

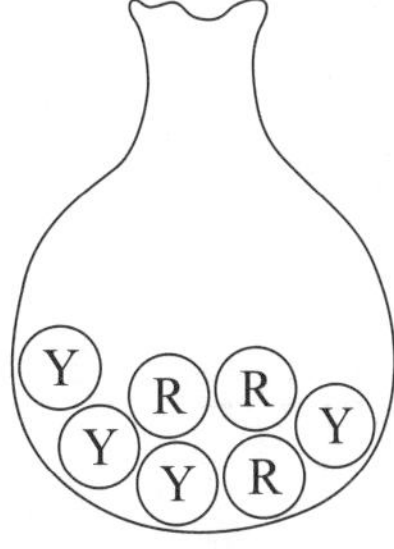

2 A fair dice is rolled 390 times. How many times would you expect to roll a multiple of 3?

3 The probability of it raining on any one day at Carnwell beach is $\frac{1}{3}$. On how many days would you expect it *not* to rain during a three-week holiday at Carnwell beach?

4 At a school fête a person pays 30p to spin the pointer opposite. The person will win the amount shown by the pointer. The game is played 480 times. What profit would the school expect to make?

5 Two bags have red (R) and black (B) balls in them, as shown.

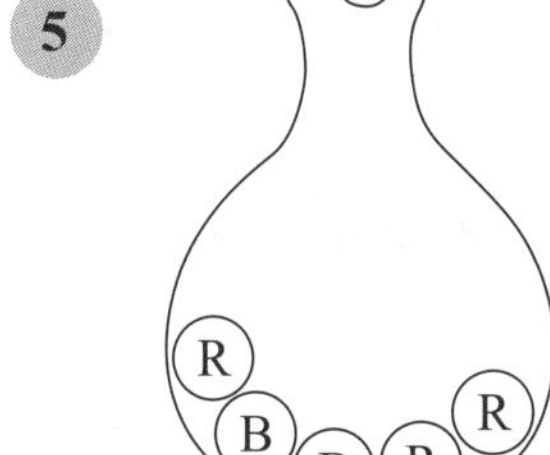

Bag A

a Find the probability of selecting a black ball from bag A.

b A black ball is taken from bag A and put into bag B. A ball is then selected at random from bag B. What is the probability that this ball is not a black ball?

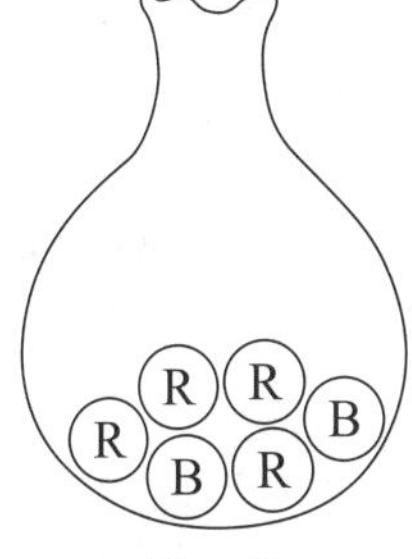

Bag B

6 Two out of every nine trains are late at Henton station. How many trains would you expect to be on time out of the next 54 trains to arrive at Henton station?

7 A coin is biased so that the probability of throwing 'tails' is 0.63. How many 'heads' would you expect when the coin is thrown 500 times?

8 Will has the Jack, Queen, King, Ace of Clubs and the Ace of Hearts. Amy chooses one of his cards and then Mark chooses one of Will's cards.

a If Amy chooses an Ace, what is the probability of Mark also choosing an Ace?

b If Amy chooses a King, what is the probability of Mark choosing an Ace?

9 A bag contains n beads of which seven are red. m beads are removed of which two are red. If one more bead is removed, what is the probability that it will be a red bead?

10 The probability of picking the winner of a horse race is p (p is a fraction). How many winners would you expect to pick for the next 45 races?

HWK 3M

Main Book page 66

1 **a** Ellie throws a coin and a dice. She could get a 'head' and a '5' (H 5). She could get a 'tail' and a '5' (T 5). List the 12 possible outcomes.

b What is the probability that Ellie would get a 'tail' and an odd number?

2 **a** Mindy uses a spinner (with the numbers 1, 2 and 3 on it) and a dice.

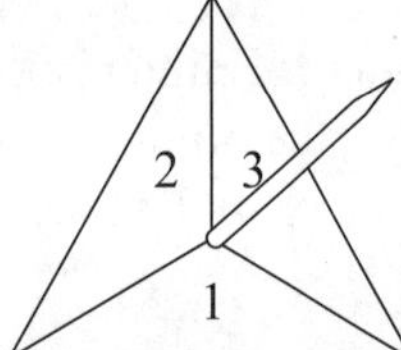

She could get a '2' with the spinner and a '4' with the dice (2, 4).
She could get a '2' with the spinner and a '5' with the dice (2, 5).
List the 18 possible outcomes.

b What is the probability that she will get an odd number with both the spinner and the dice?

3 **a** Two dice are thrown. List all possible outcomes (there are 36!) Copy and complete:

(1, 1)	(2, 1)	(3, 1)	(4, 1)	(5, 1)	(6, 1)
(1, 2)	(2, 2)	(3, 2)	...	...	...
(1, 3)	...	...	...	...	...
...	...	...	...	...	...

b What is the probability of throwing the same number on each dice?

4 A mother has three children. List all the possible outcomes to show if each child is a boy or a girl. Assuming that the probability of having a boy is $\frac{1}{2}$, what is the probability of the mother having:

a three boys **b** exactly one girl?

5 A mother has four children. Assume that the probability of having a boy is $\frac{1}{2}$. By listing all the possible outcomes, find the probability of the mother having:

a four girls **b** exactly one girl **c** exactly two girls.

HWK 4M Main Book page 68

1 A bag contains some discs. Each disc has one of three letters on it – 'T', 'R' or 'Y'. Jan randomly takes a disc from the bag and then replaces it. She does this 80 times and records the results.

Letter	T	R	Y
Frequency	23	34	23

Estimate the probability that the next disc she takes out will be

a a 'Y' **b** an 'R'.

2 Lara rolls a fair dice 120 times. Each time she records the number it lands on.

Number	1	2	3	4	5	6
Frequency	22	25	4	23	27	19

a What seems 'strange' about these results?

b How many times would you have expected the dice to land on each different number?

c If Lara rolled the dice another 120 times, would you expect her to get the same results?

3 Chad and Marie throw a shoe to see if it will land on its heel or not. Chad throws 50 times and Marie throws 130 times. The results are shown below.

Chad

Throws	50
Heel landings	28

Marie

Throws	130
Heel landings	57

The shoe is thrown again.

a For Chad, what is the probability of the shoe landing on its heel?

b For Marie, what is the probability of the shoe landing on its heel?

c Which probability is likely to be more reliable? Give a reason for your answer.

d If you put Chad's and Marie's results together, what is the probability of the shoe landing on its heel if it is thrown again?

e Based on Chad's and Marie's combined results, how many times would you expect the shoe to land on its heel if it is thrown 540 times?

4 How many tails would you expect to get if you toss a coin 50 times?
Toss a coin 50 times. Write down how your results compare to what you expected to get.
If you toss the coin another 50 times, would you expect to get the same result?

UNIT 2

2.1 Percentages 1

HWK 1M **Main Book page 86**

a Start in the top left box.

b Change the number to a fraction, decimal or percentage as required.

c Find this answer in the top corner of another box.

d Write down the letter in that box.

e Repeat steps **b**, **c** and **d** until you arrive back at the top left box.

f Write down the message.

$\frac{7}{20}$ D $(2 - 1.86) \rightarrow \%$	28% R $\left(\frac{1}{2} - 0.48\right) \rightarrow$ decimal	37.5% K $\frac{3}{8} \rightarrow$ decimal	0.095 U (20% of 16) $\rightarrow$ decimal
0.375 E (10% of 2.5) $\rightarrow$ decimal	22.5% G (10% of 0.1) $\rightarrow$ decimal	14% M $\frac{4}{25} \rightarrow$ decimal	38% W 22% $\rightarrow$ fraction
$\frac{13}{20}$ T $\frac{9}{1000} \rightarrow \%$	$\frac{31}{50}$ L 0.85 $\rightarrow$ %	$\frac{17}{100}$ S 40% $\rightarrow$ fraction	$33\frac{1}{3}\%$ H 4% $\rightarrow$ decimal
0.16 A 65% $\rightarrow$ fraction	0.15 T $\frac{1}{3} \rightarrow \%$	0.02 O 9.5% $\rightarrow$ decimal	0.05 R 0.62 $\rightarrow$ fraction

0.01 O $\frac{7}{25} \rightarrow \%$	$\frac{2}{5}$ M $\left(\frac{3}{4} - 0.3\right) \rightarrow$ decimal	3.2 N $0.35 \rightarrow$ fraction	85% D half of $0.45 \rightarrow \%$
0.25 S $\left(\frac{2}{5} - \frac{1}{4}\right) \rightarrow$ decimal	0.04 E $\frac{19}{50} \rightarrow \%$	0.9% H $(0.2 - 0.03) \rightarrow$ fraction	
0.45 A quarter of $1.5 \rightarrow \%$	$\frac{11}{50}$ O $\left(\frac{4}{5} - \frac{3}{4}\right) \rightarrow$ decimal		

HWK 2M

Main Book page 87

1 For each pair of numbers, write down which is the larger.

a $\frac{7}{10}$ 0.8 **b** 0.94 $\frac{19}{20}$ **c** 0.17 $\frac{3}{20}$

d 0.26 $\frac{7}{25}$ **e** $\frac{3}{50}$ 0.04 **f** $\frac{9}{25}$ 0.49

2 Write these numbers in order of size, smallest first.

$\frac{17}{20}$, 0.75, $\frac{9}{10}$, $\frac{18}{25}$, 0.77, 0.735

3

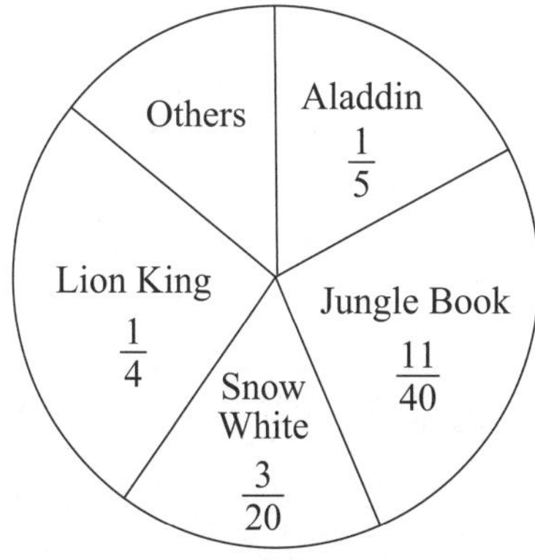

Some people were asked what their favourite Disney cartoon was. The pie chart shows the results.

a What percentage prefer Snow White?

b What percentage prefer Jungle Book?

c What is the difference between the percentages for Jungle Book and the Lion King?

d What percentage prefer 'others'?

4

80%	$\frac{12}{150}$	26%	$\frac{4}{5}$	16%	0.65	$\frac{15}{40}$	75%	$\frac{3}{25}$
0.48								0.08
0.75								$\frac{16}{20}$
$\frac{12}{25}$								$\frac{3}{8}$
$\frac{13}{20}$								65%
0.34								$\frac{21}{28}$
$\frac{13}{50}$								$\frac{2}{25}$
37.5%								$\frac{39}{150}$
0.26	$\frac{36}{75}$	$\frac{12}{65}$	8%	$\frac{3}{4}$	0.8	48%	$\frac{52}{80}$	0.375

Each number belongs to a group of four equivalent numbers (two fractions, one decimal and one percentage).

Write down each group of four numbers.

Beware: there are four numbers which do *not* belong to any group.

5 Jack eats $\frac{9}{13}$ of his food. What percentage of his food does he leave?
(Give your answer to the nearest whole number.)

6 Write in order of size, smallest first.

42%, $\frac{9}{20}$, $\frac{8}{19}$, 0.405, $44\frac{1}{2}$%, $\frac{15}{38}$

7 Which is larger and by how much?

39% of $3\frac{2}{3}$ or $0.7 \times 2\frac{1}{20}$

HWK 3M

Main Book page 88

1 John buys a house for £294 000. He has to pay a 2.5% tax called stamp duty. How much tax does he pay?

2 The cost of a £49 train ticket to London is increased by 4%. What is the new cost of the ticket?

3

Hannah buys all 3 items above in the sale. How much does she pay in total?

4 Molly's gas bill is £114 plus an extra 5% VAT (known as value added tax). How much does Molly have to pay in total?

5 A company makes kitchen units. In one year, production costs are £784 000 and transport costs are £329 000.
45% of production costs are for raw materials and the remainder are machine costs.
In the following year, the cost of raw materials rises by 18%, machine costs increase by 7% and transport costs rise by 14%

What is the overall increase in costs for this company during the following year?

6

Week 1
All prices increase by 8%

Week 7
All prices decrease by 8%

A shop increases all its prices in week 1 then, due to poor sales, decreases the prices in week 7. A jacket costs £76 at the start of week 1. How much will the jacket cost at the end of week 7?

7 Paula's car is worth £7000. After one year it loses 14% of its value.

a How much is the car worth after one year?

b It loses 14% of this new value during year two. How much is the car worth at the end of year two?

8 Seb invests £3000 in a bank for 2 years. Each year the money makes 6% interest on the amount in his account at the start of that year. How much money will Seb have after 2 years?

9 $p = \frac{a}{b^3}$

a Calculate, to 3 significant figures, the value of p when $a = 510$ and $b = 4$

b Calculate the new value of p if a is increased by 12% and b is decreased by 28%

10

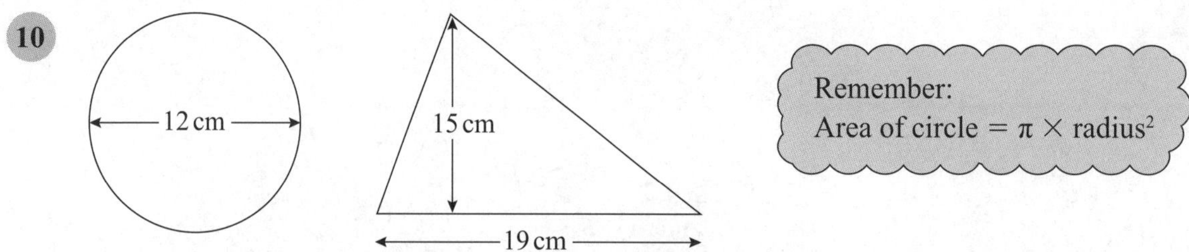

a Find the difference between the area of the triangle and the area of the circle.

b The diameter of the circle is increased by 14%. The height of the triangle is increased by 20% and the base of the triangle is decreased by 6%. Find the difference now between the area of the triangle and the area of the circle.

HWK 4M

Main Book page 89

Reminder: The quick way to work out the new value after a percentage decrease/increase is as follows:

Decrease £280 by 18%

New value = 82% of £280
= 0.82 × 280
= £229.60

0.82 is called the 'multiplier'.

Increase £540 by 11%

New value = 111% of £540
= 1.11 × 540
= £599.40

1.11 is called the 'multiplier'.

Use percentage multipliers to answer the questions in this exercise.

1 **a** Decrease £340 by 3% **b** Increase £520 by 7%
c Increase £1290 by 4.5% **d** Reduce £670 by 12.4%

2 Marvin is trying to sell his car for £2500. He is not having much luck so decides to knock 15% off the selling price. How much is he asking for his car now?

3 Lucy's garage bill is £210 plus an extra 20% VAT.
How much does Lucy have to pay in total?

4

Last year
Cornet £1.80 Sales 1060

This year
Cornet price increased by 20% Sales decrease by 20%

Each year Alfonso sells ice-creams at the Banwell festival.

a Did Alfonso make more money, the same money or less money from selling cornets this year compared with last year?

b Write down the difference in the amount of money he made.

5 Tania sells cabbages at 90p each and galia melons at £1.60 each. Towards the end of the day she reduces the price of a cabbage by 30% and the price of a melon by 25%

She then sells 14 cabbages and 9 melons. How much money does she receive in total for these cabbages and melons?

6 Alex buys a table for £350 and sells it to Jim one week later for 45% profit. Jim then sells the table on at a 20% loss. How much does Jim sell the table for?

7

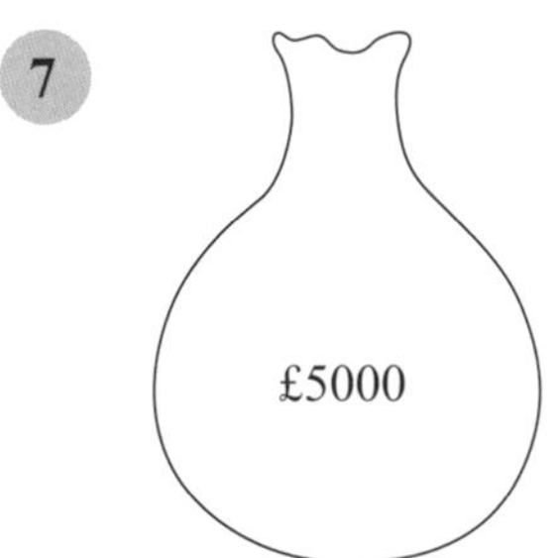

Hal invests £5000 and makes an 8% profit after one year. He leaves all the money invested and makes a further 7% profit one year later.

How much money does he now have in total?

8 The price of a cabinet at an antique shop is reduced by 6% on its price of £5400. One month later the price is reduced by a further 3%. How much will the cabinet now cost?

9

Terry invests £5000 in a building society for 4 years. Each year his money makes 4% interest on the amount in his account at the start of that year. How much money will Terry have after 4 years?

HWK 5M

Main Book page 91

1 The asking price for a house increases from £278 000 to £319 700. Work out the percentage increase in the asking price.

2 Lexa has £6000 savings. She uses some of the money to buy a £1200 bed. Work out the percentage decrease in her savings.

3 Rory takes 72 shots when playing a round of golf on Thursday. On the Friday he plays another round of golf and takes 63 shots. Work out the percentage decrease in the number of shots he takes on Friday compared with Thursday.

4

	Cost price	Selling price
E	£0.42	£0.99
L	£1.20	£2.70

Brooke makes and sells soap.
She makes economy soap (E) and luxury soap (L).
The cost price and selling price of each is shown in the table.

a Work out the percentage profit on one bar of economy soap.

b Work out the percentage profit on one bar of luxury soap.

c During one week, Brooke sells 312 economy bars of soap and 193 luxury bars of soap. Work out her overall percentage profit for these sales.

5 Malcolm commutes to work each day. The journey takes him 55 minutes.
Malcolm gets a new job and only has to commute for 38 minutes.
Work out the percentage reduction in the time he has to commute.

6 The Jenkins family usually buy 2 small boxes of flakes each week, as shown. One week they buy one large box only, as shown. Work out the percentage increase in the amount of flakes the Jenkins family have during this week.

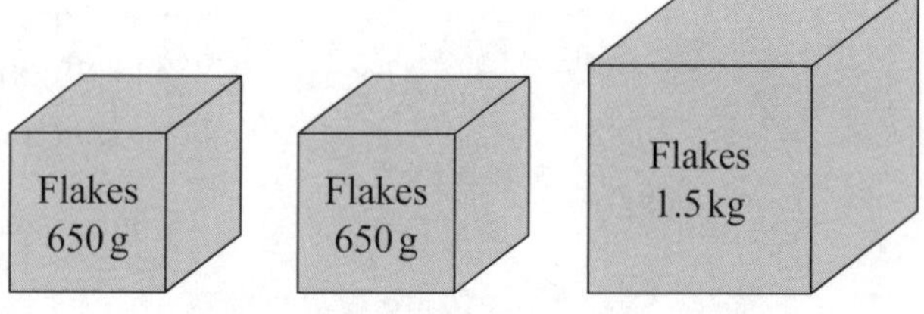

7 Julia buys 20 footballs at £6 each, 15 hockey sticks at £14 each and 30 tennis rackets at £15 each.
She sells 18 of the footballs at £11 each, 12 of the hockey sticks at £35 each and 26 of the tennis rackets at £31 each.
Work out the overall percentage profit that Julia made.

HWK 5E

Main Book page 93

1 The table opposite shows how many boys and girls were at Broomhill School in the years shown.

	2019	2020
Boys	702	
Girls		694
Total	1350	1410

a Copy and complete the table.

b Work out the percentage increase in the total number of children at the school in 2020 compared with 2019.

c Work out the difference between the percentage increase in the number of girls and the percentage increase in the number of boys in 2020 compared with 2019.

2 The number of people visiting a museum during a 4-week period is shown below.

Week	1	2	3	4
Number of people	604	541	503	445

Each week there is a decrease in the number of people. Between which 2 weeks is the largest percentage decrease? Show working out to justify your answer.

3 Molly buys 90 toy windmills for £110. On a carnival day she sells 62 windmills for £3 each and a further 23 windmills for £1.50 each. She gives the remaining windmills away free of charge. What percentage profit does Molly make?

4 Mr Riley buys bikes for £180 each and sells them at £280 each. He wants to achieve a 70% profit margin so needs to increase the selling price of a bike. How much must he increase the price by?

5 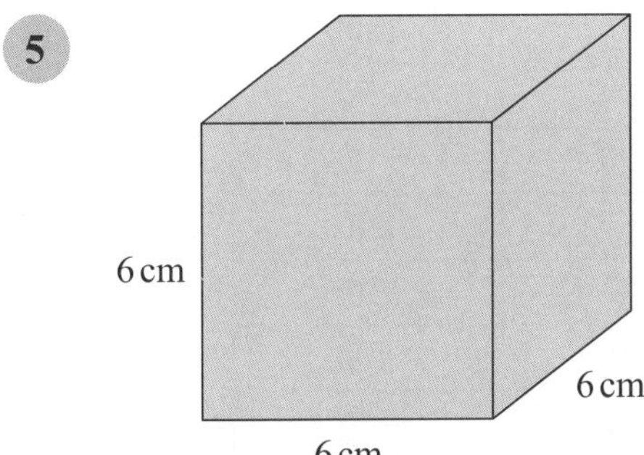

Each side of this cube is increased by 35%. Work out the percentage increase in the volume of the cube.

6 Nikhil makes wood carvings. Each carving costs £15 for the wood and Nikhil charges £18 for his labour. He sells each carving for £52.80.
Eventually the cost of the wood increases by 30%. By how much will Nikhil need to increase the selling price of each carving if he is to get exactly the same percentage profit as before?

2.2 Estimating and checking answers

HWK 1M — **Main Book page 96**

1 Work out 8×700

2 Work out a rough estimate for 7.93×706

3 Work out 50×9

4 Work out a rough estimate for 51×8.98

5 Answer 'true' or 'false' (the sign $\approx$ means 'is roughly equal to').

a 41.2×5.9
$\approx 40 \times 6$
≈ 240

b $2137 \div 98$
$\approx 2000 \div 100$
≈ 20

c 62×3989
$\approx 60 \times 4000$
$\approx 24\,000$

6 Do not use a calculator. Decide, by estimating, which of the three answers is closest to the exact answer.

	Calculation	A	B	C
a	7.3×31	2100	210	100
b	14.9×9.98	150	25	1500
c	24.8×40.2	100	1000	200
d	19.6×4.94	500	100	10
e	6.01×29.8	180	18	360
f	59.7×71.1	420	840	4200
g	$403 \div 79.12$	32 000	50	5
h	$899 \div 1.98$	450	1800	45
i	$51 \div 0.99$	50	5	200
j	$607 \div 21.8$	3	120	30
k	$79.3 + 81 + 139$	300	200	400
l	9.6×90.4	450	900	90
m	$231 + 19.6 + 41.3$	200	390	290
n	19.7×31.06	60	300	600
o	$\frac{1}{4}$ of (19.86×30.04)	300	150	15
p	4.92% of $(7103 - 89)$	350	140	700
q	$\frac{11}{21}$ of 10% of 4032	200	400	50
r	$\frac{3}{4}$ of 19% of 14.3^2	15	45	30

HWK 2M

Main Book page 97

Do not use a calculator for these questions.

1 Gareth needs to buy 19 packets of cereal at £2.49 for each packet. Estimate the total cost.

2 A book weighs 292 g. Estimate how much 31 books would weigh.

3 A book costs £9.95. Estimate the cost of 152 books.

4 Write down each calculation below and match the correct answer from the list given.

a $20.6 \div 5$ **b** 49×20.2 **c** 8.1×32

d 42×6.8 **e** $2.8 + 13.9$ **f** $3012 \div 4.8$

Answers:	259.2	16.7	989.8	627.5	4.12	285.6

5 Larry works for exactly 40 years. He works for 5 days each week and 8 hours each day. On average he earns 25p for every minute he works. At the end of the 40 years he has saved 10% of the total money he has earned. Estimate how much money he has saved.

6 Caitlin covers 0.79 m every time she takes a stride. Estimate the distance she travels if she takes 994 strides.

7 Ryan sells cups of tea for 82p each from his stall. One weekend he sells 396 cups of tea. It costs him £130 to make the tea and sort out the cups. Estimate the profit he makes on selling cups of tea during this weekend.

8

box of paper £4.95
ink cartridge £13.10
pack of photo paper £7.99

Louisa buys three boxes of paper, two ink cartridges and one pack of photo paper. Roughly how much change would Louisa get from £50?

9 Give an estimate for each of the following calculations.

a $\dfrac{2109 - 302}{87.4}$ **b** $\dfrac{3}{7}$ of 1362 kg **c** $\dfrac{19.6^2 - 197}{0.49}$

d $\dfrac{4.81 \times 19.7}{13.8 + 11.4}$ **e** 63% of £17 983 **f** $\dfrac{9.83 \times 50.03}{0.18}$

HWK 3M

Main Book page 99

1 If $56.58 \div 12.3 = 4.6$, would you expect 4.6×12.3 to equal 56.58? Give reasons for your answer.

2 Work out the following without using a calculator and check each answer using inverse operations.

a $93 - 7.68 = \square$ check $\square + 7.68$

b $2.94 \times 0.7 = \square$ check $\square \div 0.7$

c $2.536 \div 0.8 = \square$ check $\square \times 0.8$

d $1.4 \times 5.6 = \square$ check $\square \div 5.6$

e $0.8 - 0.034 = \square$ check $\square + 0.034$

3 Tom's heart beats around 100 000 times each day. Do you think this is likely or unlikely? Give reasons for your answer.

4 Copy and complete with either > or < in the boxes.

a $362 \times 0.93 \square 362$ **b** $41.8 \times 1.04 \square 41.8$ **c** $38 \div 1.3 \square 38$

d $0.65 \times 0.8 \square 0.65$ **e** $102 \div 0.95 \square 102$ **f** $1.7 \div 1.4 \square 1.7$

5 $171.08 \div 47 = 3.64$

Use the calculation above to work out

a $1710.8 \div 47$ **b** $0.17108 \div 47$ **c** 3.64×47

d 36.4×47 **e** $171.08 \div 4.7$ **f** 364×4.7

6 $180.04 \div 28 = 6.43$

Use the calculation above to work out

a $180.04 \div 2.8$ **b** $180.04 \div 0.28$ **c** 6.43×2.8

d 64.3×28 **e** 0.643×2.8 **f** $1.8004 \div 0.28$

HWK 4M

Main Book page 100

1 Write the following numbers to 2 significant figures.

a 7.6145 **b** 38 210 **c** 0.008749 **d** 387.64

2 Which of the numbers below round off to 6.78 correct to 2 decimal places?

6.714	6.769	6.773	6.782	6.774	6.786

3 Work out these on a calculator and then round off the answers correct to 2 decimal places.

a $\frac{6.99}{2.01}$ **b** $\frac{3.8^2}{4.3}$ **c** $\frac{8.21}{\sqrt{53}}$ **d** $\frac{5.14 \times 3.6}{0.93}$

e $\frac{5.2}{1.9} + 8.714$ **f** $\frac{5.25}{(1.18 + 3.27)}$ **g** $\frac{5.06^2}{4.27}$ **h** $\frac{3.134}{2.6^2}$

4 Work out $\frac{3.8 + 6.14}{0.09^2}$, giving the answer to 3 significant figures.

5 Which number below is the smallest which will round off to 8.14 correct to 2 decimal places?

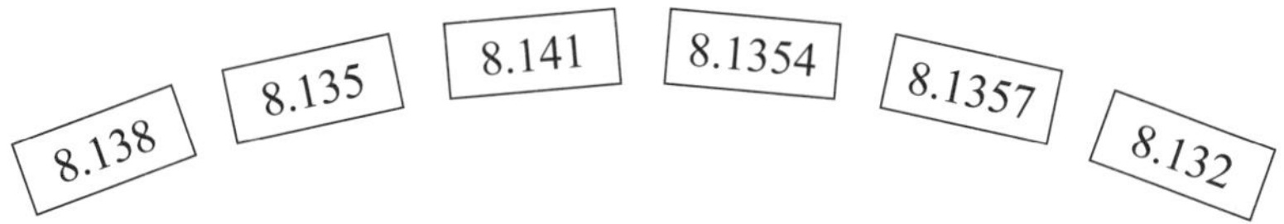

6 Jamilla says that 0.080463 is equal to 0.080 when rounded to 2 significant figures. Is she correct or not? Give a reason for your answer.

7 How many numbers below round off to 4.8 correct to 1 decimal place?

(4.861) (4.841) (4.793) (4.852) (4.768) (4.739)

8 Give these answers correct to 2 significant figures.

a $\dfrac{5.16 + 9.3}{3.7}$ **b** $\dfrac{\sqrt{46}}{9} + 3.89$ **c** $\dfrac{7.63}{8.2^2} + \dfrac{5.17}{1.3^2}$ **d** $\dfrac{5.68^2 - 17.4}{\sqrt{32.9}}$

9 What is the smallest number which rounds off to 9.3 correct to 1 decimal place?

10 What is the smallest number which rounds off to 2.38 correct to 3 significant figures?

11 0.09073 is rounded to 3 significant figures and to 3 decimal places. Write down the difference between the two answers.

2.3 Drawing and using graphs

HWK 1M/2M **Main Book pages 106/107**

For each question, complete a table then draw the graph using the scales given.

1 $y = 2x + 2$ for x-values from 0 to 5

$2x + 2$ means [x] → [$\times 2$] → [$+2$]

x	0	1	2	3	4	5
y					10	
coordinates					(4, 10)	

(x-axis: use 1 cm for 1 unit
y-axis: use 1 cm for 2 units)

2. $y = 3x + 1$ for x-values from 0 to 5

   $3x + 1$ means $\boxed{x} \rightarrow \boxed{\times 3} \rightarrow \boxed{+1}$

   (x-axis: 1 cm for 1 unit, y-axis: 1 cm for 2 units)

3. $y = \frac{1}{2}x + 2$ for x-values from 0 to 6

   $\frac{1}{2}x + 2$ means $\boxed{x} \rightarrow \boxed{\times \frac{1}{2}} \rightarrow \boxed{+2}$

   (x-axis: 1 cm for 1 unit, y-axis: 2 cm for 1 unit)

4. Draw $3x + y = 6$; take x-values from 0 to 4

5. On the same graph, draw the lines $y = 1.5x - 4$

   $y = \frac{1}{6}x$

   $x + 2y = 8$

   Take x-values from 0 to 8. Write down the coordinates of the three vertices of the triangle formed.

HWK 3M

Main Book page 108

1. Using the same axes, draw the graphs of $y = 3x - 1$, $y = 3x - 3$, $y = 3x$ and $y = 3x + 3$. Write down what you notice about each line and its equation. (Clues: where do the lines cut the y-axis? – are the lines parallel?)

2. Three of the lines below are parallel. Write down the equation of the line which is *not* parallel to the other lines.

$y = 4x + 1$	$y = 3x + 4$	$y = 4x - 2$	$y = 4x + 4$

3. Draw the graph of $y = x^2 + 2$ using x-values from 0 to 4

4. State which of the following represent straight line graphs.

$y = x^2 - 3$	$y = 4x + 2$	$y = 5x - 3$	$y = 3x^2$

5. Which line below does not cross the y-axis at (0, 5)?

$y = 5x - 1$	$y = 2x + 5$	$y = 5x + 5$

6. Write down the coordinates of the point where $y = 5x - 7$ cuts the y-axis.

7 Write down the equations of three lines which would make a diagram like the one shown opposite.

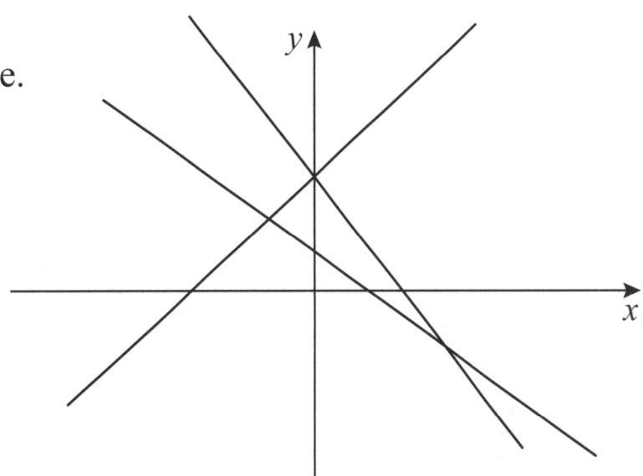

HWK 4M Main Book page 110

In questions **1** to **10** you are given the coordinates of several points on a line. Find the equation of each line.

1

x	1	2	3	4	5
y	5	6	7	8	9

2

x	1	2	3	4	5
y	5	10	15	20	25

3

x	10	12	14	16	18
y	4	6	8	10	12

4

x	20	19	18	17	16
y	0	1	2	3	4

5

x	2	4	6	8	10
y	16	32	48	64	80

6

x	1	2	3	4	5
y	1	3	5	7	9

7

x	1	2	3	4	5
y	5	7	9	11	13

8

x	1	2	3	4	5
y	2	5	8	11	14

9

x	1	2	3	4	5
y	7	12	17	22	27

10

x	1	2	3	4	5
y	11	13	15	17	19

11

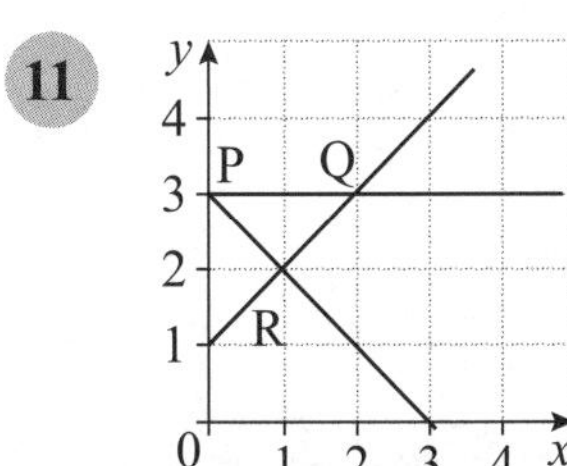

Find the equation of the line through

a R and Q **b** P and Q **c** P and R.

12

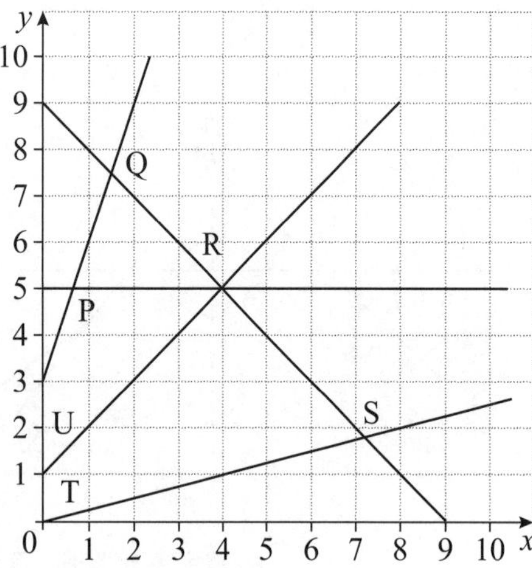

Find the equation of the line through

a P and R

b U and R

c T and S

d Q and S

e P and Q.

HWK 5M

Main Book page 111

Use $y = mx + c$ to write down the equation of each straight line.

1 Line goes up 3 for every 1 along and cuts the y-axis at (0, 1).

2 Line goes up 6 for every 1 along and cuts the y-axis at (0, −3).

3 Line goes down 4 for every 1 along and cuts the y-axis at (0, 2).

4 Line goes up $\frac{1}{3}$ for every 1 along and cuts the y-axis at (0, −5).

5 Line goes down 7 for every 1 along and cuts the y-axis at (0, −1).

Write down the gradient and y-intercept of each of the following lines.

6 $y = 2x + 9$

7 $y = 5x - 3$

8 $y = -4x + 1$

9 $y = -2x - 3$

10 $y = x + 5$

11 $y = -\frac{1}{2}x + 6$

12 $y = 7 - 4x$

13 $y = 5 - \frac{1}{3}x$

14 $y = \frac{1}{4} + 8x$

15 Write down the gradient of the line $y + 4x = 3$

16 Write down the gradient of the line $y - 2x + 1 = 0$

17 Write down the coordinates of the point where the line $y + 6x - 2 = 0$ crosses the y-axis.

18

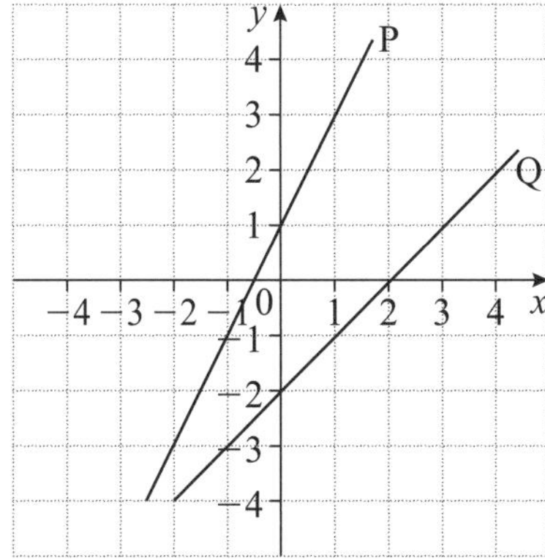

Write down the equation of each of the lines P and Q by working out the gradients and the y-intercepts.

19 Write down the equation of each of the lines A and B by working out the gradients and the y-intercepts.

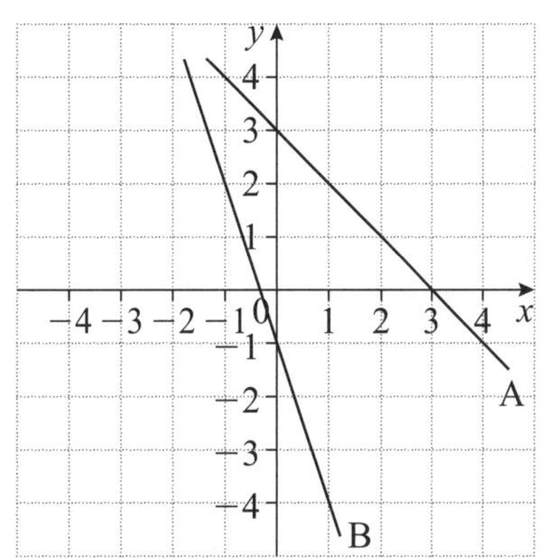

20 Which two lines below are parallel?

$y = 2 - 4x$	$y = 4x + 1$	$y - 4x = 3$	$y = 3x + 4$

HWK 6M — **Main Book page 113**

1

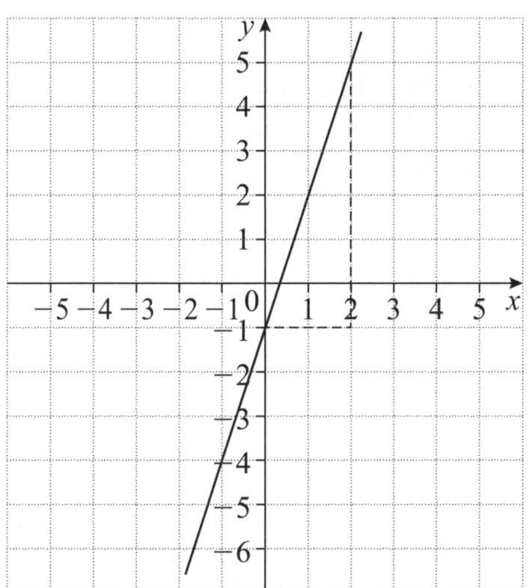

a Work out the gradient of this line.

b Write down the y-intercept for this line.

c Use $y = mx + c$ to write down the equation of this line.

2

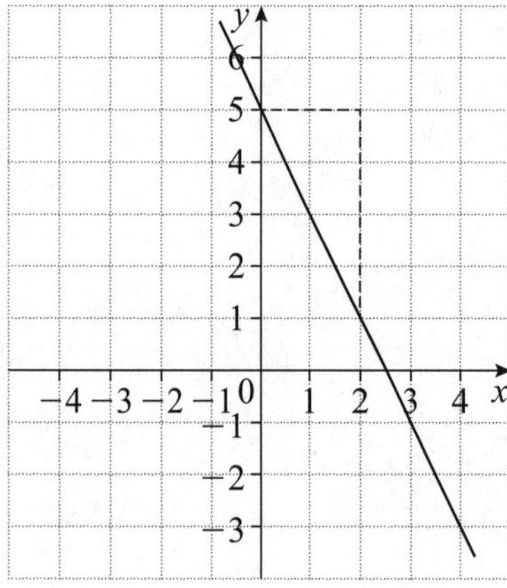

a Work out the gradient of this line (remember it is negative).

b Use $y = mx + c$ to write down the equation of this line.

3 Find the equations of the lines P, Q, R, S and T.

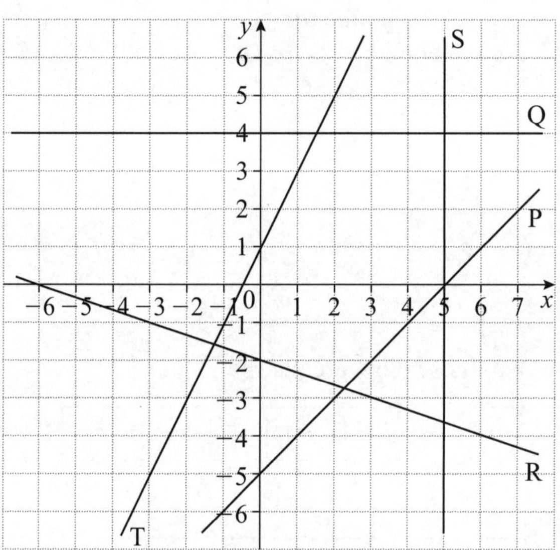

4

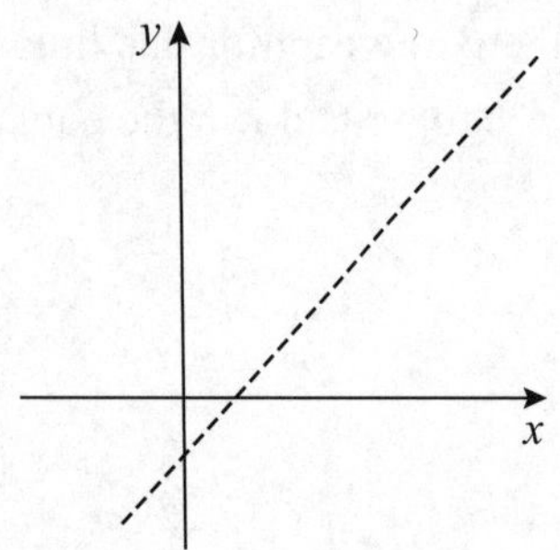

Which equation might this line have:

$y = \frac{1}{2}x - 1$ or $y = -2x - 1$?

5 Write down a possible equation for the line shown opposite.

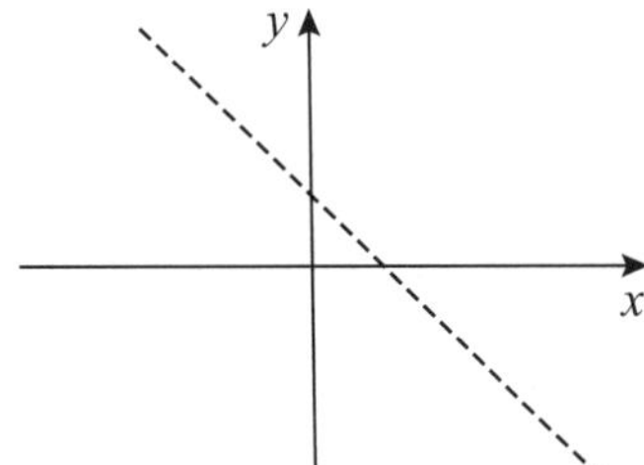

6

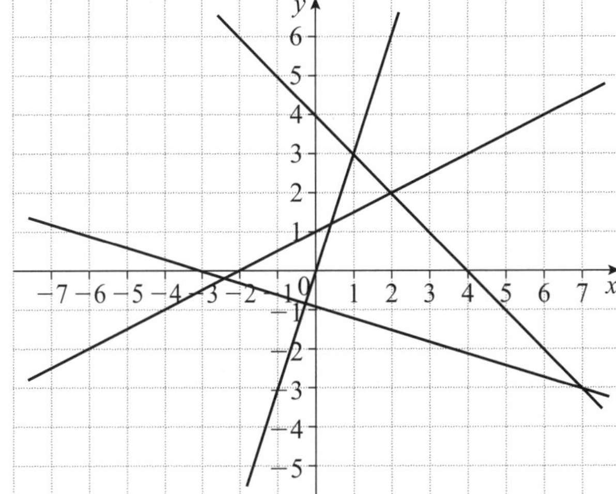

Write down the coordinates where the line $y = -x + 4$ meets the line $y = \frac{1}{2}x + 1$

HWK 6E

Main Book page 115

Draw the graph for each equation in questions **1** to **4**.

1 $y = x^2 + 4$ for x-values from -3 to 3

2 $y = x^2 + 2x$ for x-values from -3 to 3

3 $y = (x - 1)^2$ for x-values from -2 to 4

4 $y = x^2 - 6x + 9$ for x-values from 0 to 6

5 Draw the graphs of $y = (x + 2)^2$ and $y = x + 3$ for values of x from -4 to 1. Write down the x-coordinates, correct to 1 decimal place, of the two points where the line cuts the curve.

HWK 7M Main Book page 116

1 One gallon is approximately 4.5 litres.

a Draw axes, as shown, with a scale of 1 cm for 1 gallon and 1 cm for 5 litres. Draw a '×' where 45 litres are equal to 10 gallons. Draw another '×' at (0, 0).

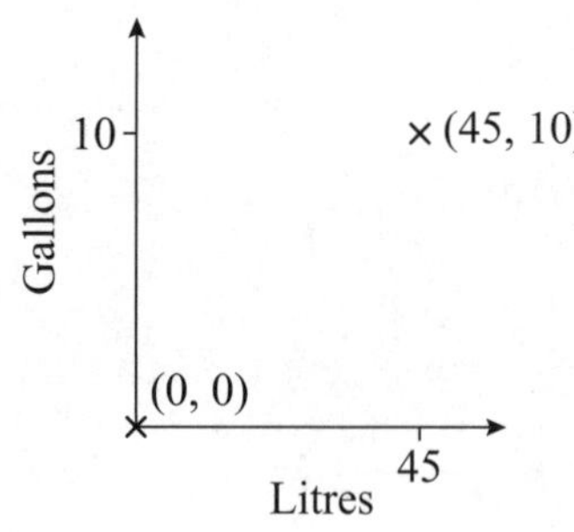

b Draw a long straight line through the two points above and use your graph to convert
i 2 gallons into litres **ii** 37.5 litres into gallons.

c Ben puts 13.5 litres of petrol into his car. This costs him £15.45. Use your graph to help you calculate the cost of 1 gallon of petrol.

2 A man climbing a mountain measures his height above sea level after every 30 minutes; the results are shown below.

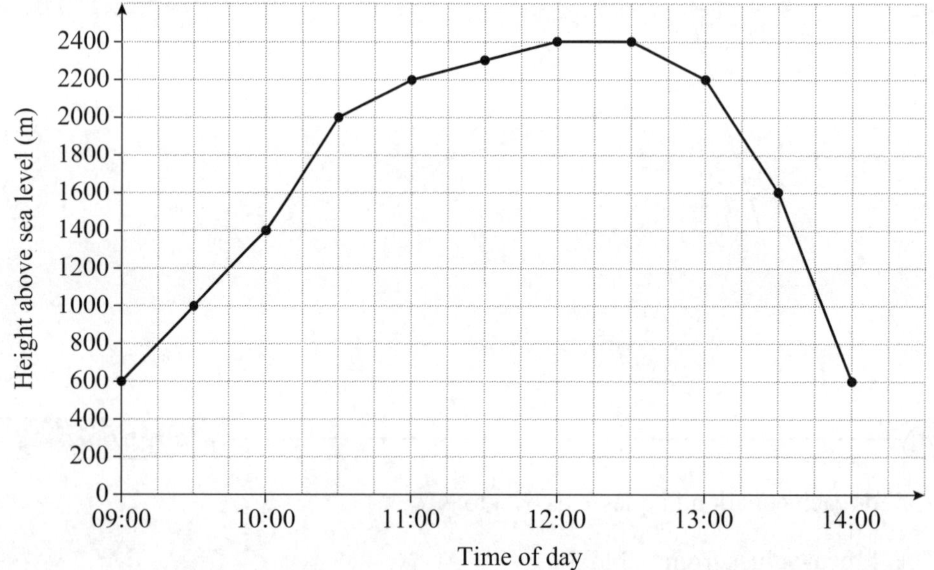

a At what height was he at 10:00 h?

b At what height was he at 13:30 h?

c Estimate his height above sea level at 09:45 h.

d Estimate his altitude at 10:45 h.

e Estimate his height above sea level at 13:45 h.

f At what two times was he 2200 m above sea level?

g How high was the mountain? (He got to the top!)

h How long did he rest at the summit?

i How long did he take to reach the summit?

3 Two tool hire firms charge the following amounts for the hire of a large tile cutter.

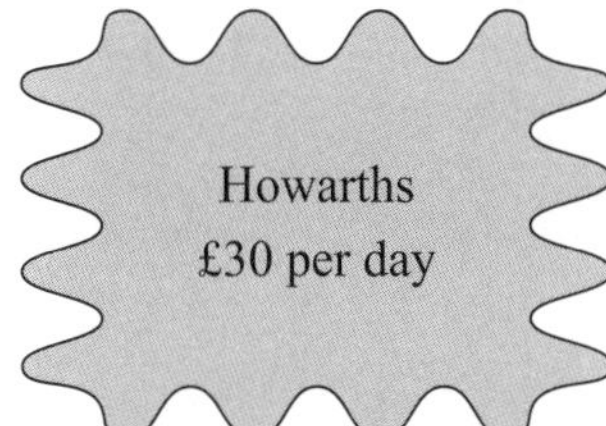

a Draw axes, as shown, for the number of days hired and the cost.

b Use the axes to draw a graph for each tool hire firm to show the cost for up to 5 days.

c Which tool hire firm is the cheaper to use for 4 days?

d For how many days' hire do both firms charge the same amount?

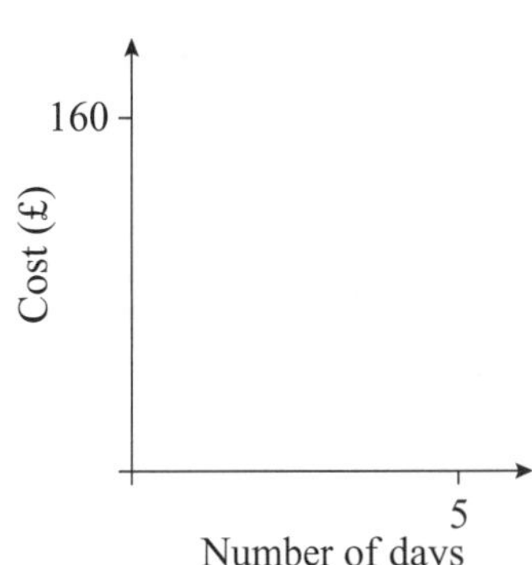

2.4 Sequences 1

HWK 1M —— **Main Book page 123**

1 Write down each sequence and find the missing numbers.

a [3] [12] [48] [ ] [ ]

b [−4] [−1] [ ] [5] [8] [ ]

c [ ] [ ] [ ] [11] [6] [1]

2 Find the next term in each sequence.

a 1, 1, 2, 3, 5, 8, …

b 26, 24, 21, 17, …

c $\frac{5}{8}, \frac{10}{16}, \frac{15}{24}, \frac{20}{32}, \ldots$

d −9, −16, −23, −30, …

e $2n, 5n, 8n, 11n, \ldots$

f $\frac{1}{2}, 0.55, \frac{3}{5}, 0.65, \ldots$

3 The first term of a sequence is 4. Write down the first four terms of the sequence if the rule is

a multiply by 3 and add 1

b double and add 4

4 Find the rule for each sequence. Each rule has two operations (similar to the rules in question **3** above).

a 3 ⟶ 9 ⟶ 21 ⟶ 45

b 1 ⟶ 3 ⟶ 11 ⟶ 43

c 1 ⟶ 6 ⟶ 31 ⟶ 156

5 Luke says the next number in the sequence [1] [2] [4] is [8]. Ali says that Luke is wrong and the next number is [7]. Tom says that both Luke and Ali are correct. *Explain* why.

6 Find the next two terms in each sequence.

a 121, 144, 169, 196, … **b** 360, 180, 60, 15, … **c** 1, 8, 27, 64, …

7 Find the missing numbers in these arithmetic sequences.

a	6		14	18		
b		23	16		2	
c		49				17

8 An arithmetic sequence has a 3rd term of 15 and a 4th term of 19. What is the 2nd term?

9 An arithmetic sequence has a 1st term of 7 and a 3rd term of 19. What is the 4th term?

10 The rule for this sequence is 'multiply by 2 and add 2'. Find the missing numbers.

( ) ⟶ (10) ⟶ (22) ⟶ ( )

11 Write down the rule for this sequence.

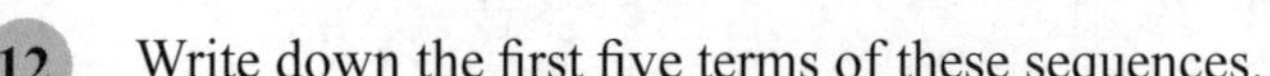

12 Write down the first five terms of these sequences.

a the second term is 9 and the rule is 'subtract 11'

b the fourth term is 35 and the rule is 'add 6'

c the first two terms are 0, 3 and the rule is 'add the two previous terms'

d the third term is 48 and the rule is 'divide by 4'

e the fourth term is -11 and the rule is 'add 9'

HWK 2M Main Book page 126

1 Here is a sequence 5, 7, 10, 14
Write the numbers in a table as shown.

Predict the numbers shown with (?) marks to find the next two terms in the sequence.

Terms	Differences
5	
7	2
10	3
14	4
(?)	(?)
(?)	(?)

2 Predict the next two terms in each sequence.

a 3, 8, 15, 24, … **b** 53, 41, 31, 23, … **c** 80, 71, 63, 56, … **d** 24, 39, 57, 78, …

3 Here is a sequence of matchstick squares.

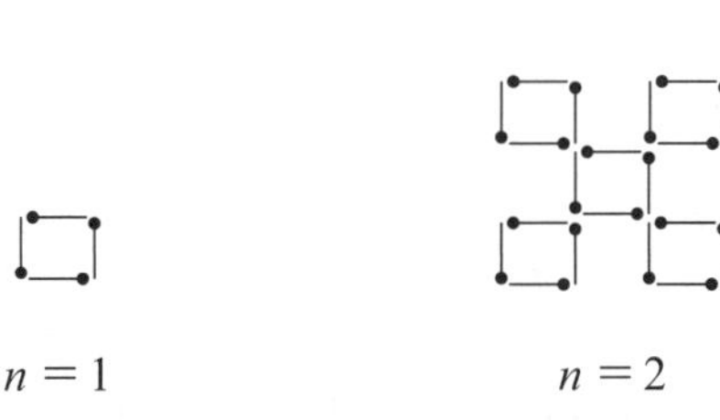
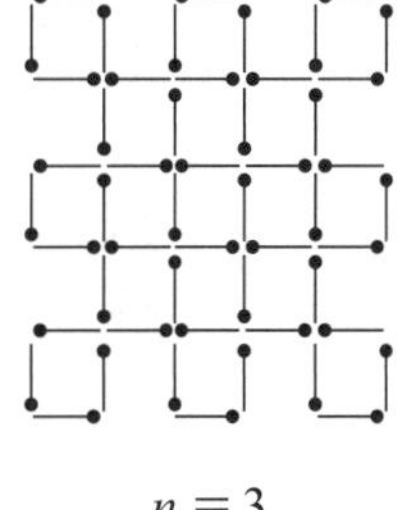

$n = 1$ $n = 2$ $n = 3$

Shape number, n	Number of matches	Difference
1	4	
2	20	16
3	52	32
4	100	48
5	?	

Use the differences to predict the number of matches in shape number 5

4 This sequence is more difficult.

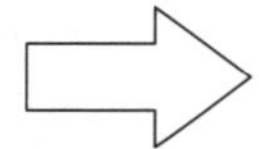

The first differences make no obvious pattern. Work out the second differences and find the missing numbers.

Number	Difference
3	
	1
4	
	4
8	
	9
17	
	16
33	

Number	Difference	Second difference
3		
	1	
4		3
	4	
8		5
	9	
17		7
	16	
33		?
	?	
?		

5 Use first, second and third differences to predict the next number in the sequences below.

a	**b**	**c**
5	7	1
7	12	9
11	20	21
20	35	46
37	61	93
?	?	?

6 Write down the first number in the sequence below which will *exceed* 1000

4, 12, 25, 50, 94, 164, …

2.5 Reflection and enlargement

HWK 1M Main Book page 133

Copy each shape on squared paper and draw the image after reflection in the broken line.

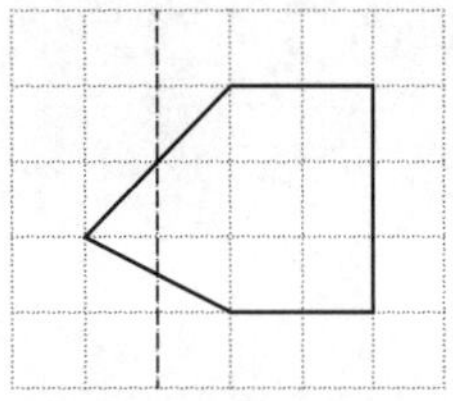

2

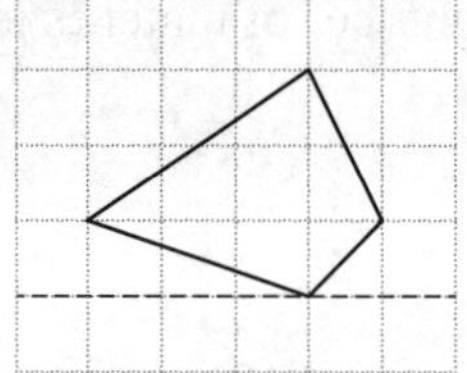

3

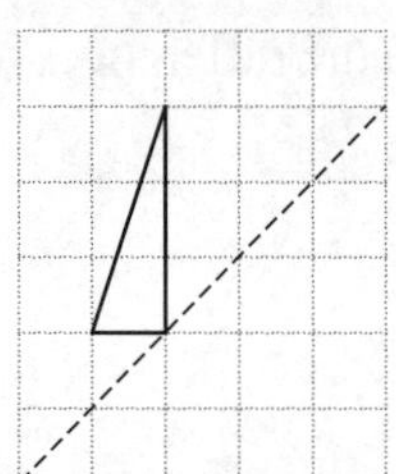

4 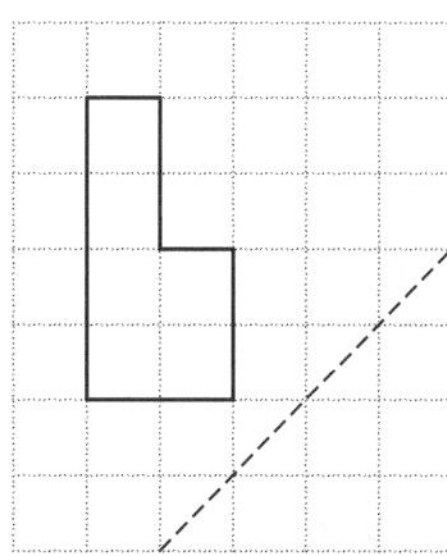

5 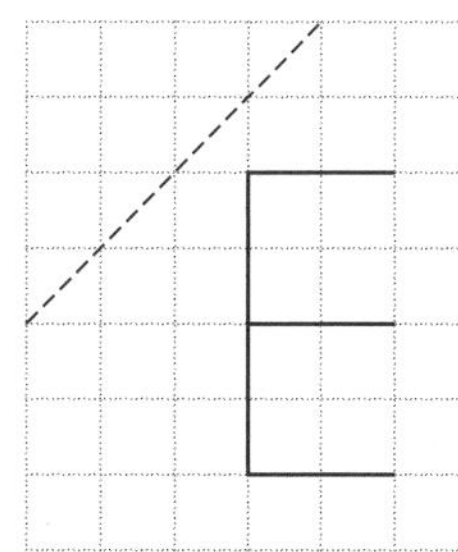

6 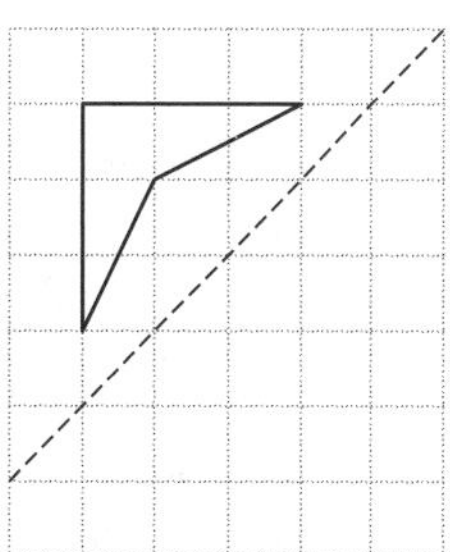

In questions 7 to 9, copy each shape and draw the image after reflection in the broken line.

7 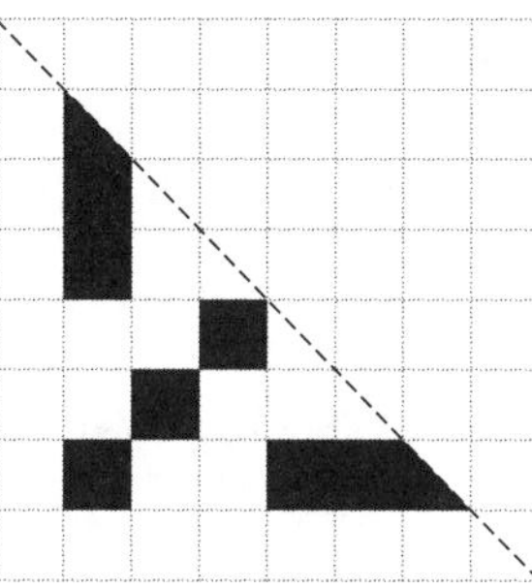

8 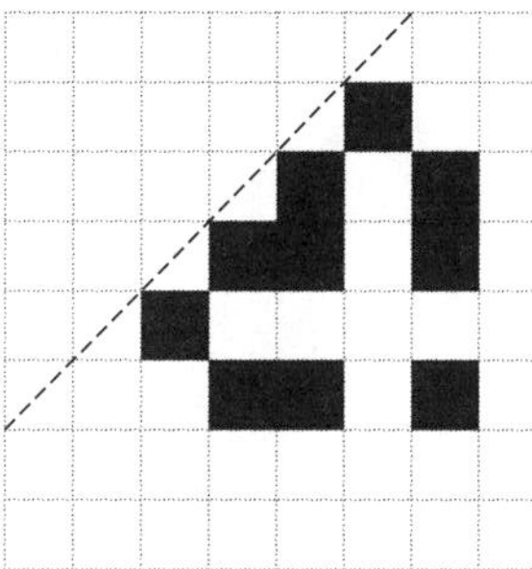

9 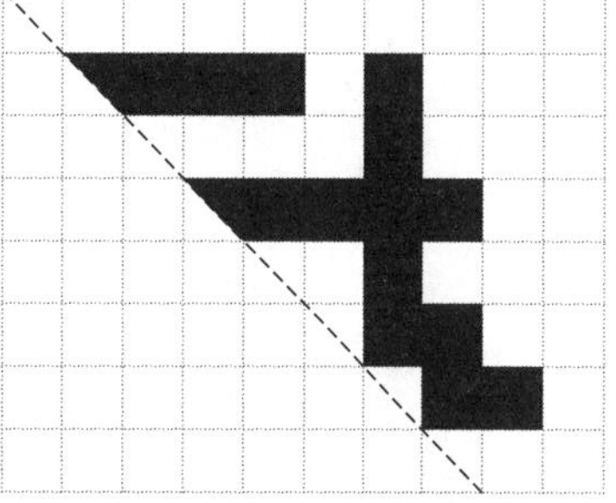

10 First reflect the shape in line 1 and then reflect the image in line 2

a 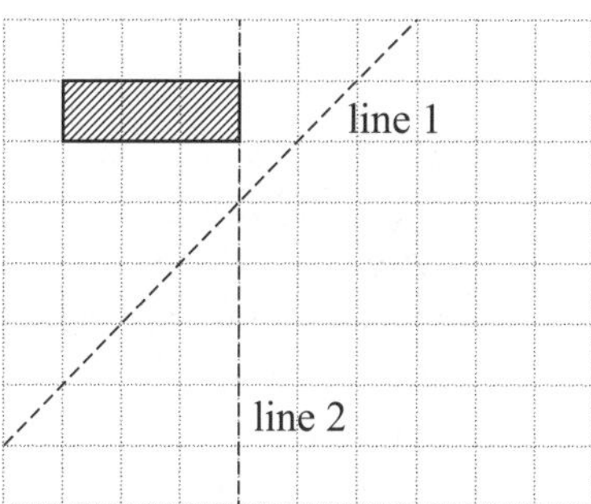

b 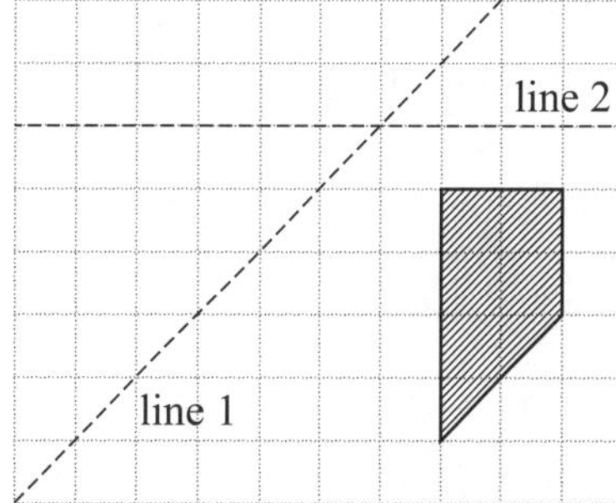

HWK 2M **Main Book page 134**

1 **a** Draw x and y axes with values from -5 to 5 and draw shape A which has vertices (corners) at (2, 2), (2, 3), (5, 3) and (5, 2).

b Reflect shape A in the x-axis. Label the image B.

c Reflect shape B in $x = 1$. Label the image C.

d Reflect shape C in $y = 1$. Label the image D.

e Write down the coordinates of the vertices of shape D.

2 Copy the diagram onto squared paper.

a Reflect triangle P in $y = x$.
Label the image Q.

b Reflect triangle Q in $x = 2$.
Label the image R.

c Reflect triangle R in the x-axis.
Label the image S.

d Write down the coordinates of the vertices of triangle S.

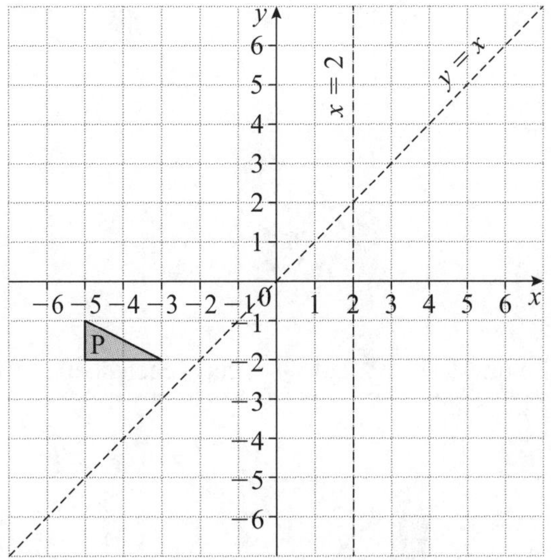

3 **a** Draw x and y axes with values from -5 to 5 and draw triangle A which has vertices at $(2, -1)$, $(2, -4)$ and $(3, -4)$.

b Reflect triangle A in the y-axis. Label the image B.

c Reflect triangle B in $y = -1$. Label the image C.

d Reflect triangle C in $x = 1$. Label the image D.

e Reflect triangle D in $y = x$. Label the image E.

f Write down the coordinates of the vertices of triangle E.

4

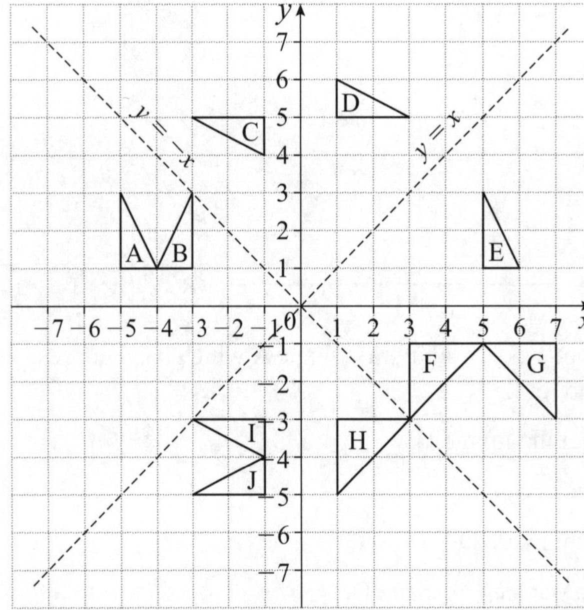

Write down the equation of the mirror line for each of the following reflections

a A → B

b B → E

c I → J

d D → E

e A → C

f C → J

g H → F

h F → G

5 **a** Find the image of the point (2, 5) after reflection in the line
i $x = 3$ **ii** $x = 40$ **iii** $y = 1$ **iv** $y = 100$ **v** $y = x$

b Find the image of the point (m, n) after reflection in the x-axis followed by reflection in the y-axis.

c Find the image of the point (m, n) after reflection in the line $y = -x$.

HWK 3M

Main Book page 137

In questions **1** to **7**, draw the shapes and then draw lines through corresponding points to find the centre of enlargement. Do not draw the shapes too near the edge of the page!

1

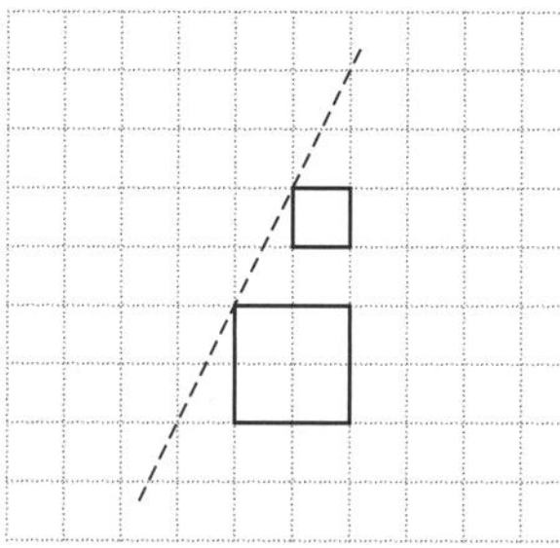

2

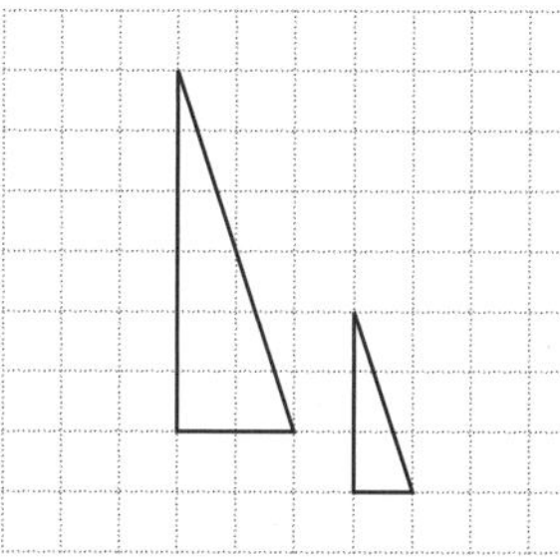

3

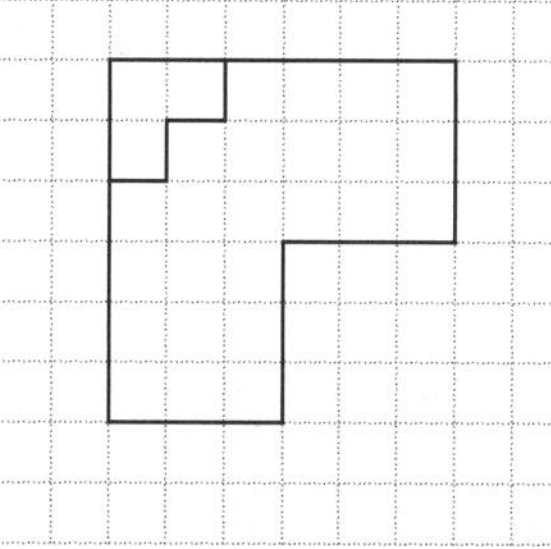

4

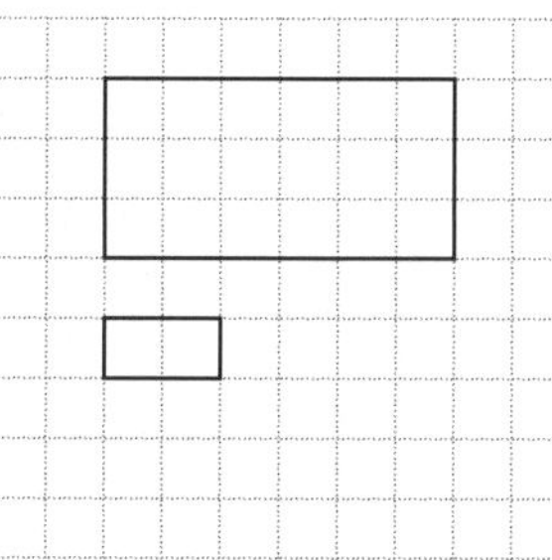

5

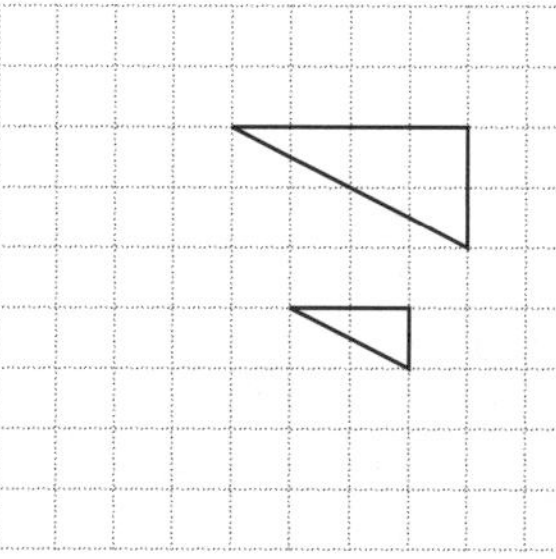

6

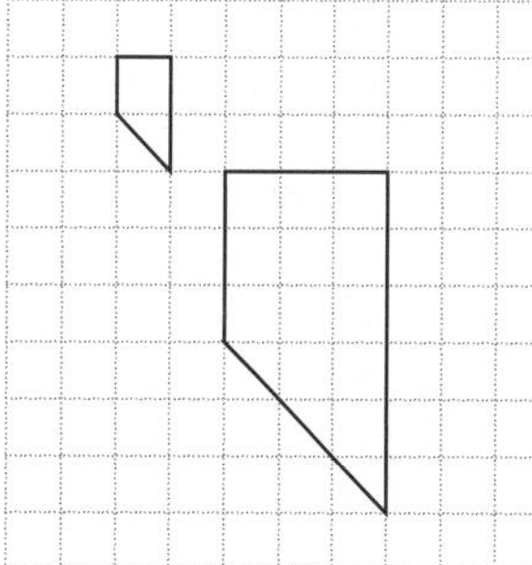

7

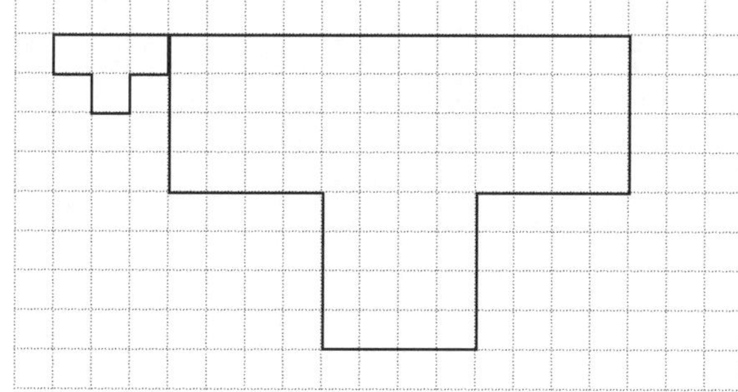

8 3 cm A 8 cm

B 4.5 cm 12 cm

Is rectangle A an enlargement of rectangle B? *Explain* your answer.

9 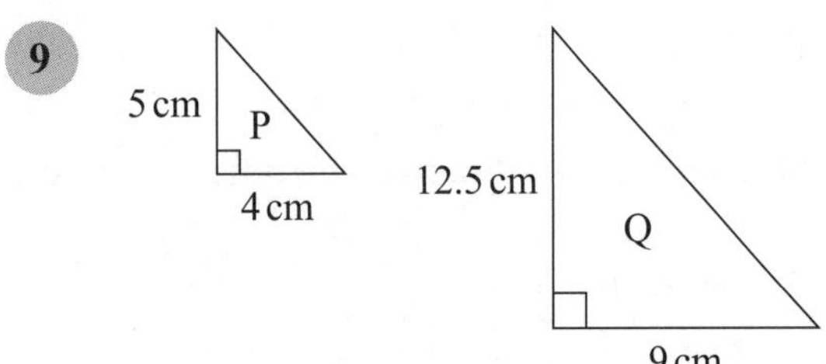

Is triangle Q an enlargement of triangle P?
Explain your answer.

10 Draw an enlargement of this picture with scale factor 2.
Shade in the letters with different colours.

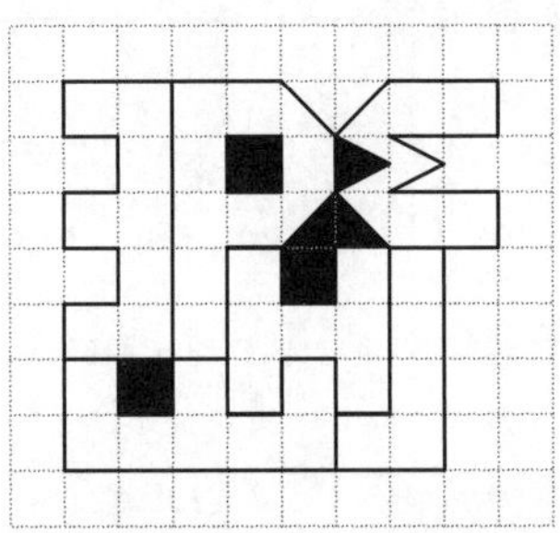

HWK 4M

Main Book page 138

1 Copy each diagram and then draw an enlargement using the scale factor and centre of enlargement given.

a 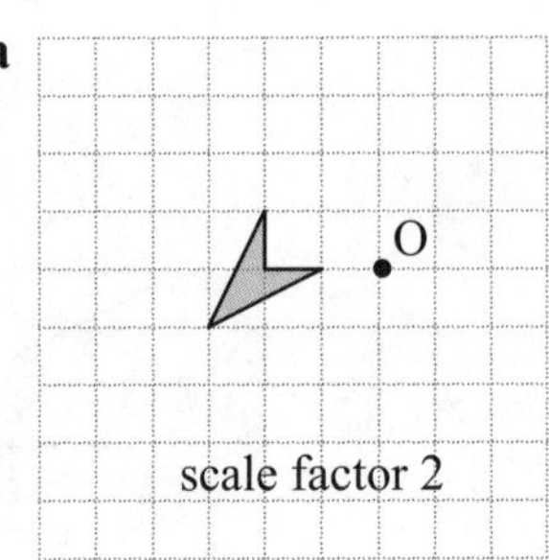

b 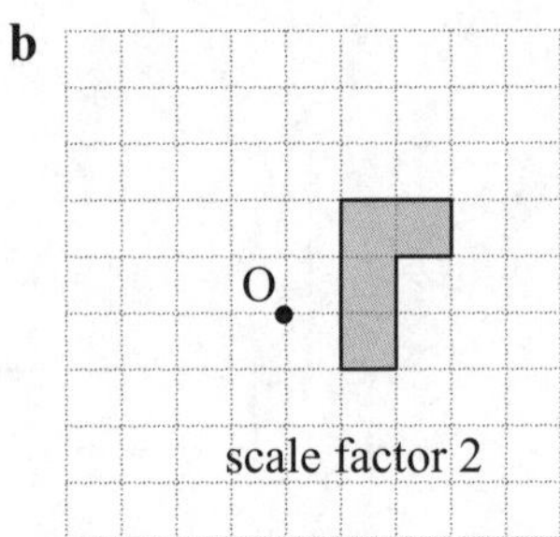

2
- **a** Copy this diagram.
- **b** Enlarge shape A with scale factor 2 and centre of enlargement (0, 0).
- **c** Enlarge shape B with scale factor 4 and centre of enlargement (0, 0).
- **d** Enlarge shape C with scale factor 3 and centre of enlargement (0, 0).
- **e** Enlarge shape D with scale factor 2 and centre of enlargement (0, 0).

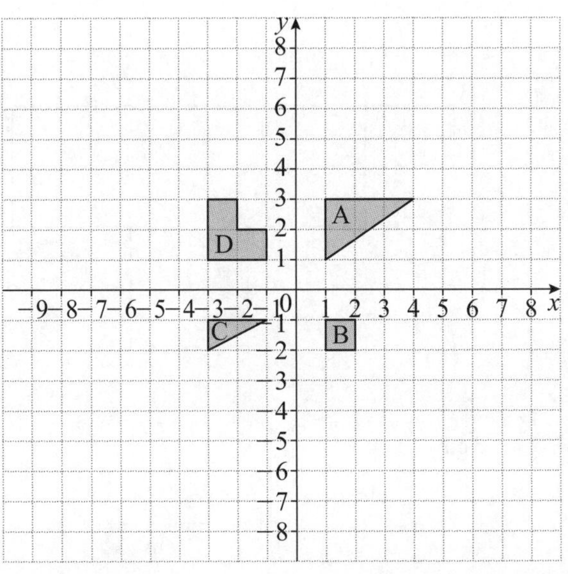

3 **a** Draw an x-axis from -8 to 8 and a y-axis from -5 to 10. Draw triangle A with vertices at (1, 1), (1, 4) and (3, 1).

b Draw triangle B, the image of triangle A under enlargement with scale factor 3, centre (5, 1).

c Draw triangle C, the image of triangle A under enlargement with scale factor 2, centre $(-1, 3)$.

d Draw triangle D, the image of triangle B under enlargement with scale factor $\frac{1}{3}$, centre $(-4, -5)$.

e Draw triangle E, the image of triangle C under enlargement with scale factor $\frac{1}{2}$, centre (5, 9).

f Which triangles are congruent to triangle A?

g Write down the ratio of the area of triangle B to the area of triangle C in its simplest form.

2.6 Rotation and combined transformations

HWK 1M **Main Book page 144**

In questions 1 to 3, draw the shape and then draw and shade its new position (the image), after the rotation stated. Take O as the centre of rotation in each case.

1

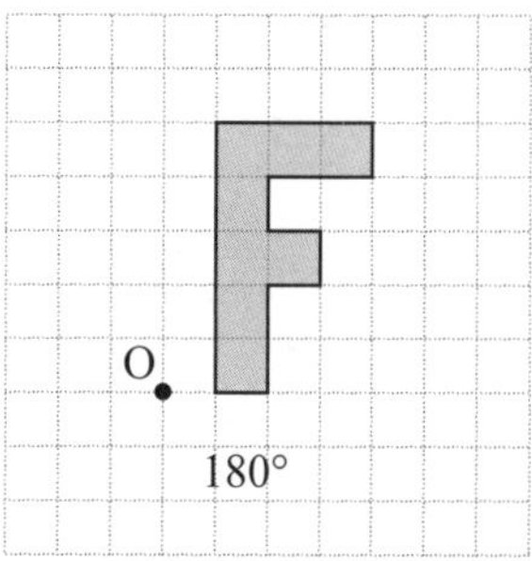

2

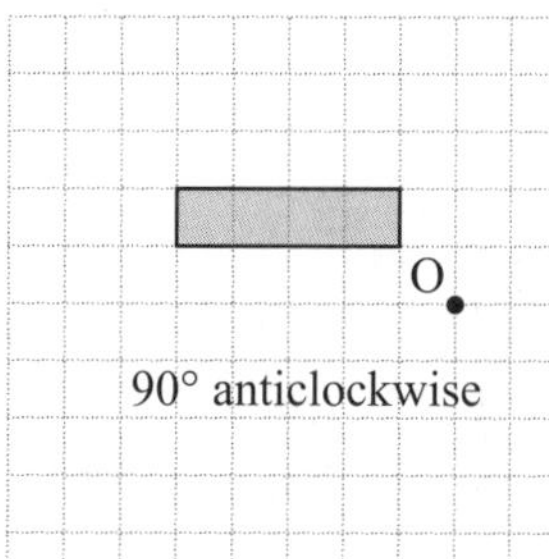

3

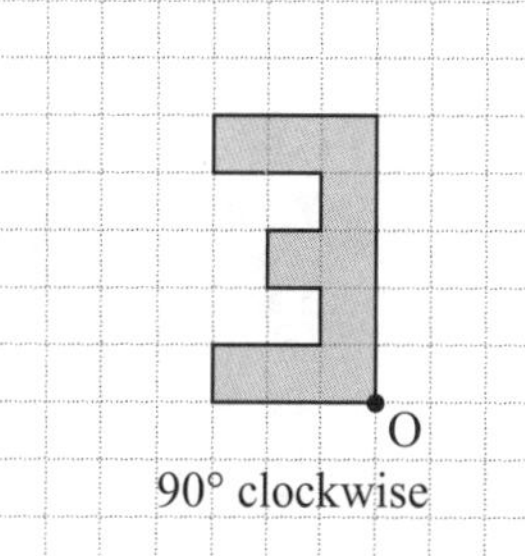

4 Copy the diagram shown, using axes from -6 to 6.

a Rotate shape P 90° anticlockwise about (0, 0). Label the new shape R.

b Rotate triangle Q 90° clockwise about $(4, -1)$. Label the new shape S.

c Rotate shape Q 180° about (0, 0). Label the new shape T.

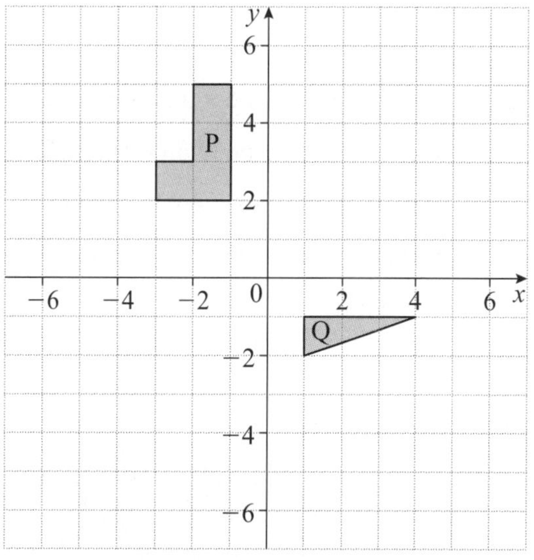

5 **a** Draw axes with values from -6 to 6 and draw triangle P with vertices at $(-3, -2)$, $(-3, -6)$ and $(-5, -2)$.

b Rotate triangle P 90° anticlockwise about (0, 0). Draw and label the new triangle Q.

c Rotate triangle Q 90° anticlockwise about $(2, -2)$. Draw and label the new triangle R.

d Rotate triangle R 180° about (3, 2). Draw and label the new triangle S.

e Rotate triangle S 90° anticlockwise about (0, 0). Draw and label the new triangle T. Write down the coordinates of each vertex (corner) of triangle T.

HWK 2M

Main Book page 145

In questions 1 and 2, copy each diagram. Use tracing paper to find the centre of each rotation.

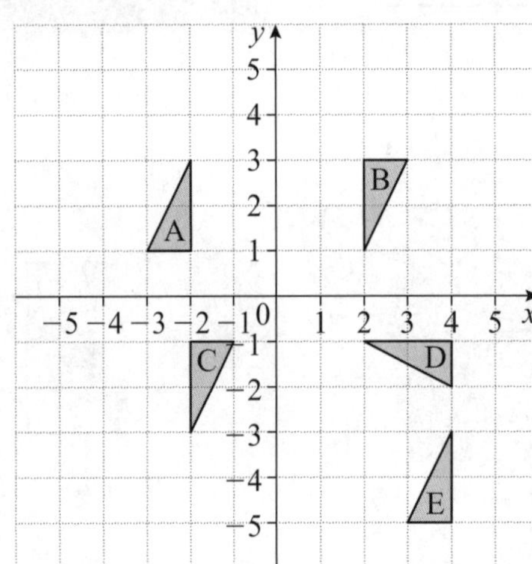

a rotation of △A onto △B

b rotation of △A onto △C

c rotation of △B onto △D

d rotation of △C onto △E

2 **a** rotation of shape P onto shape Q

b rotation of shape Q onto shape R

c rotation of shape Q onto shape S

d rotation of shape S onto shape T

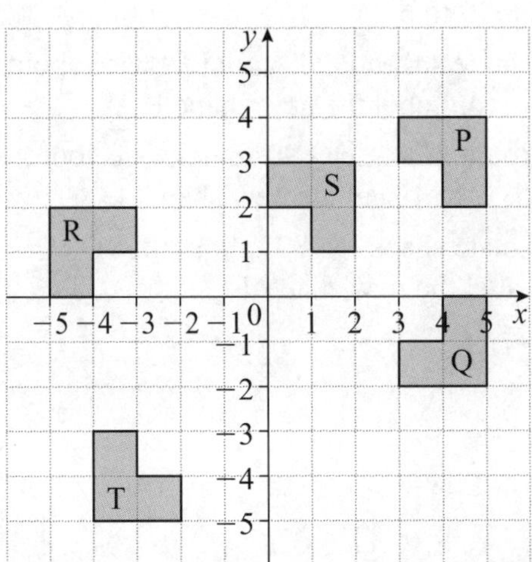

3 Draw axes with values from -8 to 8 and draw triangles with the following vertices:

triangle A:	$(-3, 3)$	$(-3, 6)$	$(-4, 3)$
triangle B:	$(1, 3)$	$(1, 4)$	$(4, 3)$
triangle C:	$(-3, 1)$	$(-4, 1)$	$(-3, -2)$
triangle D:	$(1, -6)$	$(-2, -7)$	$(-2, -6)$
triangle E:	$(2, -7)$	$(5, -7)$	$(5, -8)$
triangle F:	$(3, 1)$	$(3, 4)$	$(4, 1)$

Describe fully the following rotations or reflections.
For rotations, give the angle, direction and centre. For reflections, give the equation of the mirror line.

a triangle A → triangle B **b** A → C **c** C → D **d** B → E **e** B → F

HWK 3M

Main Book page 147

1 Copy this diagram.

a Rotate shape P 90° anticlockwise about (0, 0). Label the new shape Q.

b Reflect shape Q in the y-axis. Label the new shape R.

c Rotate shape R 90° anticlockwise about $(1, -2)$. Label the new shape S.

d Reflect shape S in the y-axis. Label the new shape T.

e Describe the single translation which will move shape T onto shape P.

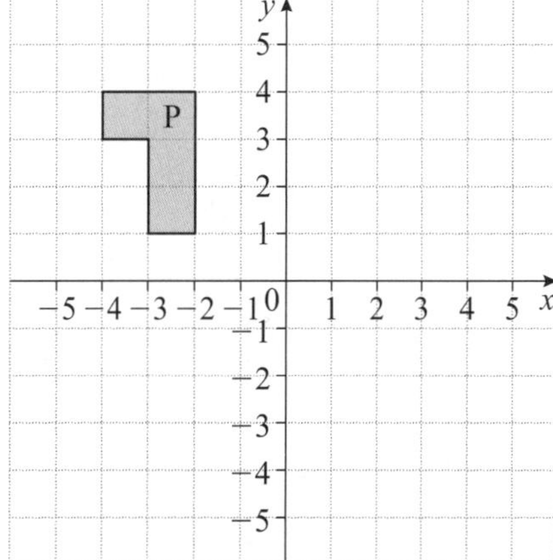

2 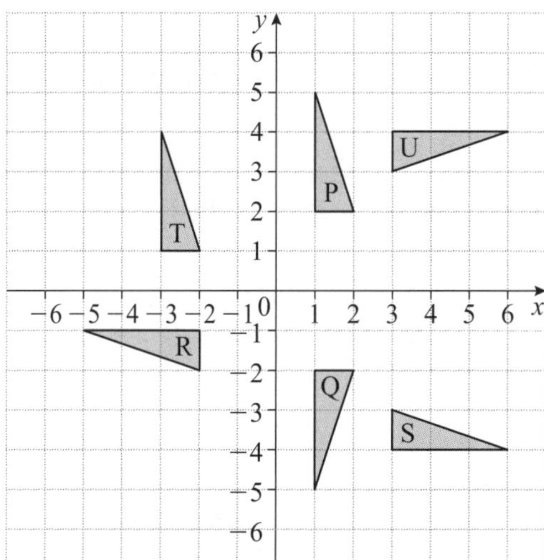

Describe fully the following transformations.

a triangle P onto triangle Q

b triangle Q onto triangle R

c triangle Q onto triangle S

d triangle P onto triangle T

e triangle P onto triangle U

f triangle S onto triangle U

3

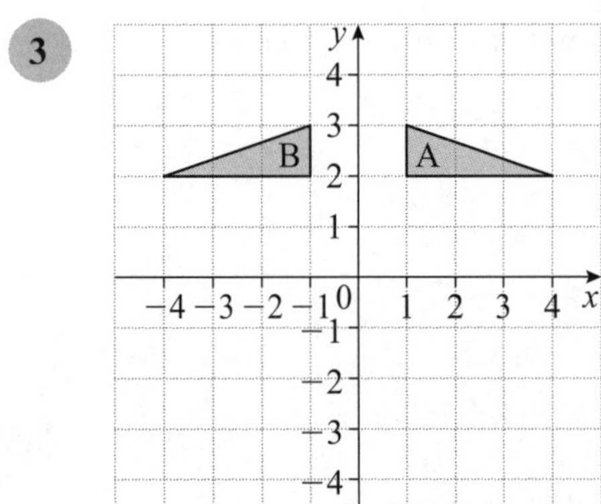

Describe the following transformations which will move triangle A onto triangle B.

a a reflection followed by a rotation

b a rotation followed by a reflection

c a reflection followed by a translation

d a translation followed by a reflection

4

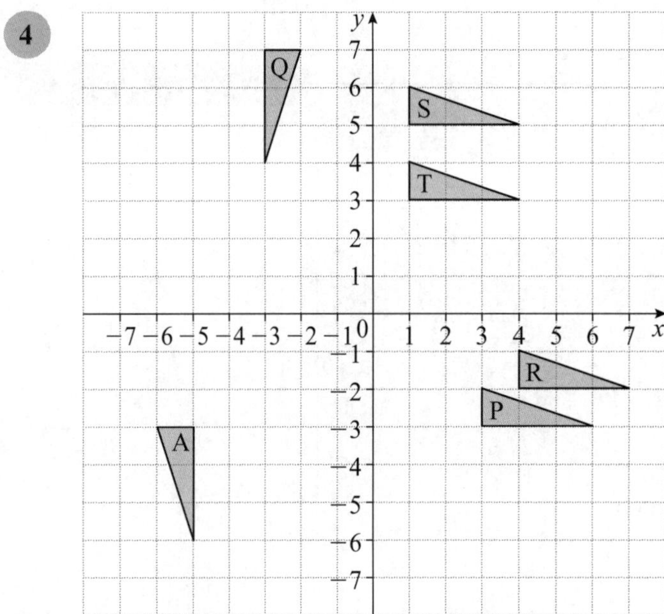

Triangle A can be transformed onto each of triangles P to T by a combination of a rotation and a reflection (in either order).

Describe the rotation and reflection for each triangle. (It may be helpful to copy the diagram first.)

5

Draw a shape of your own on a set of axes. Move this shape with one transformation followed by another.

Challenge somebody in your next maths lesson to describe the two transformations you have used. (Your diagram should have just the original shape and the final shape.)

UNIT 3

3.1 Area

HWK 1M Main Book page 169

1 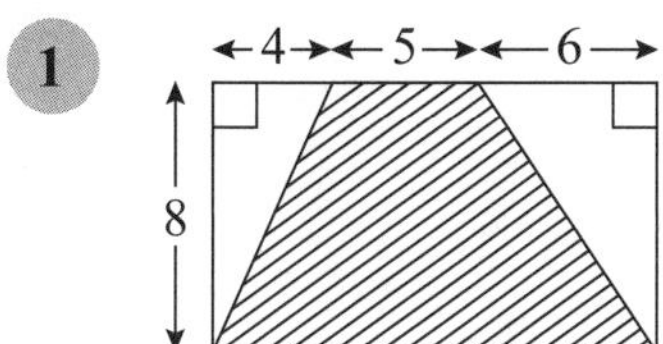

Calculate the shaded area.
(all lengths are in cm)

2 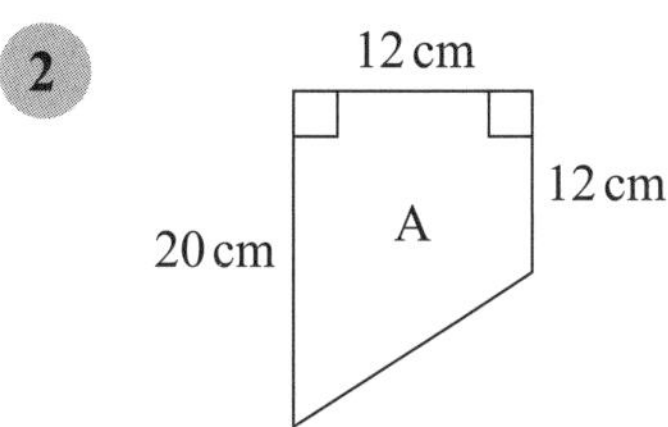

Which shape has the larger area and by how much?

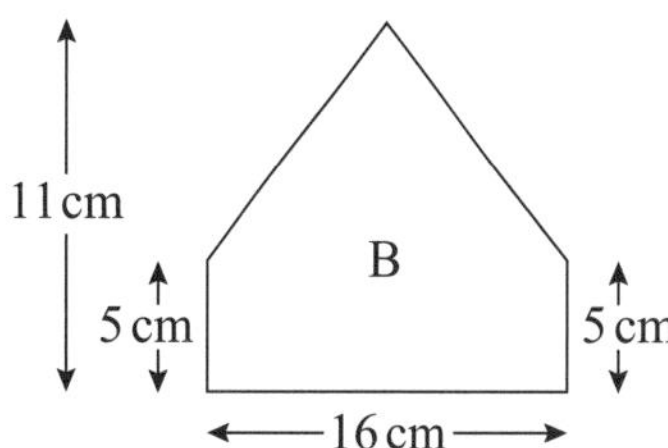

3 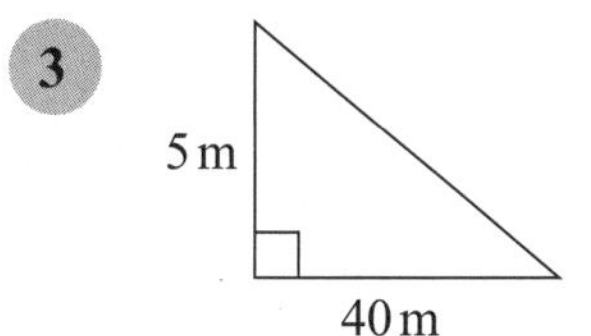

These two shapes have the same area.
Find the length of the side marked x.

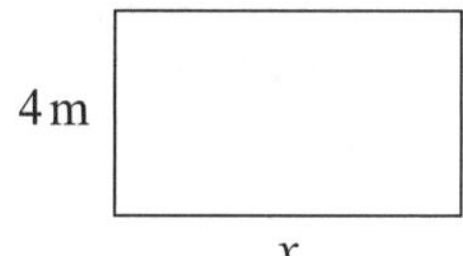

4 Calculate the area of each shape. The lengths are in cm.

a 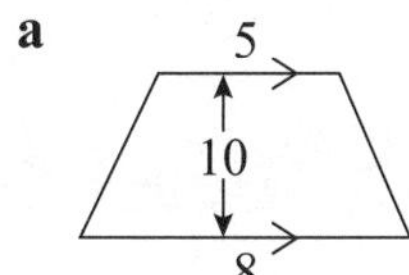

b 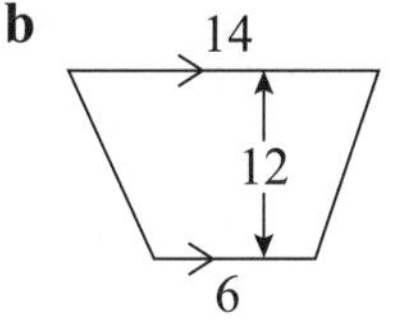

c 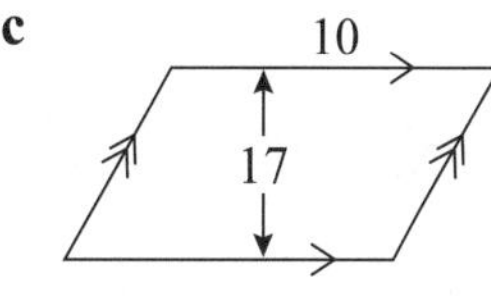

5 Calculate the value of x in each parallelogram below.

a 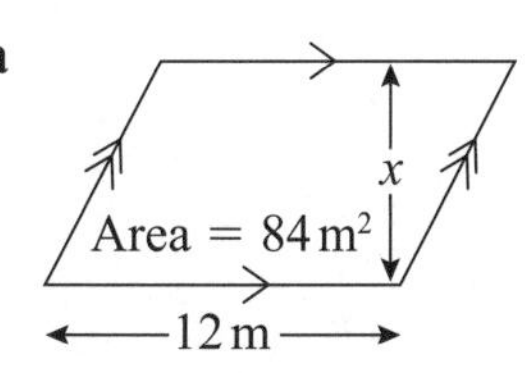

b 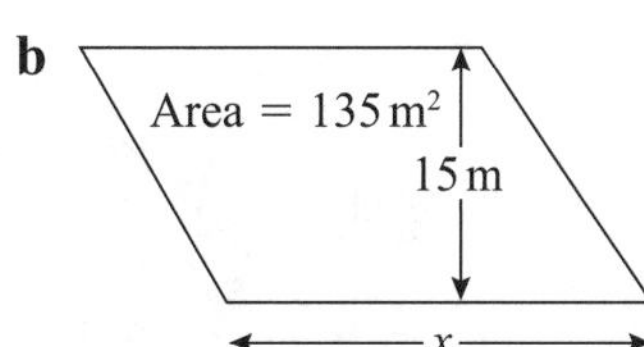

6

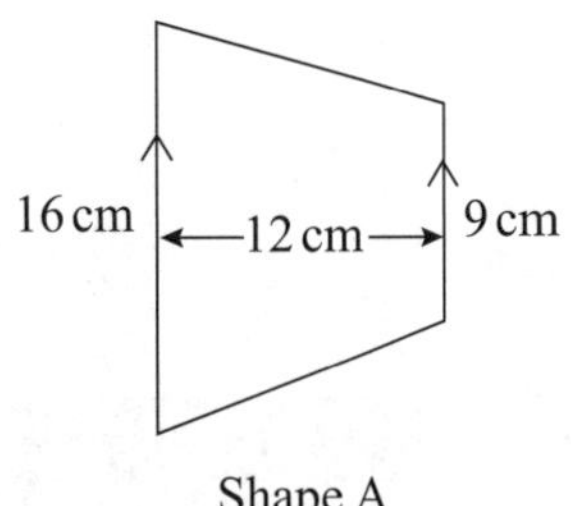

Shape A

Which shape has the larger area and by how much?

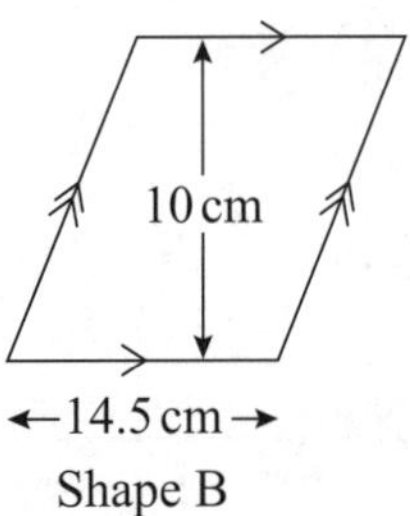

Shape B

7 Work out the area of a square of perimeter 36 cm

8 Draw any shape with an area of 5 cm^2 and perimeter 12 cm

9 Imagine this shape, which is made using squares, has an area of 160 cm^2.
Find the perimeter of this shape.

10 Ashley has to paint one side of his house.
Each pot of paint covers 20 m^2.
How many pots of paint will Ashley need to buy to do the job?

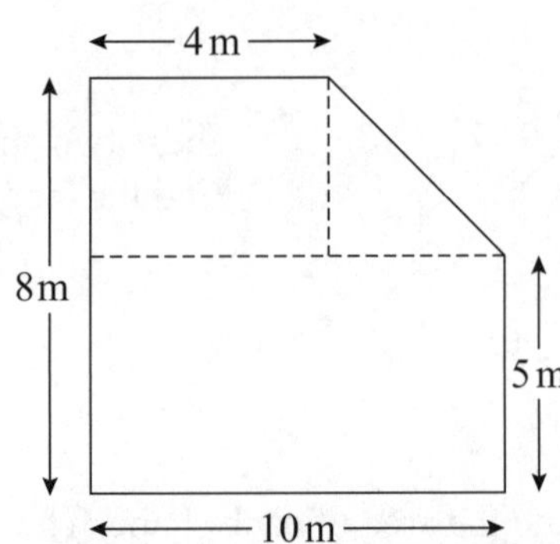

HWK 2M

Main Book page 171

1 Find the area of this shape.

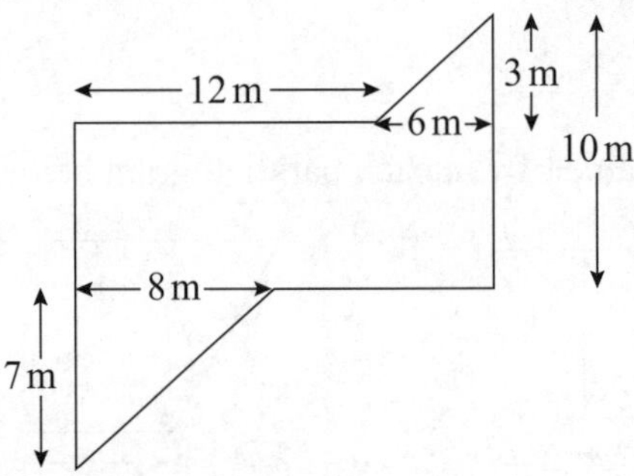

2 A triangular field has a base of $\frac{1}{2}$ km and a height of 300 m. Calculate the area of the field in hectares. (1 hectare = 10 000 m^2)

3 Square A has perimeter 20 cm. Square B has perimeter 28 cm. Rectangle C has length 14 cm and width 5 cm. The area of square P is equal to the sum of the areas of square A, square B and rectangle C. Find the perimeter of square P.

4 Alice wishes to carpet this room.

a What is the area of the room?

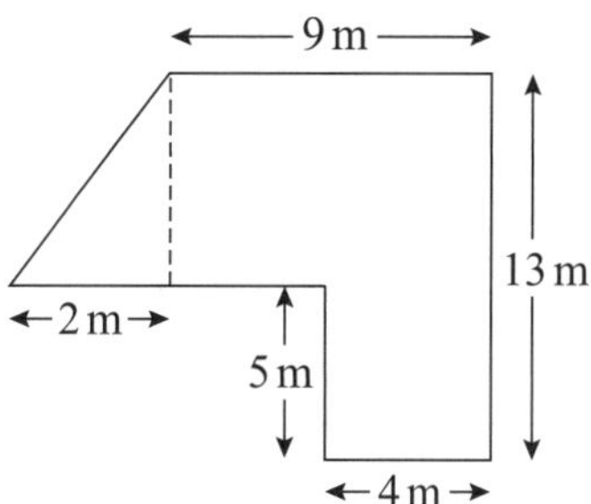

b 'Texas Twist' carpet costs £15.85 per square metre. 'Winchester Croft' carpet costs £17.25 per square metre. Alice decides to either carpet the whole room with 'Texas Twist' or to use 'Winchester Croft' for the L-shaped part only (so she does not carpet the triangular part of the room). Which is the cheaper option and by how much?

5 Calculate the area of each shaded shape. Give your answers in square units.

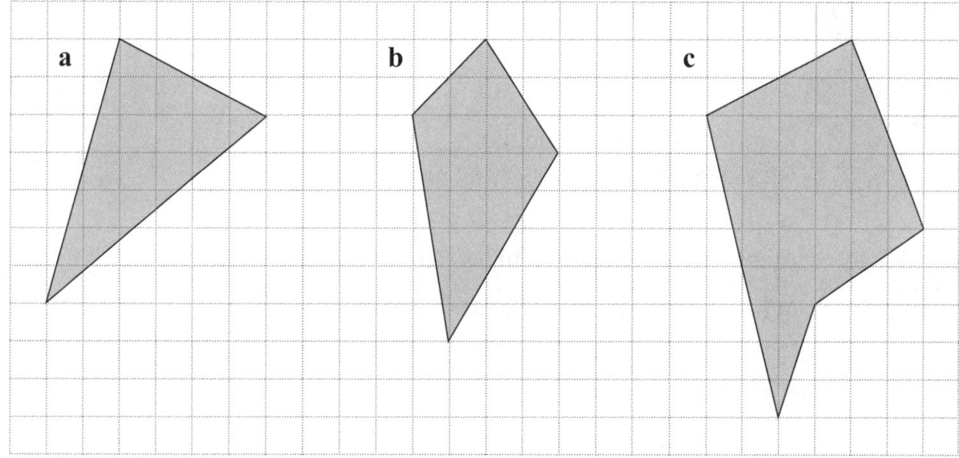

6 Jed is putting tiles onto a rectangular wall which measures 3 m by 5 m. Each tile is a square with side 10 cm. A box of 25 tiles costs £9.85.

a How many tiles does Jed need?

b How much will Jed have to pay for the tiles?

c Jed ends up breaking 5% of the tiles. How much *extra* must he spend on the tiles to finish the job?

7

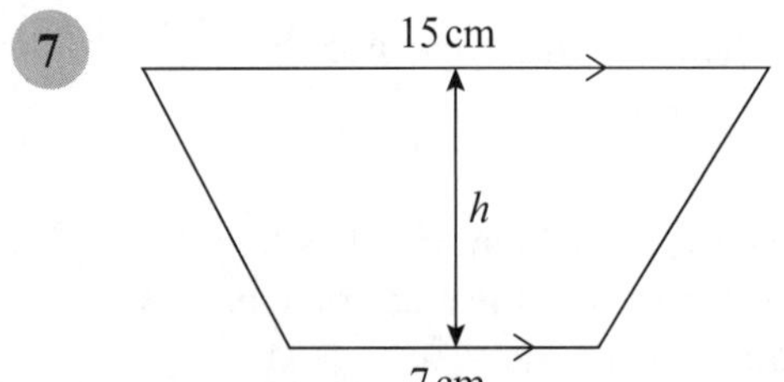

The area of this trapezium is 132 cm^2.
Find the value of h.

8

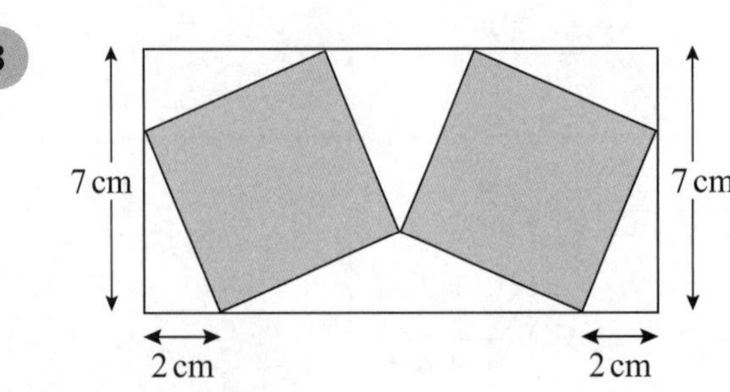

The diagram shows two squares inside a rectangle. Calculate the total area of the two grey squares.

3.2 Circles

HWK 1M — **Main Book page 178**

Remember: circumference = $\pi \times$ diameter

Give all answers to one decimal place.

1

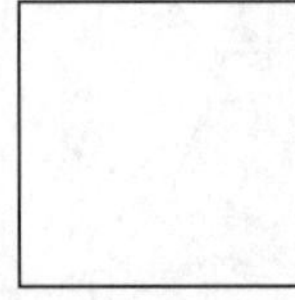

Tom walks once around the edge of a 60 m length square field.

Anna walks once around the edge of an 80 m diameter circular field.

Who walks further and by how much?

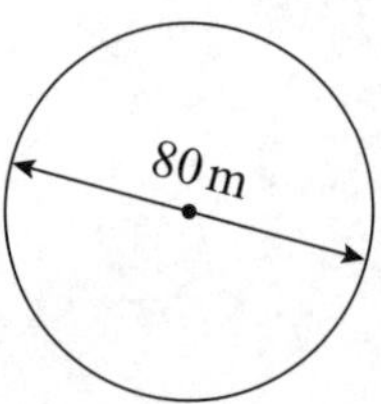

2 A coin has a radius of 8 mm. Find its circumference.

3

In a game show, a comedian lies on a circular turntable. The comedian is 1.7 m tall.

If the turntable is spun around four complete rotations, how far will the top of the comedian's head travel?

4 The wheels on a bike have a diameter of 59 cm. Alf travels 25 m on this bike.
How many times do the wheels go round *completely*?

5

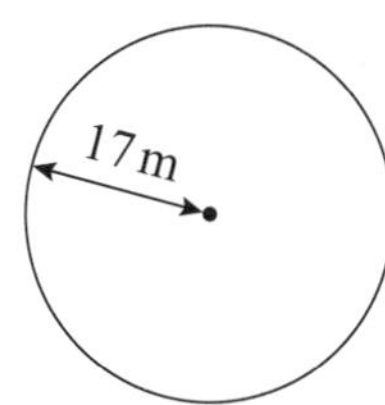

A dog runs around this circular pond at a speed of 2.5 m/s. How long does it take the dog to run all the way round the pond twice? Give your answer to 1 decimal place.

6 The circumference of a circular field is 400 m. Calculate the diameter of the field to the nearest cm.

7 A circle has a perimeter of 563 cm. Calculate the radius of the circle to the nearest cm.

8 The wheels on Mary's model car have a diameter of 3.2 cm. The wheels on Wayne's model car have a radius of 1.3 cm. Both cars are pushed so that their wheels rotate completely 50 times. How much further does Mary's car travel than Wayne's?

9

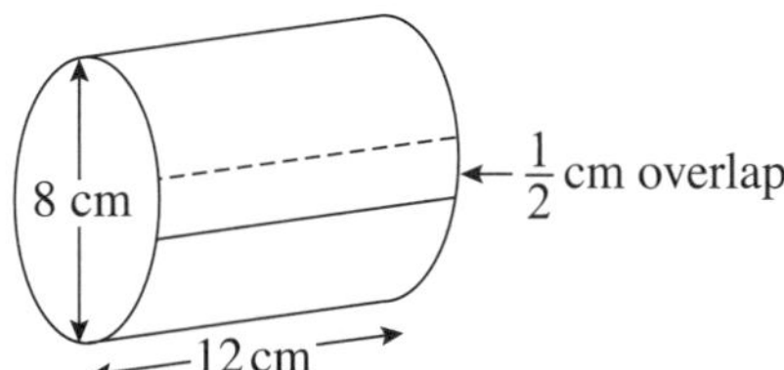

A rectangular piece of paper is wrapped around a tin with a $\frac{1}{2}$ cm overlap for fixing. Calculate the area of the piece of paper. Give your answer to 1 decimal place.

10 John and his dad go for a bike ride. John's bike wheels have a radius of 49 cm and his dad's bike wheels have a radius of 62 cm. During part of the journey, his dad's bike wheels rotate 530 times. How many complete rotations do John's bike wheels make during the same part of the journey?

HWK 2M

Main Book page 180

Calculate the perimeter of each shape. All shapes are either semicircles or quarter circles. Give answers correct to 1 decimal place.

1

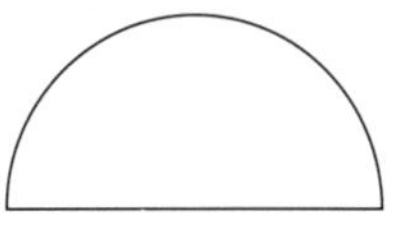

2

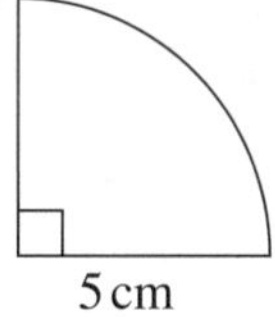

3

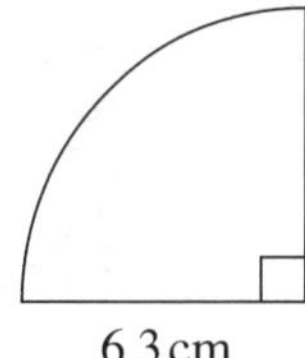

4

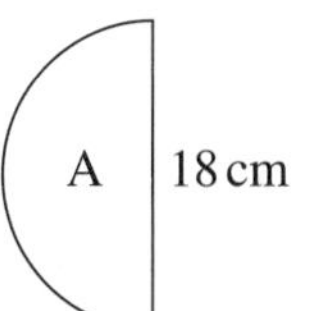

Which shape has the longer perimeter and by how much?

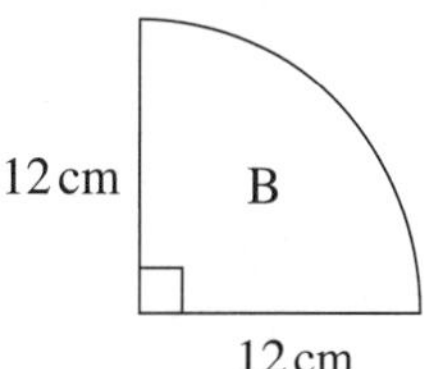

5 This shape is made from a triangle and a semicircle. Calculate the total perimeter of this shape.

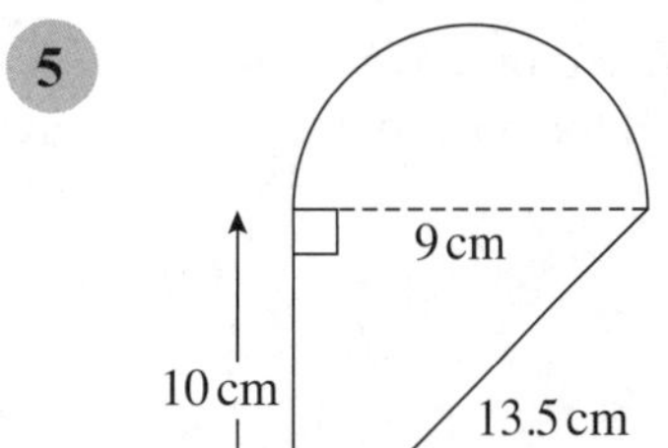

6 Calculate the perimeter of this shape correct to 1 decimal place.

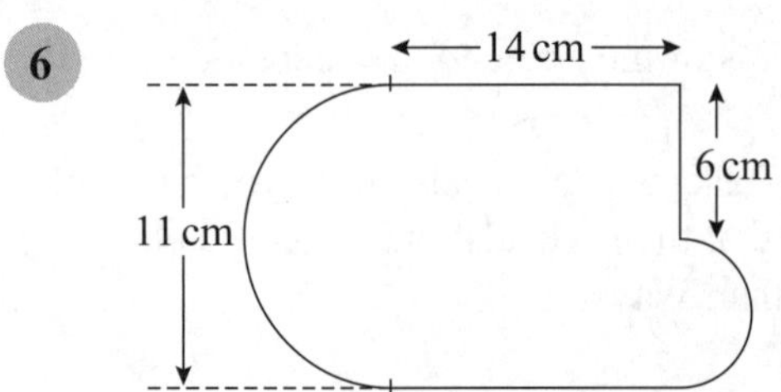

7 Calculate the perimeter of each shape.

a

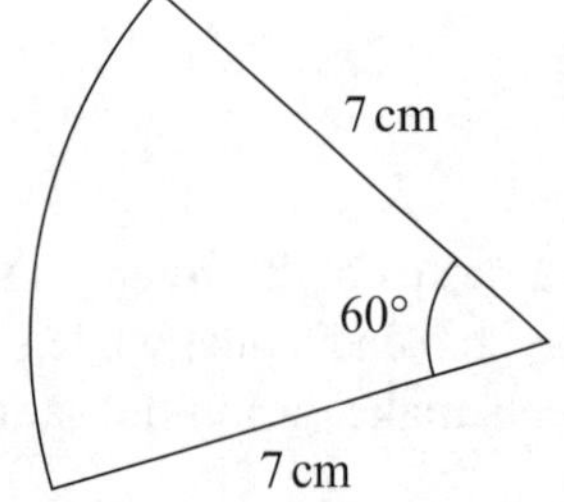

b

12 cm
120°
12 cm

HWK 3M — Main Book page 181

Give all answers correct to one decimal place in this exercise.

1 Calculate the shaded area.

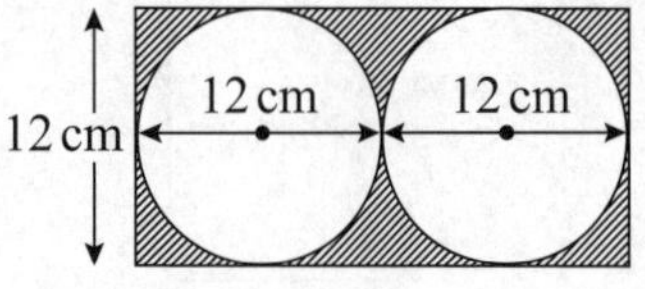

In questions **2** to **4**, find the area of each shape. All arcs are either semicircles or quarter circles.

2

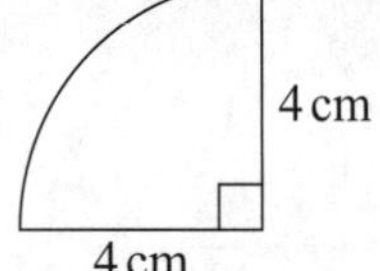

3

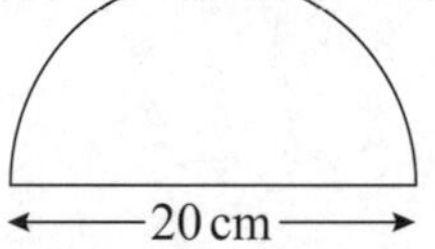

4

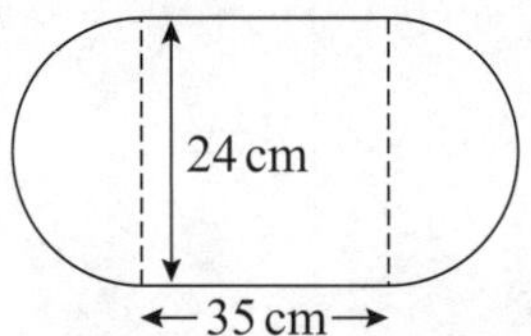

5 A circular lawn has diameter 60 m. In the centre of the lawn is a circular pond with a radius of 5 m. What is the area of the lawn without the pond?

6 This shape is made from a rectangle and a quarter circle. Calculate the total area of the shape.

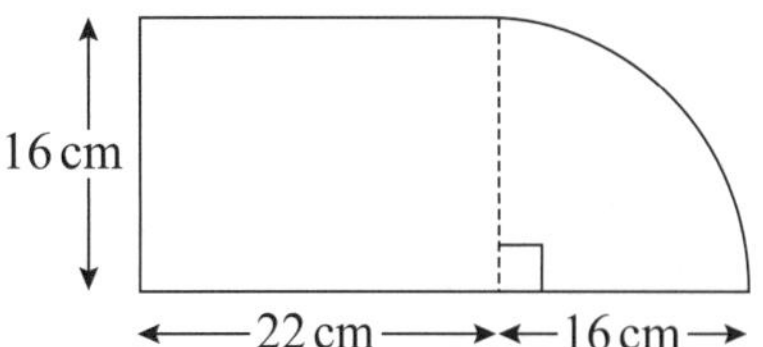

7 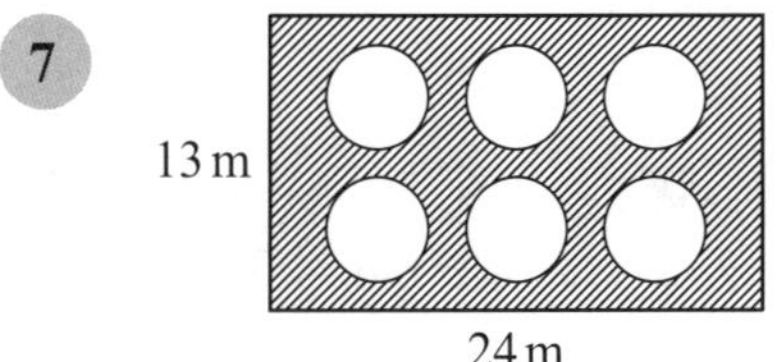

The shaded part of this design is to be painted blue. Each circle has a diameter of 5 m. Calculate the blue area.

8 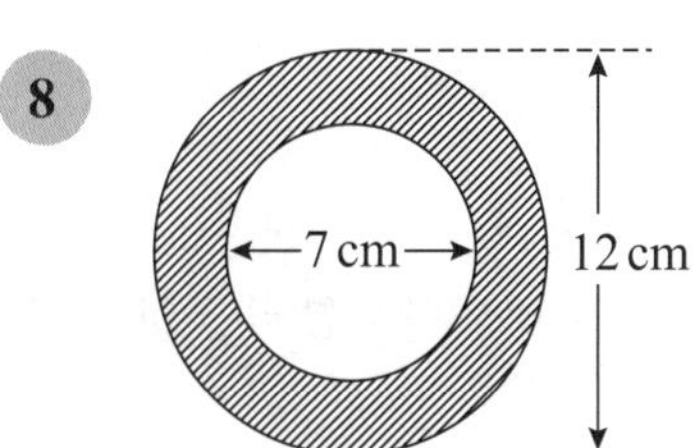

Find the shaded area.

9 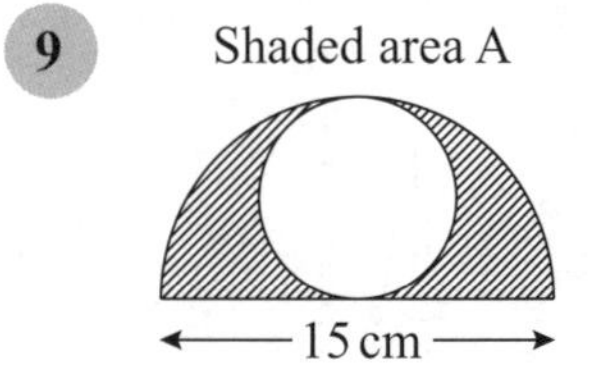

Which shaded area is greater and by how much?

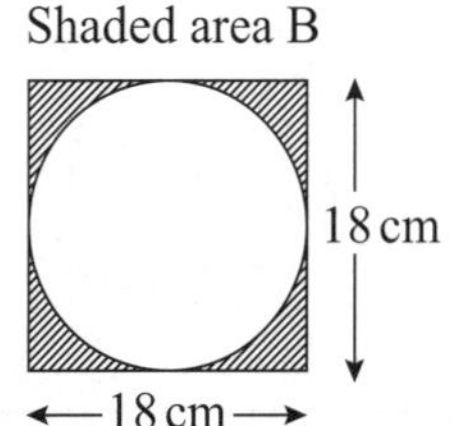

10 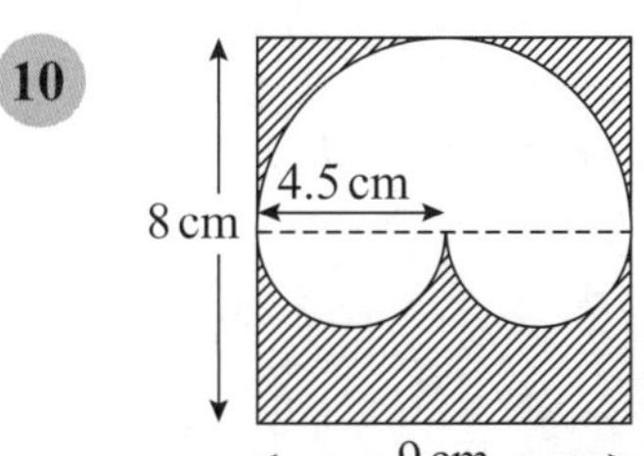

Calculate the shaded area.

3.3 Number – calculations review

HWK 1M — **Main Book page 188**

1 Work out, without a calculator

a 0.0654 ÷ 3 **b** 0.82 − 0.157 **c** 12.74 ÷ 7 **d** 429 × 83

e 928 ÷ 32 **f** 144 000 ÷ 60 **g** 7 − 3.014 **h** 688 ÷ 43

2 Colin weighs 63.64 kg and Marie weighs 51.87 kg. How much heavier is Colin?

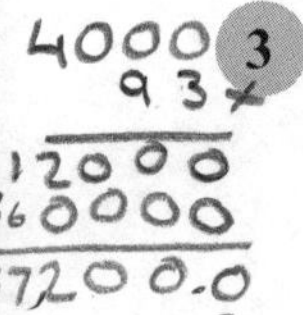

3 Work out, without a calculator

a 9.3 × 4000 **b** 4.92 × 0.25 **c** 0.169 × 1000 **d** 36 + 16.2

e 0.82 − 0.073 **f** 0.312 ÷ 6 **g** 8.19 × 0.5 **h** 6.4 × 3000

i 0.019 + 3.685 **j** 6 − 0.018 **k** 0.86 × 7 **l** 0.513 ÷ 9

4 Charlie is sponsored £3.20 per kilometre for a charity run. How much money is he given if he runs 13.8 km?

5 A drama group from a school put on a charity show. 39 tickets are sold at £23 each and 68 tickets are sold at £12 each. The show costs £423 to put on. The remaining money is split equally between 6 charities. How much money does each charity receive?

6 Copy and complete

a 3.9 + ☐ = 6.34 **b** 0.28 ÷ ☐ = 0.0028 **c** 9 − ☐ = 4.44

d ☐ − 0.19 = 0.34 **e** ☐ × 0.5 = 1.69 **f** ☐ + 2.91 = 10.15

HWK 2M — **Main Book page 189**

For each of the scales, work out the measurement shown by the arrows.

1
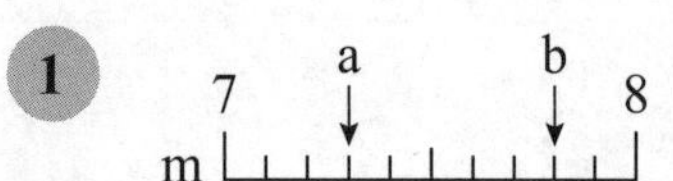

2
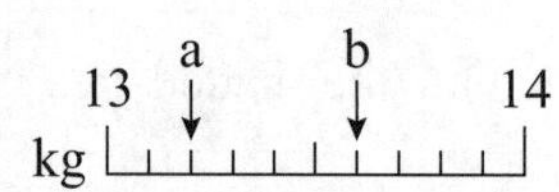

3
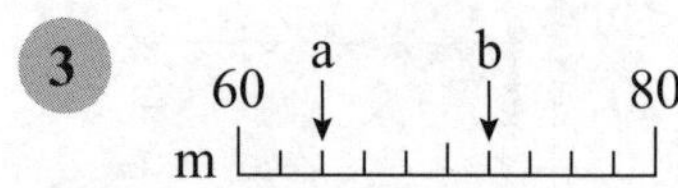

4 **5** **6**
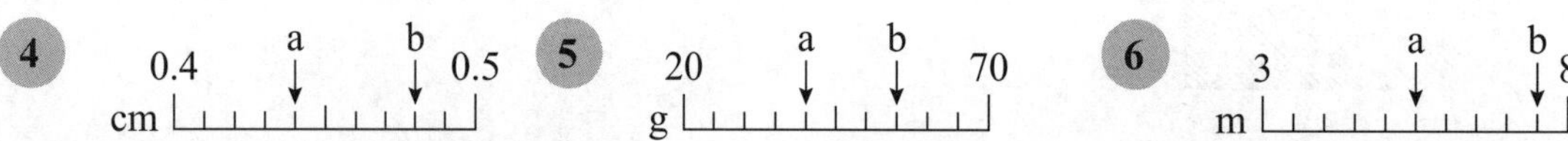

7 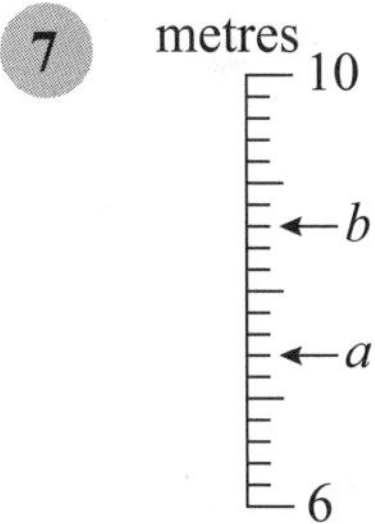

Work out the difference between the values at b and a.

8 Copy the line and locate the numbers.

4.02	3.96	3.92	4.08	4.06

3.9 4.1

9 Copy the line and locate the numbers.

2.35	2.365	2.38	2.31	2.325

2.3 2.4

10 Write down the measurement shown by each arrow below.

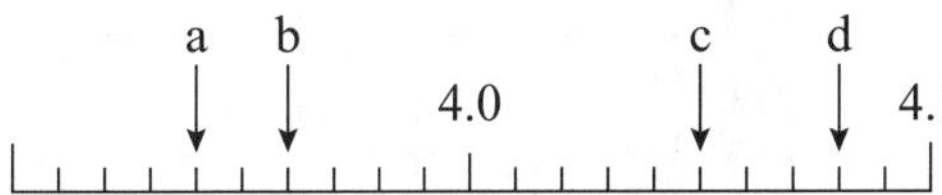

11 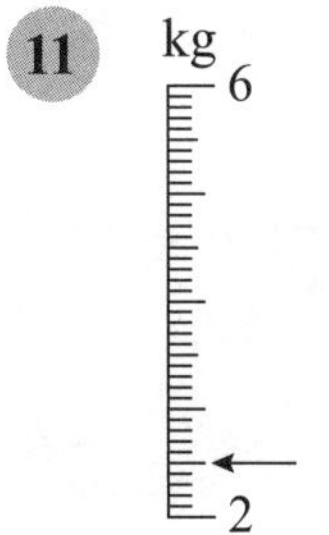

The weight of some cheese is shown on the scale. The price of cheese is £5.80 per kg. How much does this piece of cheese cost?

12 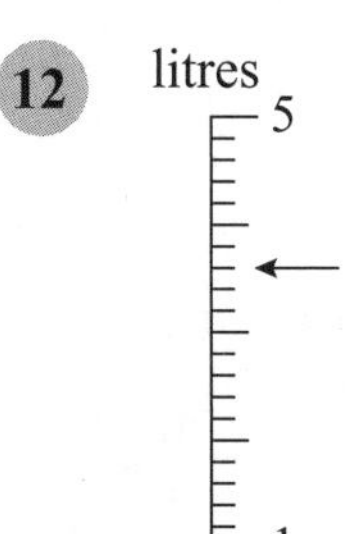

Petrol costs £1.38 per litre. What is the cost of the petrol indicated by the arrow opposite? Give the answer to the nearest penny.

HWK 3M

Main Book page 191

1 Answer 'true' or 'false'.

a $0.3^2 = 0.9$ **b** $0.1 \times 0.2 = 0.2$ **c** $0.5^2 = 0.25$

2 A 4 m width of carpet costs £8.35 per metre. Calculate the cost of 6.4 m of carpet.

3

0.9 m

A

1.6 m

Which shape has the larger area and by how much?

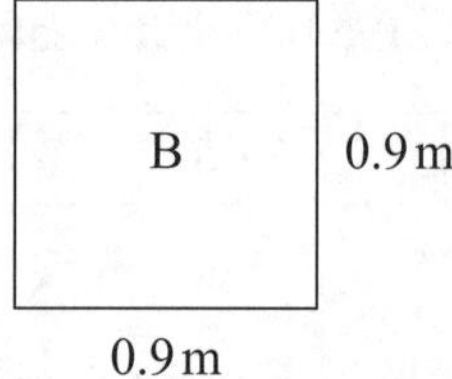

4 Work out, without a calculator. Check each answer by finding an approximate answer.

a 8.7×37.3 **b** 0.86×62.3 **c** 71.6×0.95 **d** 0.342×47

5 Copy and complete the multiplication square.

×	0.3	0.05	7	1.2	0.9
0.6					
0.05					
1.1					
0.8					
4					

6 £1 can be changed for $1.46

a How many dollars do you get for £300?

b How many dollars do you get for £550?

7 Copy and complete

a $0.4 \times \square = 0.024$ **b** $\square^2 = 0.0025$ **c** $\square \times 0.08 = 0.096$

8 Work out the difference between 6.18×0.089 and 0.068×3.06

HWK 4M

Main Book page 192

1 Answer 'true' or 'false'.

a $0.4 \div 0.01 = 4$ **b** $31 \div 0.1 = 310$ **c** $45 \div 0.01 = 450$

d $0.8 \div 0.01 = 800$ **e** $1 \div 0.01 = 100$ **f** $0.9 \div 0.1 = 9$

2 Work out, without a calculator

a $6.39 \div 0.3$ **b** $0.72 \div 0.4$ **c** $0.49 \div 0.2$ **d** $1.158 \div 0.6$

e $3.78 \div 0.3$ **f** $0.1174 \div 0.02$ **g** $0.01352 \div 0.08$ **h** $9.52 \div 0.7$

i $0.0126 \div 0.09$ **j** $0.6656 \div 0.8$ **k** $0.01528 \div 0.002$ **l** $0.0655 \div 0.005$

3 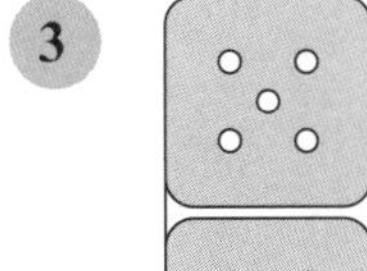

A domino is 4.8 cm long. Hundreds of dominoes are laid in a line 1680 cm long. *Exactly* how many dominoes are used?

4 On average a chocolate raisin weighs 0.9 g.
How many chocolate raisins will there be in a packet which weighs 76.5 g?

5 Caroline works at a garage and is paid £8.20 per hour. Scott also works at the garage and is paid £7.50 per hour.
During one week, Caroline earns £164 and Scott earns £240. Work out the total number of hours Caroline and Scott worked during that week.

6 **a** Start in the top left box below.
b Work out the answer to the calculation in the box. *Do not use a calculator.*
c Find the answer in the top corner of another box.
d Write down the letter in that box.
e Repeat steps **b**, **c** and **d** until you arrive back at the top left box. What is the message?

1.8 0.7×0.9	172.8 O $4.32 \div 0.08$	0.714 E 0.8^3	1300 E 46×0.6	0.057 N $0.08 \div 0.001$	2.16 T 0.08^2
3.6 E $6^3 \times 0.01$	80 O $0.9^3 - 0.8^2$	16.86 U 0.28×200	2080 E $0.4^2 - 0.103$	54 F $0.73 - \frac{2}{5}$	56 T 4.8×36
27.6 O $19 - 2.14$	0.63 G $0.144 \div 0.04$	0.33 H 1.7×0.42	0.0064 M $13 \div 0.01$	0.089 W $0.468 \div 0.26$	0.512 R 5.2×400

3.4 Using a calculator

HWK 1M Main Book page 199

1. Answer 'true' or 'false'.

   a $(3 + 4)^2 = 49$ **b** $8^2 - 4 = 12$ **c** $8 + 3 \times 2 = 22$

   d $5^2 - 3^2 = 16$ **e** $19 + 3 \times 4 = 31$ **f** $4 \times (6 + 3) = 27$

   g $(4^2 + 2^2) \div 5 = 4$ **h** $\frac{25 - 8 \times 2}{3} = 3$ **i** $5 + 6^2 \div 9 = 9$

In questions **2** to **10**, find the missing signs (+, −, ×, ÷). There are no brackets.

2. 8 2 3 = 19
3. 5 3 1 = 2
4. 4 18 3 = 10
5. 20 2 15 = 25
6. 9 16 4 = 21
7. 5 9 2 = 23
8. 16 14 2 1 = 10
9. 10 2 3 4 = 17
10. 9 4 2 3 = 14

The next six questions have brackets.

11. 4 5 2 = 12
12. 8 3 4 = 44
13. 8 2 4 3 = 42
14. 9 4 1 7 = 10
15. 15 25 7 3 = 4
16. 8 5 6 20 = 18
17. Copy each question below and insert brackets so that each calculation gives the correct answer.

    a $13 + 17 \div 5 = 6$ **b** $5 + 20 \div 3 + 2 = 5$ **c** $10 - 6 \div 1 + 3 = 1$

HWK 2M Main Book page 200

Work out and give the answer correct to 2 decimal places.

1. $\frac{9.23 - 2.14}{6.49}$
2. $(7.12 + 4.93 - 1.86)^2 \times 1.6$
3. $\frac{5.6}{1.93} + 4.18$
4. $\frac{11.6 - 3.14}{2.12 + 5.9}$
5. $\frac{7.94}{2.16^2}$
6. $\frac{1.93^2}{5.06 - 2.1}$
7. Jade sells security devices. She makes 8 selling trips to the north-west of England during one month. Each trip costs her £49.50. During the month she sells 7 burglar alarms and 12 security spotlights. She makes £179 profit for each burglar alarm sold and £23 for each spotlight. How much money will she make in total during this month?
8. Jimmy squares the number 4.7 then adds on 28. Abbie subtracts 3.6 from 10 then cubes the answer. Calculate the product of the two final answers.

9 Calculate the following, giving your answer to 2 decimal places.

$$\frac{(7.8^2 + 1.9)^2 - 6.3^2}{(8.91 - 3.6)^2 + 6.4 \times 3.4}$$

10 Use a calculator to work out

a $\frac{2}{3} \times \left(\frac{3}{4} - \frac{1}{5}\right)$ **b** $\frac{9}{10} \div \left(\frac{3}{5} - \frac{3}{20}\right)$ **c** $\left(\frac{4}{9} + \frac{2}{5}\right) \times \frac{3}{4}$

d $\frac{5}{7} \times \left(2\frac{1}{4} - \frac{7}{8}\right)$ **e** $\left(3\frac{1}{2}\right)^2 + \frac{5}{6}$ **f** $\dfrac{2\frac{1}{2} + 3\frac{2}{5}}{1\frac{1}{5} - \frac{5}{6}}$

11 $1\frac{3}{5}$ cm

A

$2\frac{1}{2}$ cm

Which shape has the larger area and by how much?

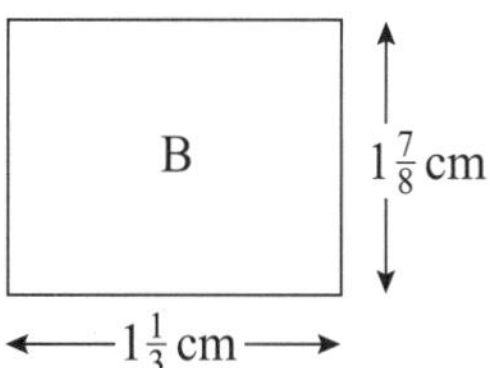

12 Copy and complete this multiplication table.

×		$\frac{1}{5}$	$2\frac{1}{4}$		
	$\frac{1}{2}$				
$1\frac{1}{3}$					
$\frac{7}{9}$	$\frac{14}{27}$			$\frac{35}{54}$	
		$\frac{4}{25}$			$\frac{2}{5}$
					$\frac{1}{3}$

13 Copy and complete

a $\frac{4}{5} \times \left(\frac{3}{4} - \square\right) = \frac{1}{15}$ **b** $\left(2\frac{1}{3} + \square\right) \times \left(3\frac{1}{2} - 2\frac{7}{8}\right) = 1\frac{53}{72}$

c $\left(3\frac{1}{4}\right)^2 - 2\frac{3}{4} \times \square = 6\frac{7}{16}$ **d** $\left(1\frac{2}{3} \div \frac{3}{5} + \square\right) \times \left(\frac{1}{2}\right)^3 = \frac{73}{180}$

HWK 3M

Main Book page 201

Work out the following. Give each answer correct to 1 decimal place where appropriate.

1 $-9 \div (-2)$

2 $-18 - 14$

3 $-6.2 \times (-3.1)$

4 $4.8 - (-3.72)$

5 $-46 \div 4.13$

6 $(-8.12)^2$

7 $\dfrac{(-7) \times 2}{-5}$

8 $9 - 4.6^2$

9 $\dfrac{8 - (-0.17)}{2.3}$

10 $\left(\dfrac{-3.6}{1.92}\right) - (-2.8)$

11 $(-7.2 - 3.93)^2$

12 $49 - (-4.6)^2$

13 Copy and complete

a $-3.7 + \square = 12.1$

b $5.17 + \square = -11.03$

c $\dfrac{-12.48}{\square} = -2.6$

d $4.3 \times \square = -29.24$

14 Which calculation gives the larger answer and by how much?

A $(-4.9)^2 + 4.52$

B $(-5.2 + 10.31)^2 - 2.06$

15

Ron's items
2 tins of paint at £11.99 each
4 paintbrushes at £3.45 each
300 g of nails at £7/kg
12 m of wallpaper at £4.70/metre

a Who has the most expensive bill, Ron or Amy?

b What is the difference in the two bills?

Amy's items
2 paintbrushes at £4.25 each
200 g of nails at £8/kg
14 m of wallpaper at £4.55/metre
3 batons of wood at £6.80 per baton

16 Give answers correct to 1 decimal place.

a $\dfrac{4.9}{8} + \dfrac{6.3}{17}$

b $\sqrt{\dfrac{80.6}{4.17 + 3.8}}$

c $\dfrac{385}{7.6^3 + 123}$

d $2.9^4 - \left(\dfrac{2.8}{3.4}\right)^2$

e $\dfrac{(-4.62) \times 1.8}{(-2.53)}$

f $\dfrac{3}{5}$ of $\left(\dfrac{4.9^2}{3.72}\right)^2$

g 5.4% of 6% of 1270

h $4.6^5 - 7.3^4$

i $\dfrac{7.3^2 + \sqrt{15.4}}{5.8^2 - \sqrt{98}}$

j $(7\% \text{ of } 48.6)^4$

k $\dfrac{8}{9}$ of $\left(\dfrac{5}{6} - \dfrac{2}{5}\right)^2$

l $\sqrt{\dfrac{\sqrt{15} - 1.8^2}{2.73^3 - \sqrt{12}}}$

3.5 Upper and lower bounds

HWK 1M **Main Book page 207**

1. The length of a book is measured at 26.3 cm, to the nearest mm.

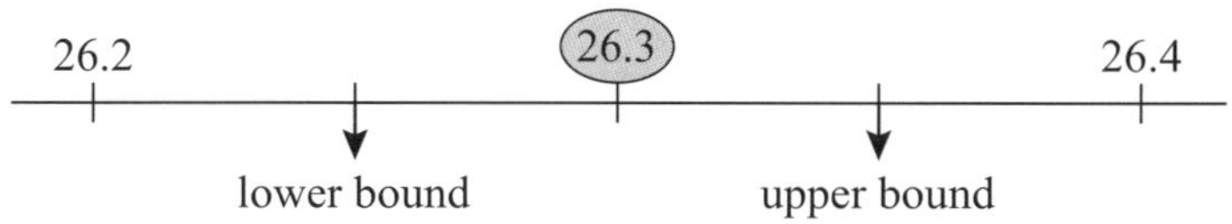

Write down **a** the lower bound **b** the upper bound.

2. The capacity of a bottle is 700 ml, to the nearest millilitre. Write down the lower and upper bounds for this capacity.

3. The length of a paper clip is 49 mm, to the nearest mm. Write down the lower and upper bounds for this length.

4. A dog weighs 31.4 kg, to the nearest 0.1 kg. Write down the lower and upper bounds for this weight.

5. The weight of a person is 90 kg, to the nearest 10 kg. What is the lowest amount that this person might weigh?

6. Remember: the error interval for a weight is:

   lower bound $\leqslant$ weight $<$ *upper bound*

   Copy and complete each error interval below.

   a A volume is 726 ml to the nearest ml, so □ $\leqslant$ volume $<$ □

   b A height is 17.1 cm to the nearest 0.1 cm, so □ $\leqslant$ height $<$ □

   c A speed is 8.2 m/s to 1 decimal place, so □ $\leqslant$ speed $<$ □

   d An area is 14.62 m^2 to 2 decimal places, so □ $\leqslant$ area $<$ □

   e A mass is 638.293 kg to 3 decimal places, so □ $\leqslant$ mass $<$ □

   f A time is 45 seconds to the nearest 5 seconds, so □ $\leqslant$ time $<$ □

7. A teapot contains 900 ml of tea, to the nearest 10 ml. Two mugs each have a capacity of 450 ml, to the nearest ml. Explain clearly why it might *not* be possible to completely fill both the mugs from this teapot.

8 A lift has this sign in it.
The weights of nine people are shown below.
Each weight is measured to the nearest kg.

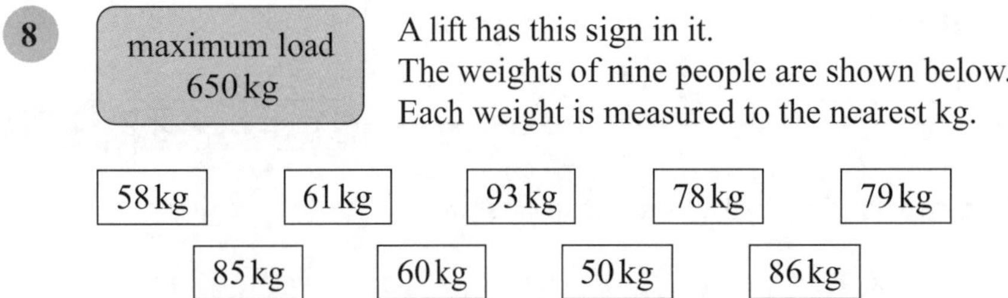

Is it 'safe' for all nine people to travel in the lift? Give a clear reason for your answer.

HWK 2M

Main Book page 208

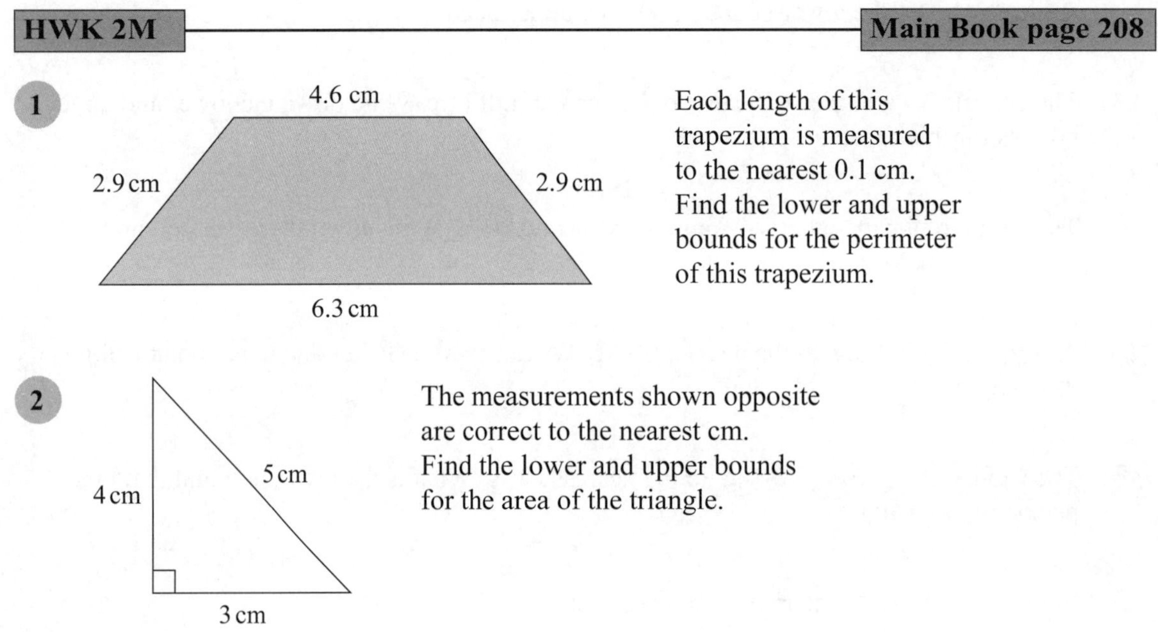

1 Each length of this trapezium is measured to the nearest 0.1 cm. Find the lower and upper bounds for the perimeter of this trapezium.

2 The measurements shown opposite are correct to the nearest cm. Find the lower and upper bounds for the area of the triangle.

3 A pen weighs 28.2 grams to the nearest 0.1 gram. What is the lowest possible weight of 30 pens?

4 The length of one of the sides of a regular hexagon is 4.3 cm to the nearest 0.1 cm. Work out the difference between the upper and lower bounds for the perimeter of the hexagon.

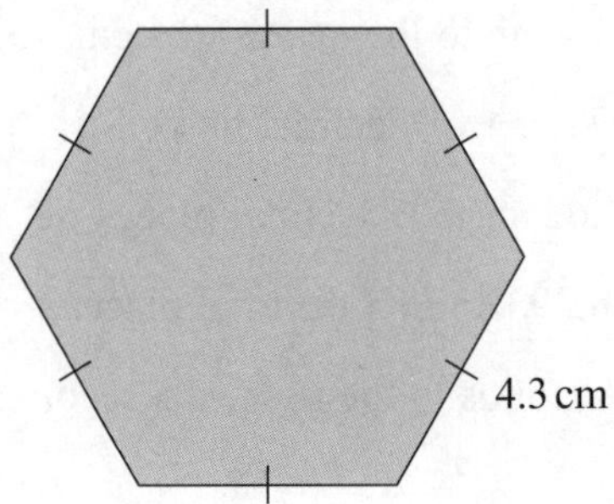

5 Two Christmas tree decorations both weigh 275 g to the nearest gram. What is the greatest possible difference in the actual weights of the two Christmas tree decorations?

6 The measurements shown on the rectangle are correct to the nearest millimetre. Work out the difference between the upper and lower bounds for the area of the rectangle.

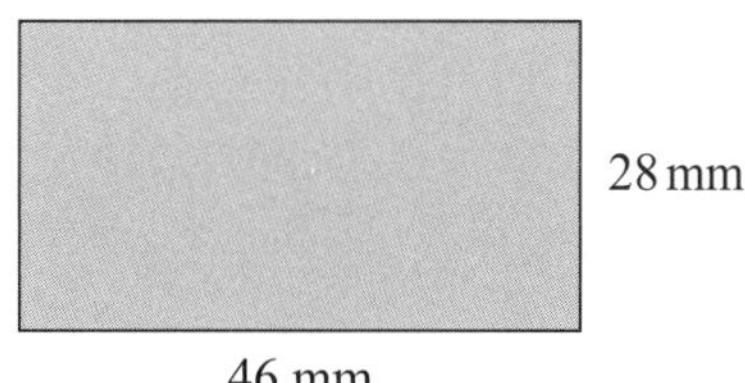

7 If $a = 4.7$ and $b = 12.8$, all measured correct to 1 decimal place, calculate

a the value of $\frac{a}{b}$, using the upper bound for a and the upper bound for b

b the value of $\frac{a}{b}$, using the upper bound for a and the lower bound for b

c the greatest value of $\frac{a^2}{b}$

8 If $x = 11.72$ and $y = 5.91$, all measured correct to 2 decimal places, calculate

a the greatest value of $\frac{x}{y}$

b the greatest value of $x - y$

c the lowest value of $x - y$.

d *Explain* why you know that your answer to part **c** is the lowest possible value.

3.6 Expanding brackets and equations

HWK 1M — **Main Book page 213**

In questions 1 to 6, answer 'true' or 'false'.

1 $3(x + 2) = 3x + 5$

2 $5(x - 4) = 5x - 20$

3 $2(4x + 3) = 14x$

4 $6(2x - 1) = 11x$

5 $4(2x + 7) = 8x + 28$

6 $3(2x - 1) = 6x - 3$

7 Copy and complete

a $4(3x - \square) = 12x - 8$

b $7(\square + 3p) = 42 + 21p$

c $3(\square - \square) = 15a - 24$

d $\square(4 + \square) = 20 + 35n$

In questions 8 to 19, remove the brackets and simplify.

8 $4(x + 3) + 2(x + 5)$

9 $5(x + 1) + 7(x + 3)$

10 $6(2x + 3) + 2(x + 7)$

11 $3(3x + 2) + 5(2x + 7)$

12 $4(3x + 1) + 3(5x + 2)$

13 $7(4x + 2) + 2(8x - 3)$

14 $6x + 3(2x - 1)$

15 $5(3x + 2) - 7x$

16 $4(2 + 5x) - 3x + 7$

17 $3 + 9(2x + 1) + 5x$

18 $3(4x + 3) - 4x + 2(x + 5)$

19 $6(3x - 2) - x + 4(2x + 3)$

20

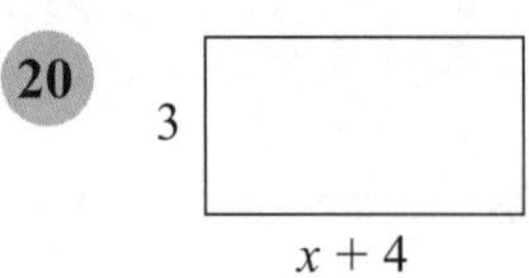

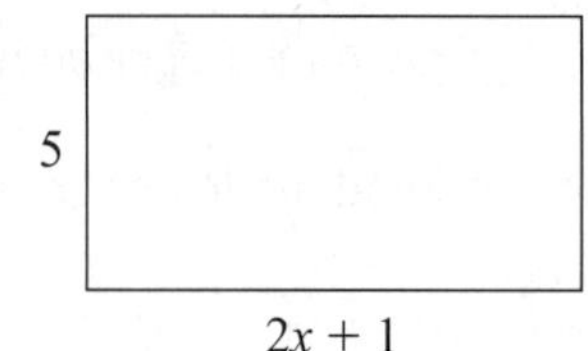

Write down an expression for the sum of the areas of these two rectangles. Simplify your answer.

21 Simplify $4(3x + 1) + 2(2x + 6) + 7(x + 8)$

22 Simplify $3(5x + 4) + 4(2 + 8x) + 8(2x + 5) + 2(1 + 7x)$

HWK 2M

Main Book page 214

In questions **1** to **6**, answer 'true' or 'false'.

1 $-4(x + 3) = -4x + 3$

2 $-8(m - 2) = -8m - 16$

3 $-3(n + 2) = -3n - 6$

4 $-9(a - 3) = -9a + 27$

5 $-5(2 - y) = -10 + 5y$

6 $-2(4 + 3p) = -8 - 6p$

In questions **7** to **14**, remove the brackets and simplify.

7 $3(x + 4) + 2(x - 3)$

8 $5(2x + 3) + 3(x - 2)$

9 $4(2x + 6) + 3(4x - 5)$

10 $5(3x + 4) - 4(2x - 3)$

11 $6(2x - 1) + 5(3x + 2)$

12 $7(2x + 3) - 5(x + 3)$

13 $8(4x + 7) - 4(3x + 8)$

14 $6(5x + 9) - 2(10x - 1)$

15

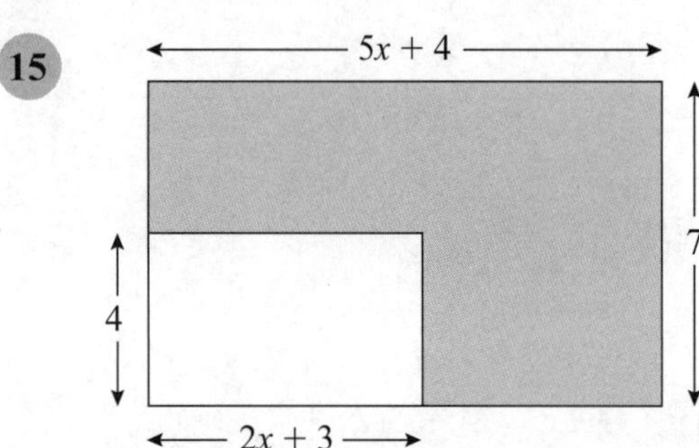

Write down an expression for the shaded area. Simplify your answer.

16 Copy and complete

a $4(2x + 1) - \square(x - 3) = 3x + \square$ **b** $6(3x + 2) - \square(\square + 2) = 13x + 2$

In questions **17** to **19**, remove the brackets and simplify.

17 $4(2a + 5b) - 5(a + 2b) + 3(3a - 4b)$

18 $7(5m + 6n) - 4(7m - 3n) - 5(m + 3n)$

19 $5(2x + 9y) - 6(x + 5y) + 3(4x + 7) - 4(2x - 1)$

20

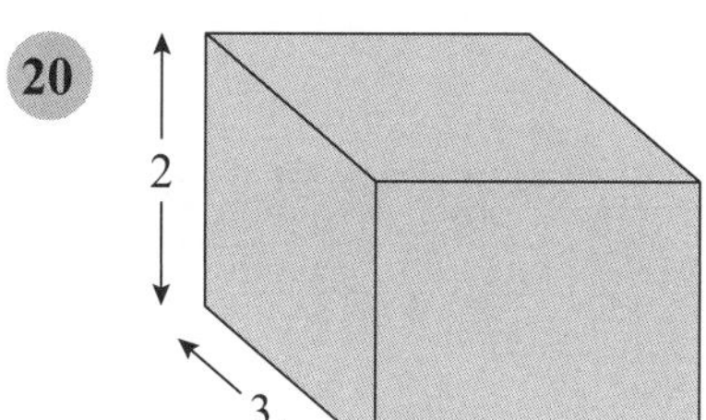

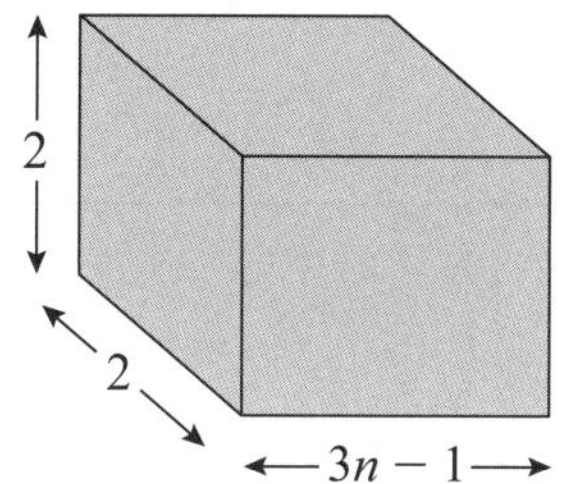

Write down and simplify an expression for the sum of the volumes of these two cuboids.

HWK 3M

Main Book page 216

Remove the brackets and simplify.

1 $(x + 6)(x + 7)$ **2** $(x + 5)(x + 6)$ **3** $(x - 4)(x - 2)$

4 $(x - 1)(x + 8)$ **5** $(x + 7)(x - 2)$ **6** $(x + 9)(x - 4)$

7 $(x - 4)(x - 5)$ **8** $(x - 3)(x + 10)$ **9** $(x + 11)(x - 7)$

10

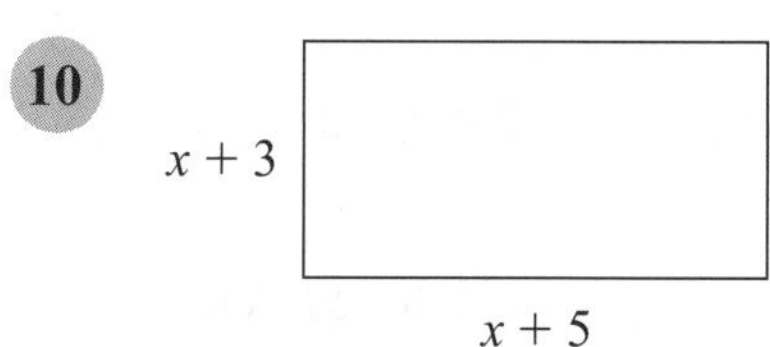

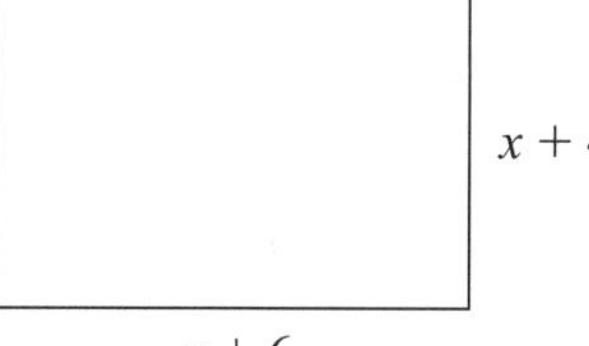

Write down and simplify an expression for the total area of these two rectangles.

11 Expand and simplify

a $(2x + 1)(5x + 3)$ **b** $(6x - 1)(2x + 3)$ **c** $(4x - 5)(5x + 7)$

12 Natasha says that $(x + 3)^2 = x^2 + 9$. Is she correct? Give a reason for your answer.

13 Expand and simplify

a $(x - 5)^2$ **b** $(x + 7)^2$ **c** $(x + 6)^2 + (x - 2)^2$

14 Write down and simplify an expression for the total area of the squares shown opposite.

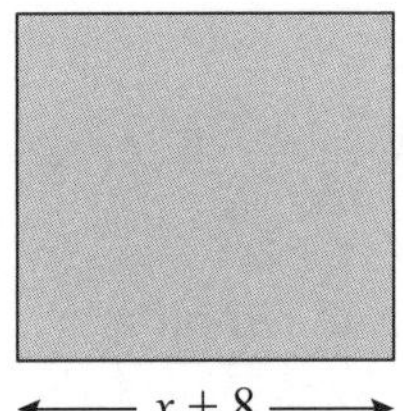

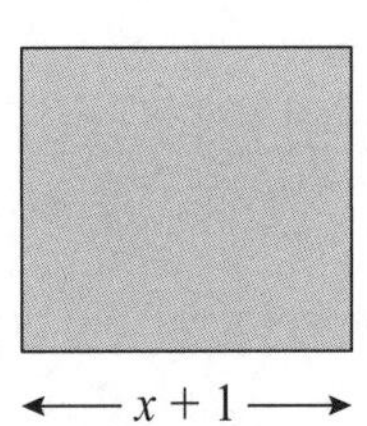

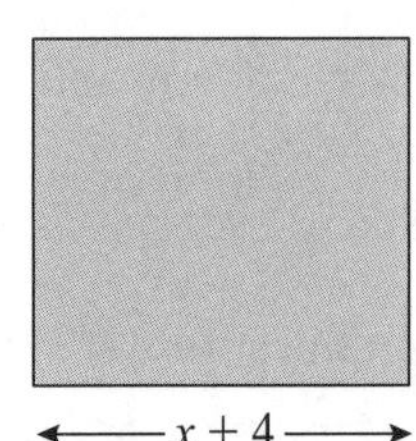

15 Expand and simplify

a $(x + 8)^2 - (x - 5)^2$

b $(x + 9)^2 - (x + 6)^2$

c $(3x + 2)(4x - 3) - (x - 2)^2$

d $(x + 10)^2 - (5x + 2)(3x - 7)$

HWK 4M

Main Book page 217

Solve

1 $3(n + 5) = 36$

2 $6(n + 2) = 24$

3 $8(n - 3) = 40$

4 $7(2n - 3) = 49$

5 $4(2n + 1) = 36$

6 $10(n - 6) = 30$

7 $4(2n - 7) = 60$

8 $6(5n + 2) = 42$

9 $2(n - 40) = 20$

10 $4(n + 2) = 10$

11 $12(2n - 1) = 4$

12 $7(n + 4) = 33$

13 Dom has £n. He spends £20. He then looks at a £100 coat in a shop which costs five times the money he now has left.

a Write down an equation involving n.

b Find n.

Solve

14 $4(3n + 1) = 40$

15 $30 = 2(n + 6)$

16 $25 = 5(2n - 3)$

17 $90 = 3(n + 10)$

18 $7(2n - 9) = 7$

19 $120 = 8(n + 5)$

20 $15 = 4(2n + 3)$

21 $6(4 + 5n) = 114$

22 $2 = 3(5n - 1)$

In questions **23** to **30**, form an equation with brackets and then solve it to find the number.

23 If we add 7 to the number and then double the result, the answer is 58

24 If we subtract 15 from the number and then multiply the result by 3, the answer is 48

25 If we subtract 14 from the number and then multiply the result by 6, the answer is 66

26 If we double the number, add 1 and then multiply the result by 3, the answer is 117

27 If we treble the number, subtract 7 and then multiply the result by 5, the answer is 445

28 If we multiply the number by 4, subtract 13 and then multiply the result by 2, the answer is 18

29 If we add 7 to the number and then multiply the result by 9, the answer is 65

30 If we treble the number, subtract 8 and then multiply the result by 3, the answer is 12

HWK 5M

Main Book page 218

Solve

1 $6p + 10 = 4p + 16$

2 $7y - 3 = 4y + 18$

3 $4m + 7 = 2m + 11$

4 $10a - 12 = 5a + 18$

5 $6y - 32 = 2y + 28$

6 $8x + 13 = 6x + 23$

7 $10m + 14 = 6m + 66$

8 $5p - 27 = 2p + 33$

9 $2 + 5x = x + 42$

10 $9y - 12 = 3y$

11 $4n = 3n + 45$

12 $7p - 22 = 2p + 18$

13 $11 + 6a = 9a - 16$

14 $8m - 28 = m$

15

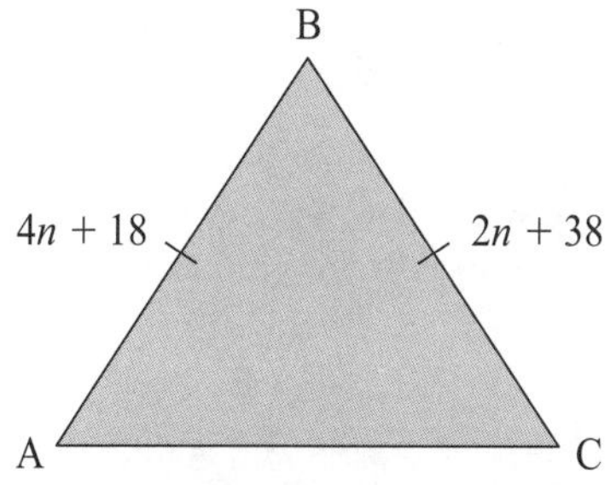

B

$4n + 18$

$2n + 38$

A

C

The sides AB and BC are equal.

Find the value of n then write down the length of side AB, assuming all values are in cm.

Solve these equations involving brackets.

16 $10(n + 4) = 9(n + 5)$

17 $6(n - 4) = 3(n + 2)$

18 $6(3n - 1) = 2(5n + 5)$

19 $8(n - 2) = 2(2n + 6)$

20 $15n + 6 = 3(4n + 3)$

21 $4(3n - 5) = 2(5n + 4)$

22 $7(n + 3) = 2(15 + 2n)$

23 $5(4 + 2n) = 2(3n + 10)$

24 $6n + 18 = 3(3n - 2)$

25 $5(4n - 2) = 3(12n - 6)$

HWK 5E

Main Book page 219

Solve

1. $4(2x - 1) = 5(x + 2) - 2$
2. $53 + 3(p - 2) = 4(3p + 5)$
3. $2(3m + 1) + 16 = 6(2m - 3)$
4. $5(4a - 2) = 2(5a - 35)$
5. $7(2n + 5) = 3(3n - 15)$
6. $4y + 4 + 2y = 2(2y + 7)$
7. $9(2w - 7) = 12 + 3(5w + 2)$
8. $5(3x + 5) + 3 = 4(2x - 7)$
9. $7q + 3(2q - 1) = 8q + 17$
10. $33 + 8n = 5(4n - 3)$

Now solve these.

11. $2(9y - 7) = 4(3y + 2) - 4$
12. $16 + 20m = 8(3m - 5)$
13. $4(6x + 5) - 12x = 2(5x + 4)$
14. $7(3a - 2) = 7 + 6(2a + 7)$
15. $5(3n + 7) = 4(3n - 4) + 6$
16. $2 + 4(3p - 5) = 10(2p + 3)$

Solve

17. $\frac{3x}{7} - 2 = 4$
18. $\frac{4x + 3}{3} = 5$
19. $\frac{5x}{8} + 7 = 10$
20. $(x + 4)(x + 2) = (x + 3)(x + 5)$
21. $(x + 6)(x - 2) = x(x + 5)$
22. $(x + 7)(x - 3) = (x + 6)^2$

HWK 6M

Main Book page 219

1. This rectangle has an area of $120\,cm^2$.
   Form an equation and solve it to find x.

2. If I treble a number, take away 4 and then multiply the result by 3, the answer is 51.
   Find the number.

3 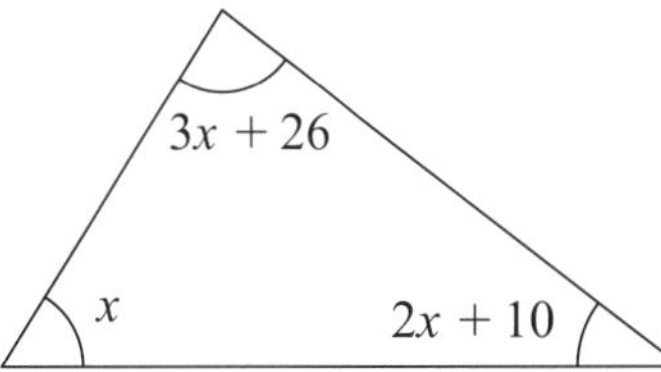

a Form an equation involving x.

b Solve the equation to find x.

c Write down the value of each angle in the triangle.

4 The sum of four consecutive numbers is 114. Find the four numbers.

5 PQ and QR are the equal sides in an isosceles triangle. Find the value of n.

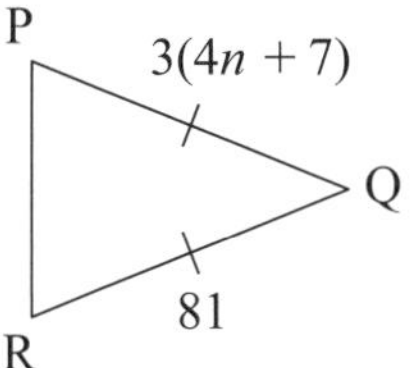

6 Alex has £$(6n + 3)$ and Fiona has £$(3n + 15)$. If they both have the same amount of money, form an equation involving n. Solve the equation and write down how much money Fiona has.

7 The perimeter of this rectangle is 38 cm

a Form an equation involving x.

b Solve the equation to find x.

c Write down the values of the length and width of the rectangle.

8 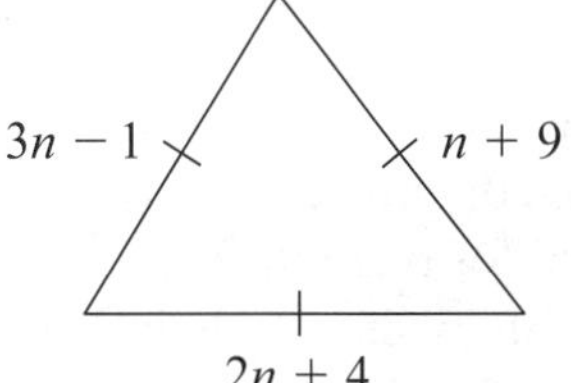

Work out the actual perimeter of this equilateral triangle. All lengths are in cm.

HWK 7M

Main Book page 221

1 The angles in a quadrilateral are $x°$, $3x°$, $(2x + 15)°$ and $63°$. Find the angles in the quadrilateral.

2 Dave weighs $(5x + 3)$ kg and Angie weighs $(4x + 7)$ kg. They weigh a total of 136 kg. Find the value of x then write down how much each person weighs.

3 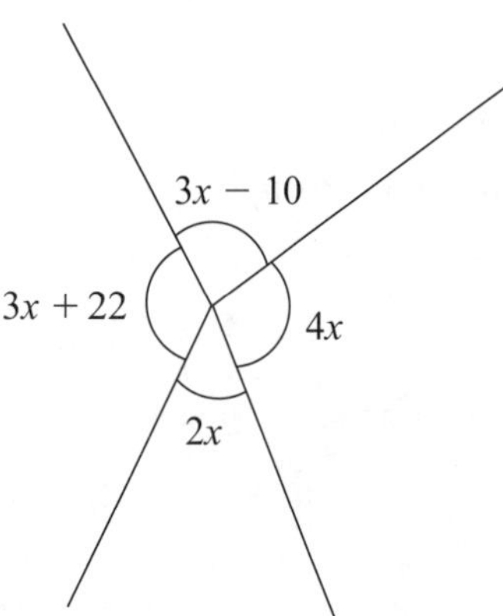

Form an equation involving x, then use it to find the value of each angle shown.

4 The velocity v of a particle is given by the formula $v = u + at$.
Find the value of t if $u = 15$, $a = 10$ and $v = 105$

5 The displacement s of a particle is given by the formula $s = ut + \frac{1}{2}at^2$.
Find the value of u if $a = 10$, $t = 6$ and $s = 228$

6 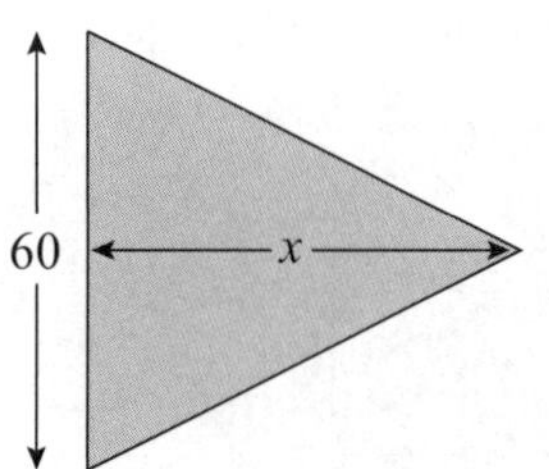

The triangle and the trapezium have the same area. Find x.

$3x + 2$

6

$5x + 8$

7 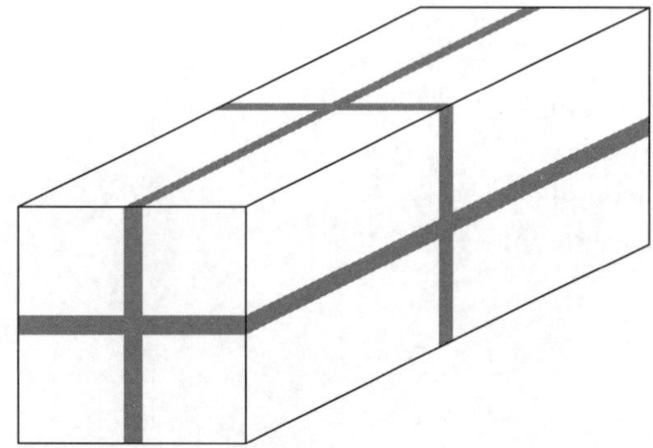

The length of a box is three times its width.
The height of the box is 2 cm more than its width.
Ribbon is tied around the box as shown in grey on the diagram.
10 cm is used for tying the ribbon.
Find the length, width and height of the box if a total of 258 cm of ribbon is used.

8 The sum of five consecutive *even* numbers is 240. Find the five numbers.

9 Gary scores x goals for his football team during one season. Wayne scores four times as many goals as Gary. Michael scores seven goals more than Wayne and Steve scores three goals less than Wayne.

If the four players score a total of 69 goals between them, how many goals does each player score?

UNIT 4

4.1 Averages and range

HWK 1M — Main Book page 240

1 | 5 | 6 | 13 | 8 | 6 | 5 | 8 | 4 | 10 | 4 | 8 |

For the list of numbers above, find

a the mean **b** the median **c** the mode **d** the range.

2 The numbers below show the scores of ten golfers.

$-3, -1, -5, +2, +3, -6, -4, -3, +2, -4$

Write down the median score.

3 Nine people have weights 52 kg, 63 kg, 51 kg, 48 kg, 62 kg, 59 kg, 60 kg, 62 kg and 56 kg.

a Find the mean weight of the nine people.

b Two more people join the group. They weigh 79 kg each. Find the mean weight of all 11 people.

4 | 3 | 7 | ? | 10 |

The numbers on these cards have a mean average equal to 6. Write down the missing number.

5 The numbers 7, 4, 9, 2, 7 and n have a median equal to 6. Write down the value of n.

6 Nine children get the following marks in a test: 36, 50, 54, 59, 37, 62, 52, 51, 49

Gemma scored the mean average mark. Was she in the bottom half or the top half of this list of marks?

7 Set A: | 8 | 10 | 5 | 9 | 6 | 7 | 4 |

Set B: | 12 | 1 | ? | 8 | 9 |

The mean average of set B is the same as the mean average of set A. Find the missing number.

8 Children in class 8A are given a maths test. Their marks are recorded below.

17 23 19 28 15 17 22 28 19 20
24 8 21 15 28 16 27 29 21 23

a Find the mean mark and the range of the marks.

b Children in class 8B took the same test. Their mean mark was 24 and the range of the marks was 12. Use the means and the ranges to compare the test marks for classes 8A and 8B.

9 | 8 | 17 | 7 | ? | Work out the mean average of these four numbers if the median is 10

HWK 2M Main Book page 242

1 The six numbers below are all positive and have a range of 39. Find the value of n.

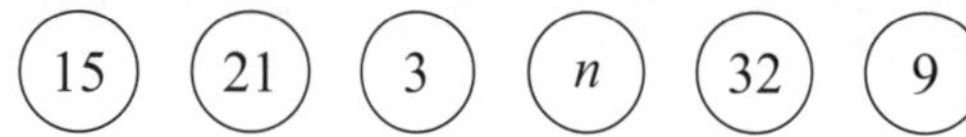

2 Seven numbers have a mean of 9 and a median of 8

Write down three possible missing numbers.

3 The mean of seven numbers is 8. Another number is added to the list, making the mean of the eight numbers equal 9. What was the new number that was added to the list?

4 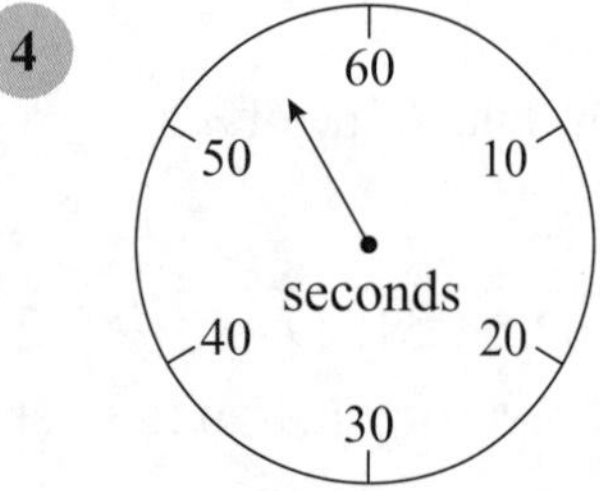

Two groups of people were asked to estimate when one minute had passed. Their estimates are shown in the boxes below. The times are given in seconds.

Group X	54	61	60	55	62	66	61	51	52

Group Y	59	58	67	50	63	69	71	67

a Work out the mean estimate and the range for group X.

b Work out the mean estimate and the range for group Y.

c Write one or two sentences to compare the estimates for the two groups.

5 The mean weight of 4 girls is 49 kg. The mean weight of 6 boys is 55 kg. Find the mean weight of the 10 boys and girls combined.

6 19 people have a mean height of 1.7 m. Another person of height 1.9 m joins the group. What is the mean height of all 20 people?

7 Two groups of young children were asked how much pocket money they received each week. The results are shown below:

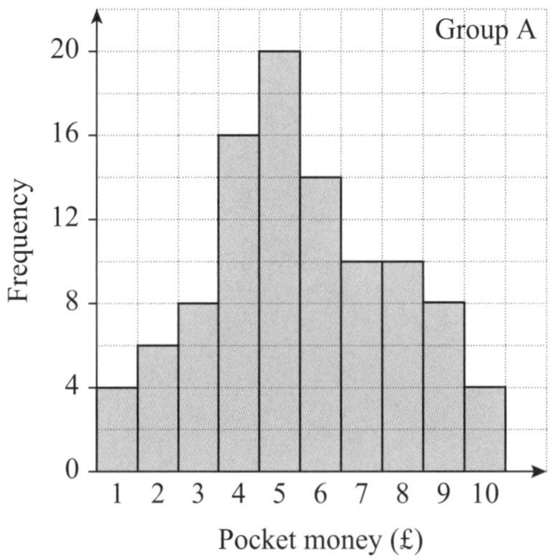

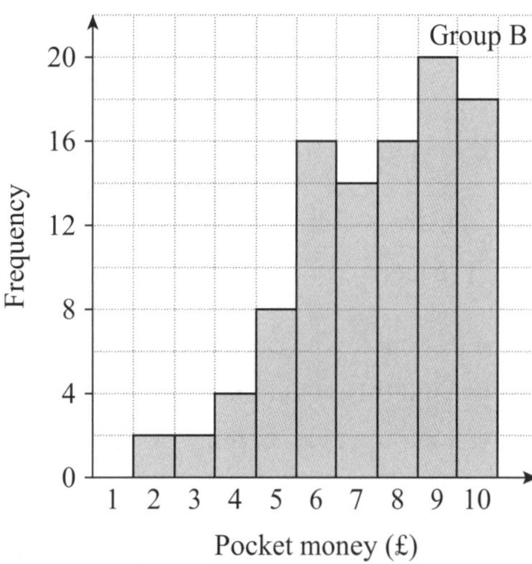

Write down one or two sentences to compare the weekly pocket money received by children in Group A and Group B.

8 The mean height of n girls is p metres. The mean height of m boys is q metres. Write down an expression for the mean height of all the boys and girls combined.

9 Here are six cards and you are told that x is a positive whole number.

$x + 3$	$x - 3$	$3x + 3$
$4x + 7$	$x + 5$	$x + 2$

a Find, in terms of x,

i the median of the six cards

ii the range of the six cards

iii the mean of the six cards.

b The range is 8 greater than the median.
Find the value of x.

HWK 3M

Main Book page 244

1 The frequency table shows the weights of 50 apples in a box.

Weight	90 g	100 g	110 g	120 g	130 g
Frequency	8	11	17	9	5

a Calculate the mean weight of the apples.

b Find the modal weight of the apples (i.e. the mode).

c Find the median weight of the apples.

2 40 children were asked how many drinks of water they had during one day. The findings are shown in the frequency table below.

Number of drinks	0	1	2	3	4	5	6
Frequency	3	5	6	7	12	5	2

a Calculate the mean number of drinks.

b Find the modal number of drinks (i.e. the mode).

c Find the median number of drinks.

3 Tom wants to know if a 'city' family or a 'village' family spends more or less each week on food. He asks 25 families in a city and 25 families in a village to share their weekly food bill. The results are shown in the frequency tables below.

City	
Food bill (£)	Frequency
80	0
100	4
120	8
140	6
160	7

Village	
Food bill (£)	Frequency
80	5
100	5
120	10
140	4
160	1

a Calculate the mean weekly food bill for the 'city' families.

b Calculate the mean weekly food bill for the 'village' families.

c Which group of families spends more each week on food? Can you suggest a possible reason for this?

4 The table shows the number of cars owned by some families in a street.

a If the modal number of cars is 2, find the largest possible value of n.

b If the mean number of cars is 2.28, find n.

Number of cars	Frequency
1	5
2	11
3	n
4	3

4.2 Charts, including scatter graphs

HWK 1M/2M/3M **Main Book page 250**

1 The scatter graph shows the waist sizes and weights of some people.

a How many people weighed more than 70 kg?

b How many people had a waist size of less than 36 inches?

c Answer *true* or *false*: 'In general as waist size increases, weight increases.'

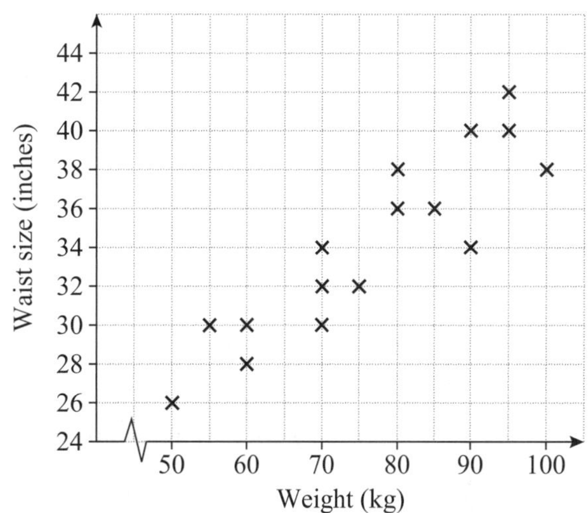

2 The scatter graph shows the heights of some people and how many shirts they own.

a How many people are more than 150 cm tall?

b How many people own fewer than 8 shirts?

c Answer *true* or *false*: 'In general as the number of shirts increases, height increases.'

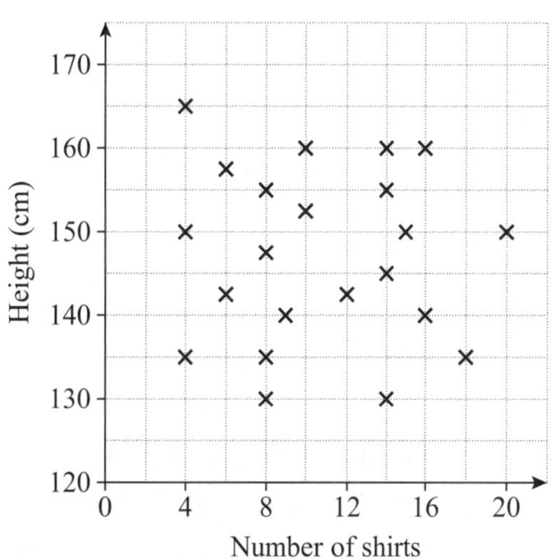

3

French test	German test
13	14
19	17
16	17
8	8
16	15
3	4
10	11
20	19
18	18
7	5
4	18
11	12
18	19
10	8
12	10
9	9
15	16

The table shows two test scores obtained by 16 children in Year 8 for French and German.

a Draw the axes shown below and complete the scatter graph.

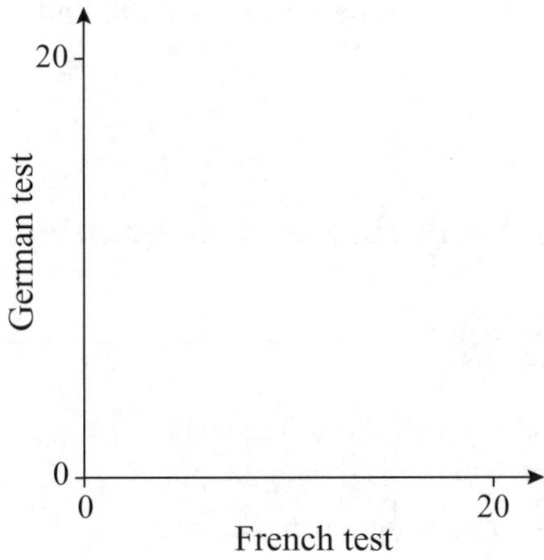

b Describe the correlation, if any.

c One of the points does not follow the trend (called an *outlier*). Write down the German test mark for this outlier.

4 Describe the correlation, if any, in these scatter graphs.

a

b

c

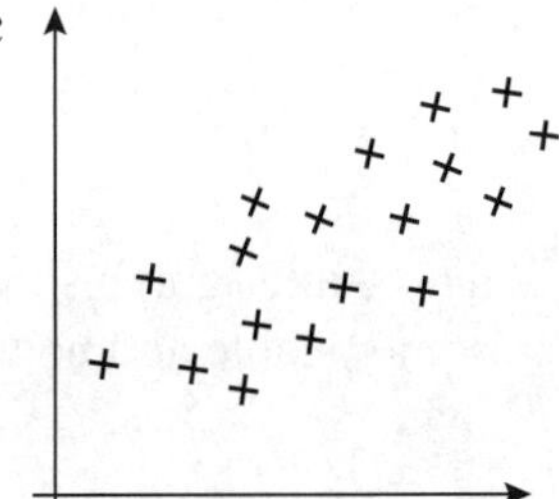

5 If scatter graphs were drawn with the quantities below on the two axes, what sort of correlation would you expect to see in each case?

a salary; value of home lived in

b maths ability; shoe size

c number of pages in a book; time to read the book

d petrol used by a car; further distance that a car could travel

e time spent by a person at the gym; time the person takes to run 5 miles

HWK 4M/5M Main Book page 255

1 The heights of two groups of teenagers are measured. The heights for each group are shown in the frequency diagrams below.

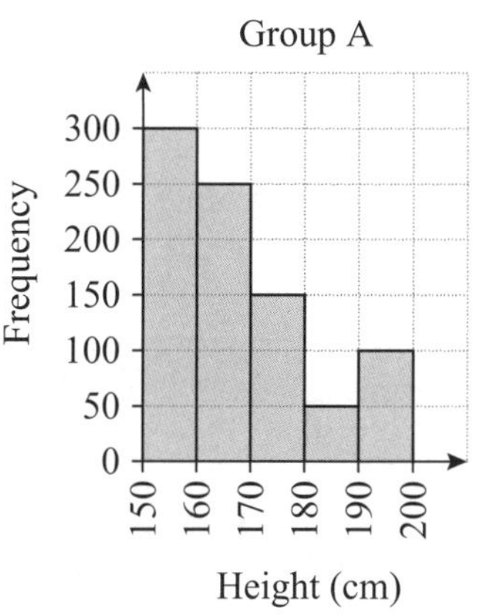

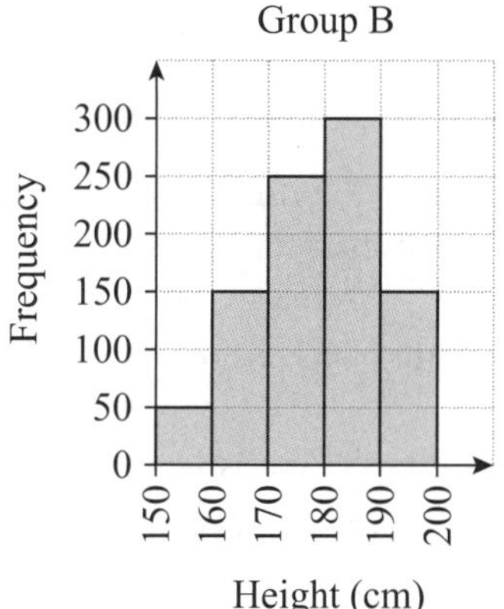

a Which group of teenagers is generally taller?

b Which frequency diagram would you expect if you measured the heights of all the teenagers in a sixth form college? Explain your answer.

2 **a** 18 ten-year-old children run a 400 metre race. Their times t (in seconds) are shown below.

64, 63, 86, 75, 81, 92, 74, 77, 85, 93, 76, 65, 84, 91, 73, 83, 76, 75

Put the heights into groups.

Class interval	Frequency
$60 \leqslant t < 70$	
$70 \leqslant t < 80$	
$80 \leqslant t < 90$	
$90 \leqslant t < 100$	

b Draw a frequency diagram like those in question 1.

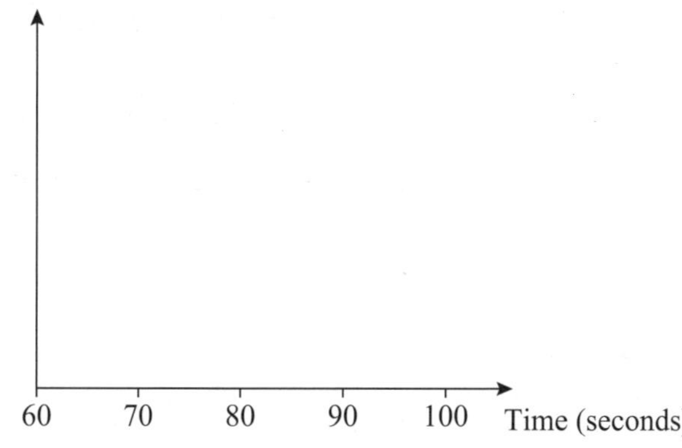

c The same children run a 400 metre race when they are seventeen years old. Their times t (in seconds) are shown below.

67, 56, 65, 57, 53, 74, 59, 53, 71

68, 52, 66, 75, 61, 54, 62, 56, 63

Put the heights into groups similar to part **a**.

d Draw a frequency diagram like those in question **1**.

e Write a sentence to compare the times shown by each frequency diagram. Suggest a reason for the difference.

3 72 people were asked what their favourite type of chocolate was.
The results are shown in the table opposite.

a Work out the angle on a pie chart for one person.

b Work out the angle for each type of chocolate and draw a pie chart.

Type of chocolate	Frequency
milk	32
dark	30
white	10

4 A group of children are measuring the lengths of leaves for a biology experiment. The stem and leaf diagram opposite shows the length of each leaf.

a What is the median length of a leaf?

b What percentage of the leaves are greater than 7.5 cm in length?

Stem	Leaf
5	2 3 7 7
6	0 1 1 4 8 9
7	0 0 2 3 3 7 7 7
8	1 5 5 7 8
9	0 2 4

Key: 7|3 means 7.3 cm

5

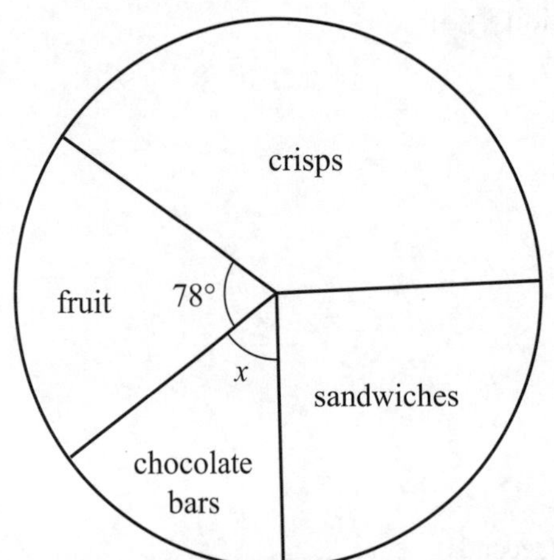

Year 8 children who bring packed lunches to school are asked what main items they have in their lunch. The pie chart opposite shows the results.

40% of items are crisps and $\frac{1}{4}$ are sandwiches.

Calculate the size of angle x in the pie chart.

6 The weights, in kg, of 22 members of a football squad are shown below. Draw an ordered stem and leaf diagram to show this data.

68	79	59	64	63	68	71	76	58	82	71
73	81	64	68	59	72	69	74	80	66	70

7 900 pupils in Cork Field School and 350 pupils in Manor High School were asked what they enjoyed doing most at weekends. The results are shown in the two pie charts.

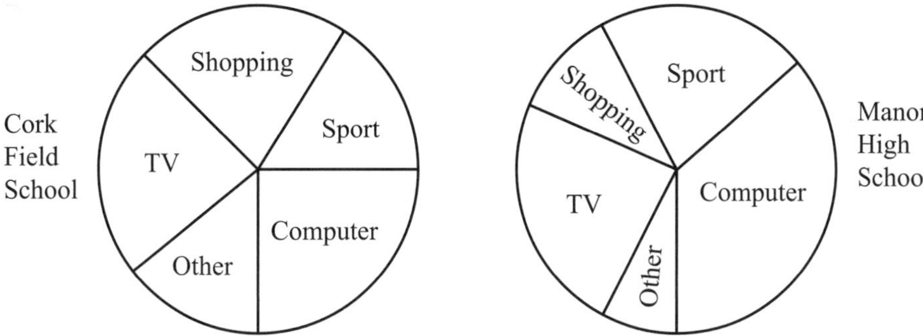

Did more pupils in Manor High School choose using the computer than pupils in Cork Field School or less? *Explain* your answer.

4.3 Pythagoras' theorem

HWK 1M — **Main Book page 265**

Use Pythagoras' theorem in this exercise and give answers correct to 2 decimal places. The units are cm unless you are told otherwise.

1 Find the side marked with a letter.

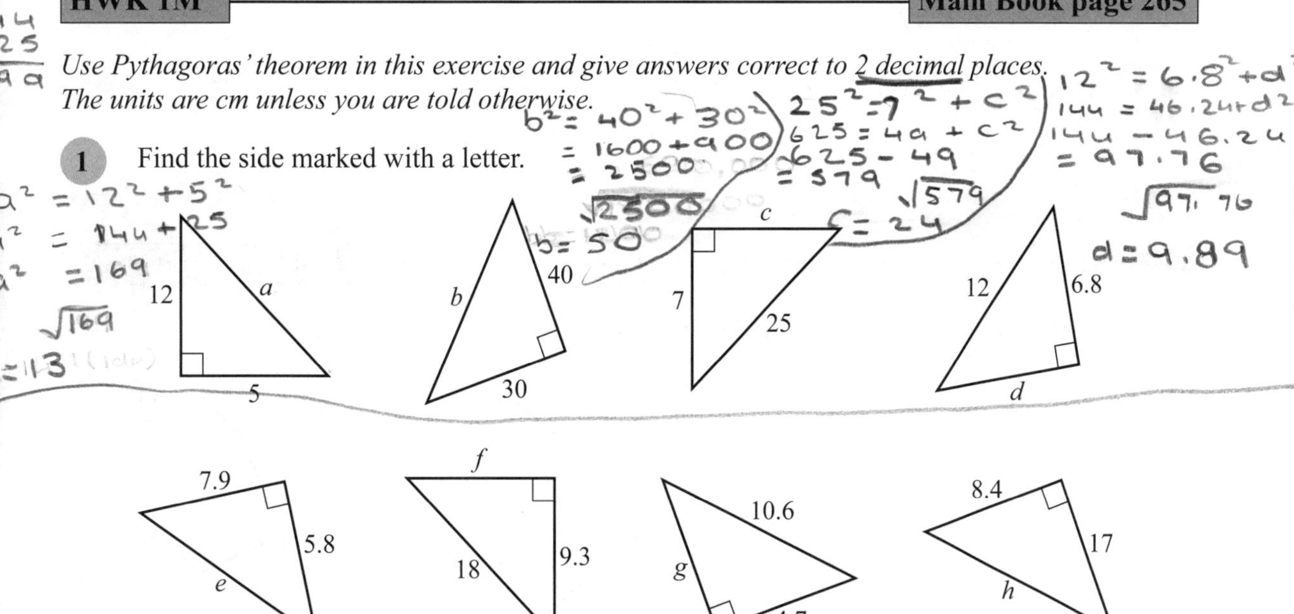

2 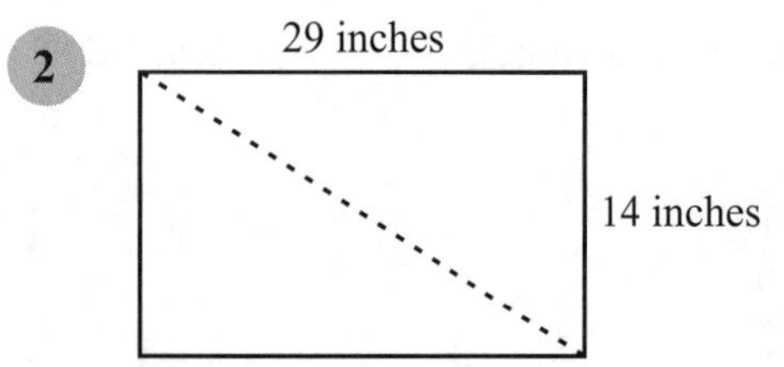

Calculate the length of the diagonal of this rectangular TV screen.

3 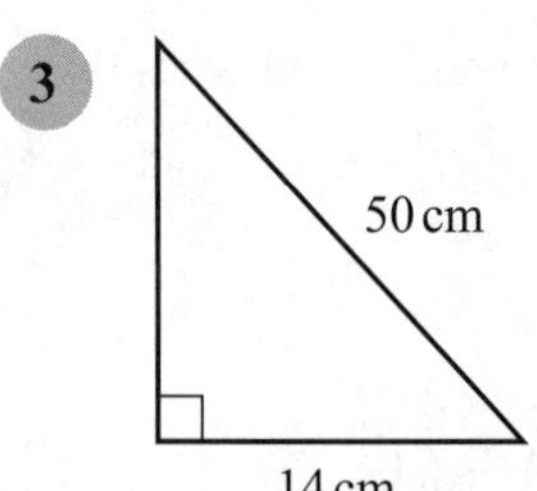

Calculate the area of this triangle.

4 A ladder of length 6 m rests against a vertical wall, with its foot 2.3 m from the wall. Will the ladder reach a window which is 5.5 m above the ground? *Explain* your answer.

5 Find the value of x if this square has a diagonal of length 17 cm.

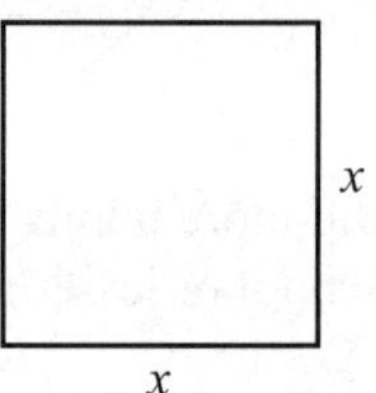

6 A balloon flies 25 miles north and then a further 18 miles west. How far is the balloon from its starting point?

7 Calculate the area of this isosceles triangle.

8 cm

7 cm

7 cm

HWK 2M — Main Book page 267

Give answers correct to 2 decimal places if necessary.

1 Find the length x. All lengths are in cm.

a

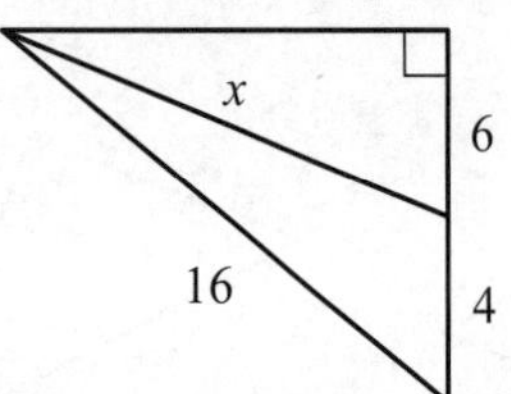

b

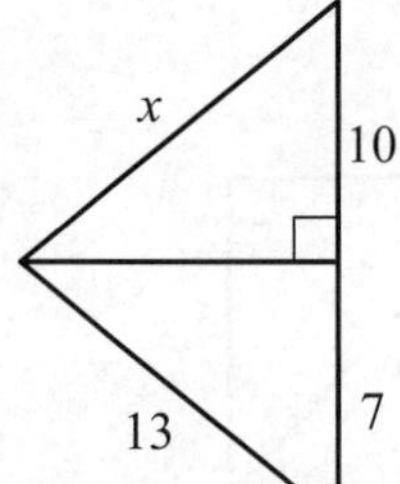

c

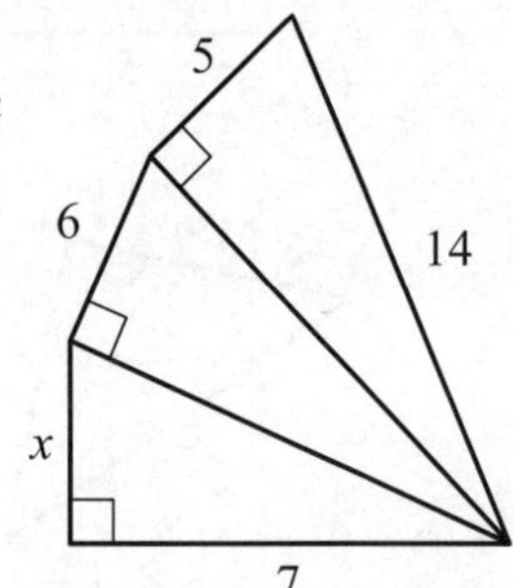

2 ABCD is a parallelogram. The area of a parallelogram is found using base $\times$ height.
Calculate the area of ABCD.

3

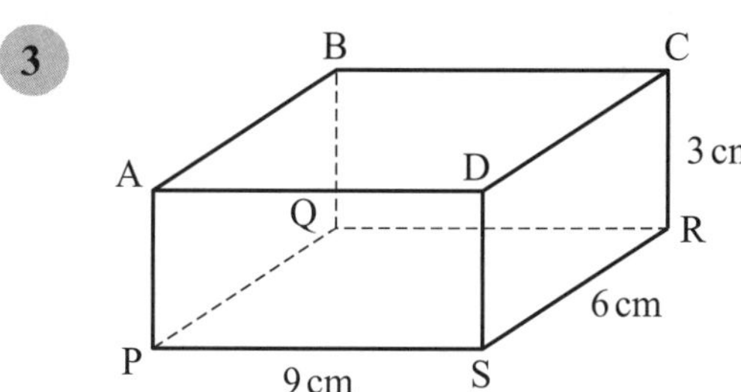

a Use triangle PQS to find the length QS.

b Use triangle BSQ to find the length of BS.

4 Find the length of the diagonal XY in the cuboid opposite.

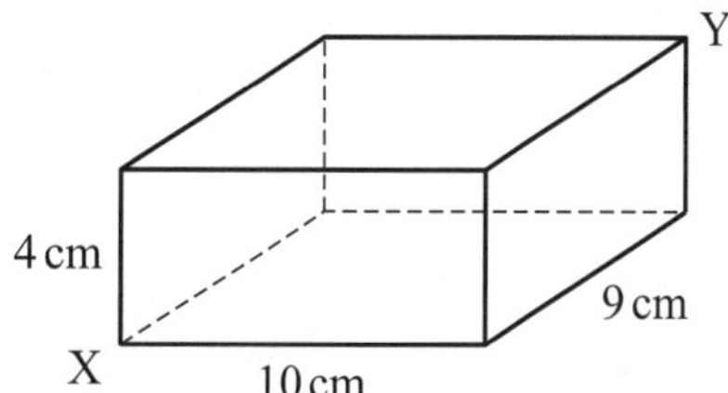

5 Find the length of the longest pencil which would fit into a rectangular box measuring 15 cm $\times$ 9 cm $\times$ 4 cm

6

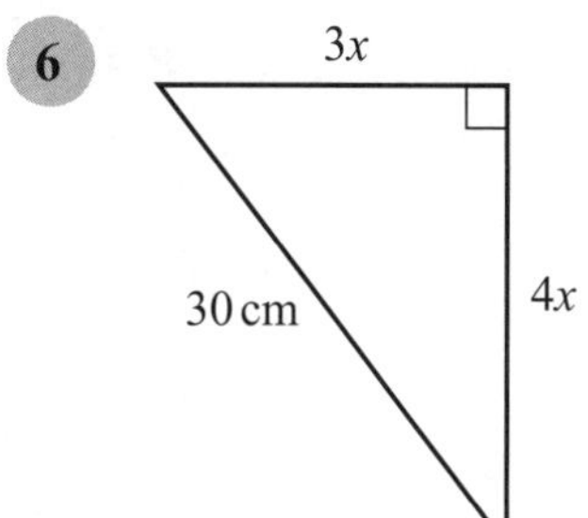

Calculate the value of x.

4.4 Bearings and scale drawing

HWK 1M **Main Book page 275**

1

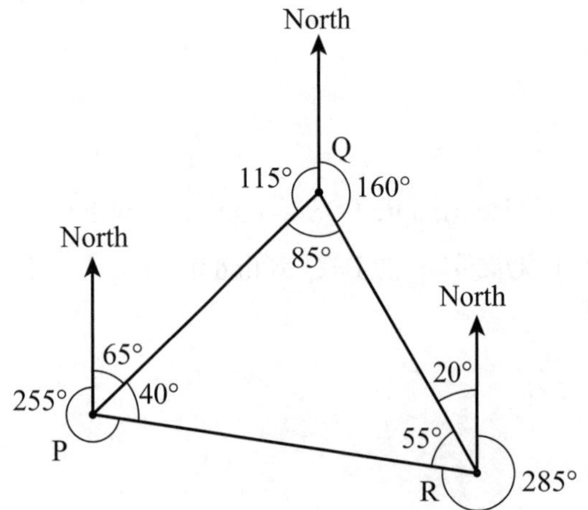

Write down the bearing of

a Q from P

b R from Q

c R from P

d P from R

2 Measure the bearing of

a A to B **b** C to D **c** E to F **d** G to H

e I to J **f** K to L **g** M to N

3 Draw lines to show the following bearings.

a 065° **b** 170° **c** 250° **d** 155° **e** 310°

4 A ship sails from A to P then to B. Another ship sails from C to Q then to D.

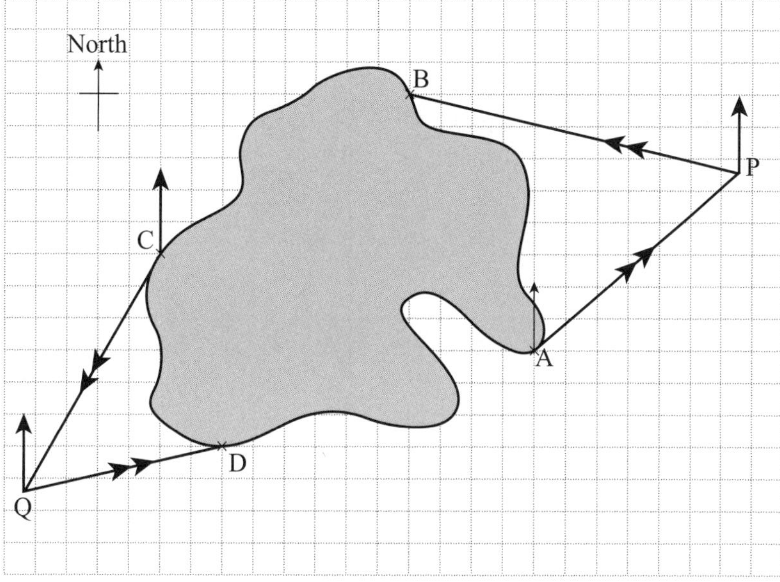

a Measure the bearing of A to P.

b Measure the bearing of P to B.

c Measure the bearing of C to Q.

d Measure the bearing of Q to D.

 **5**

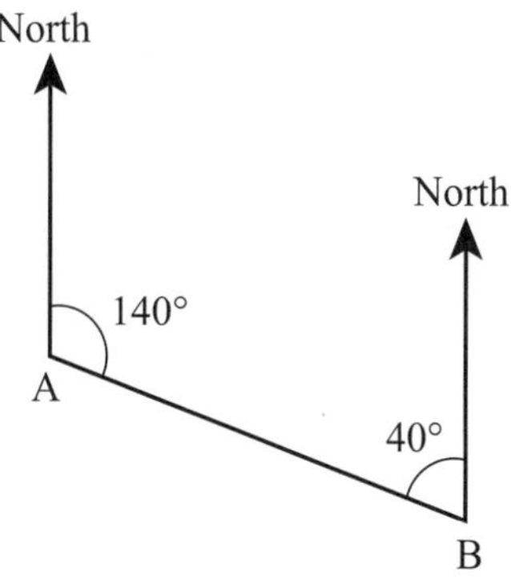

a Write down the bearing of B from A.

b Write down the bearing of A from B.

6 The bearing of point P from point Q is 105°. What is the bearing of point Q from point P?

7 The bearing of point X from point Y is 230°. What is the bearing of point Y from point X?

HWK 2M

Main Book page 277

In questions 1 to 5, use a scale of 1 cm to represent 1 km. Draw an accurate scale drawing to help you answer each question.

1 A ship sails 7 km due north and then a further 5 km on a bearing of 075°

How far is the ship now from its starting point?

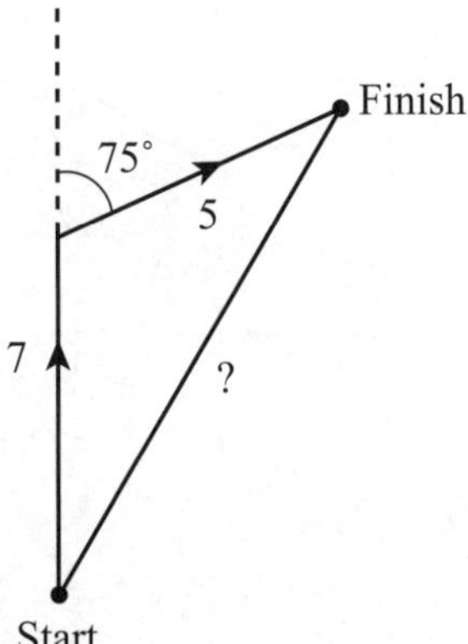

2 A ship sails 6 km due north and then a further 6 km on a bearing of 080°

How far is the ship now from its starting point?

3 Sarah and Barclay are standing at the same point A. Sarah walks for 7 km on a bearing of 050°. Barclay walks for 6 km on a bearing of 310°. How far is Sarah from Barclay now?

4 A ship sails due south for 6 km and then on a bearing of 120° for 3 km.
How far is the ship now from its starting point?

5 Draw a point P with a cross.
Point Q is 7 km from P on a bearing of 072° from P.
Point R is 5 km from P on a bearing of 190° from P.
What is the bearing of R from Q?

6 Use a scale of 1 cm for 10 km. Palton is 100 km from Beale on a bearing of 090°.
A group of hikers is on a bearing of 045° from Beale and on a bearing of 325° from Palton.

a Make a scale drawing to show the position of the hikers.

b The group of hikers now travels 30 km on a bearing of 255°. What is the bearing of the hikers from Beale now?

7

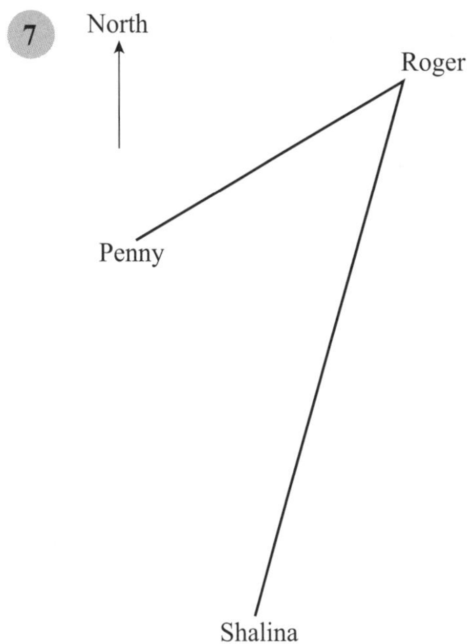

Penny is 20 km from Roger on a bearing of 245°. Shalina is 35 km from Roger on a bearing of 205°

a Draw an accurate diagram using a scale of 1 cm for 5 km.

b Penny now travels 15 km on a bearing of 200°. Shalina travels 25 km on a bearing of 065°. How far now is Penny from Shalina and what is the bearing of Penny from Shalina?

4.5 Trigonometry

HWK 2M — **Main Book page 287**

For each triangle below, find the sides marked with letters, correct to 1 decimal place. All lengths are in cm.

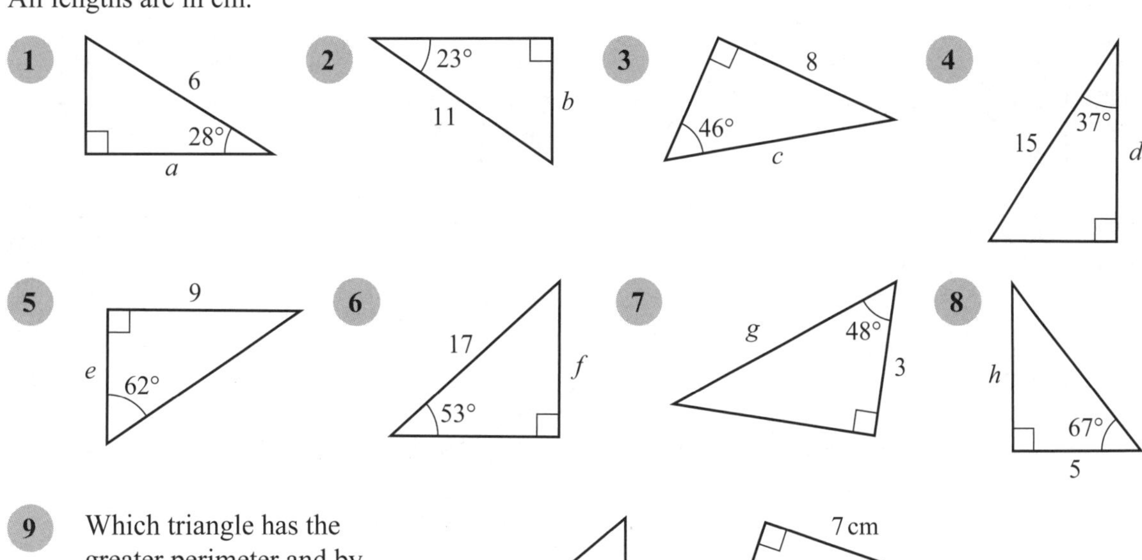

9 Which triangle has the greater perimeter and by how much?

10 cm
A
42°
7 cm
B
36°

10 In triangle DEF, $D\hat{F}E = 90°$, $D\hat{E}F = 57°$ and EF = 9 cm. Find the length DF.

11 Calculate the area of triangle ABC.

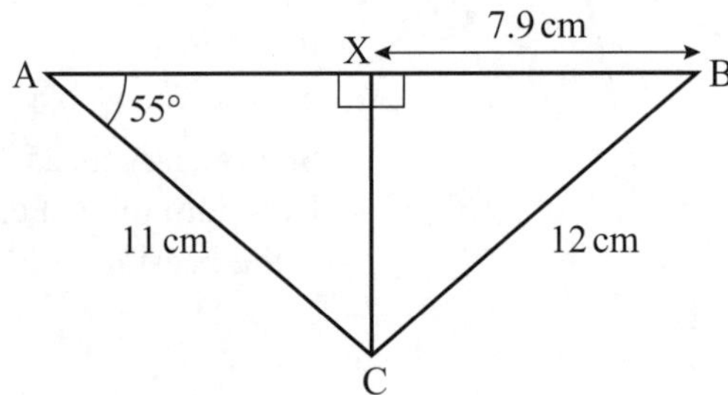

HWK 3M Main Book page 288

For each triangle below, find the angles marked, correct to 1 decimal place. All lengths are in cm.

1

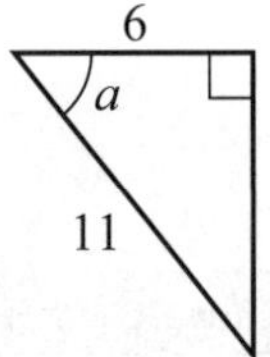

2

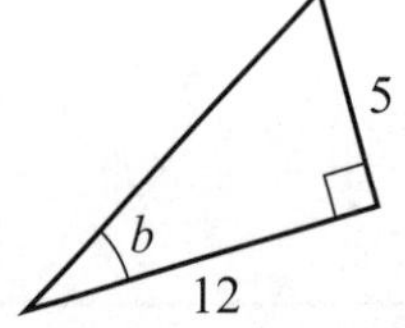

3

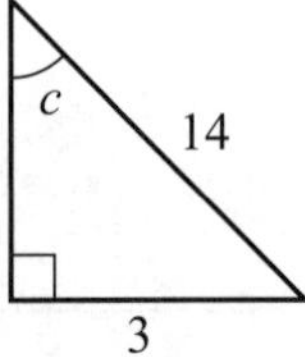

4

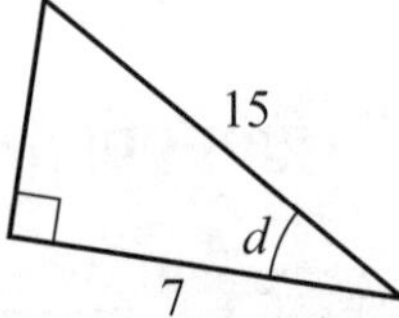

5

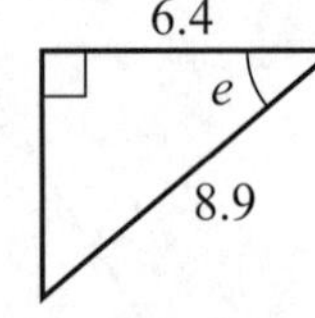

6

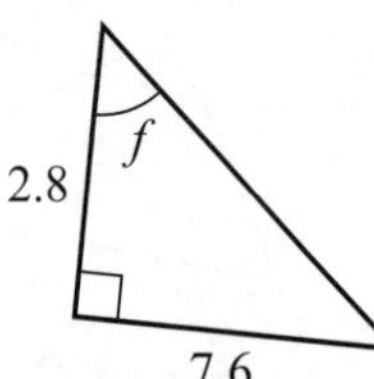

7

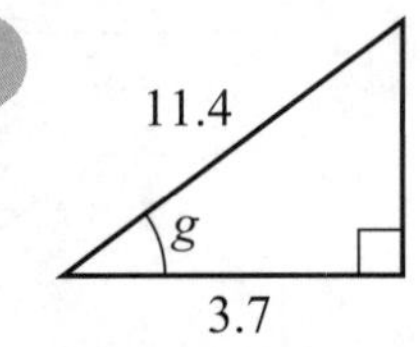

8

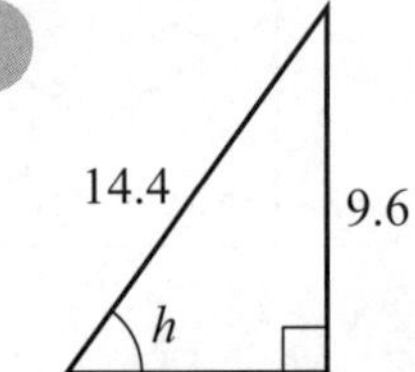

9 Calculate the value of $C\hat{B}D$.

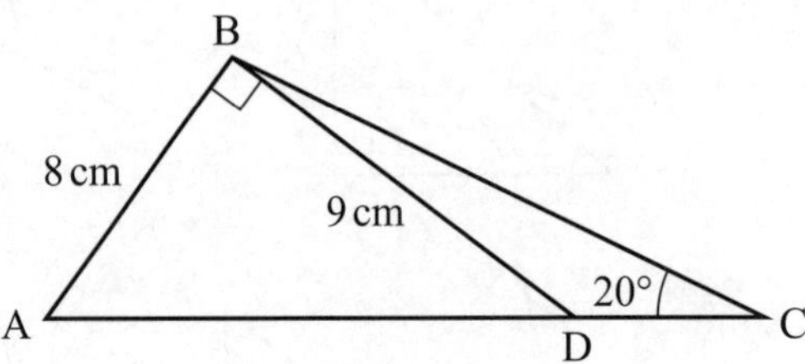

10 In triangle PQR, $P\hat{Q}R = 90°$, QR = 6 cm and PR = 17 cm. Work out $Q\hat{P}R$.

11

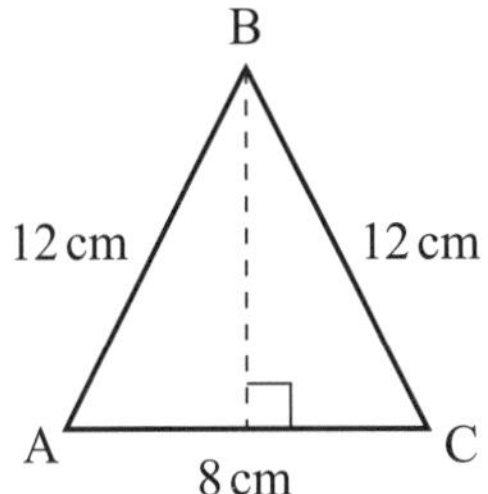

Work out the value of $A\hat{B}C$.

12 Work out the value of $Q\hat{P}R$.

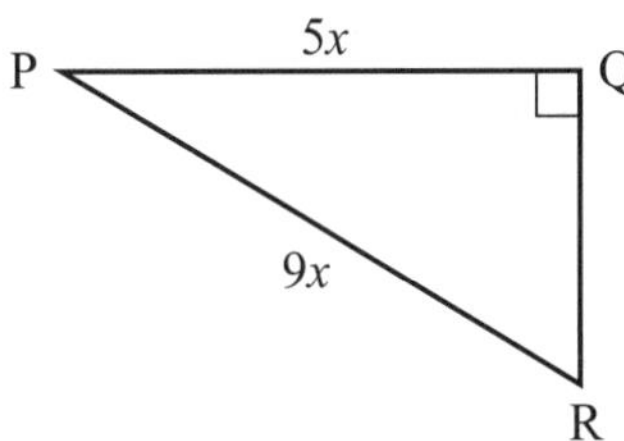

13

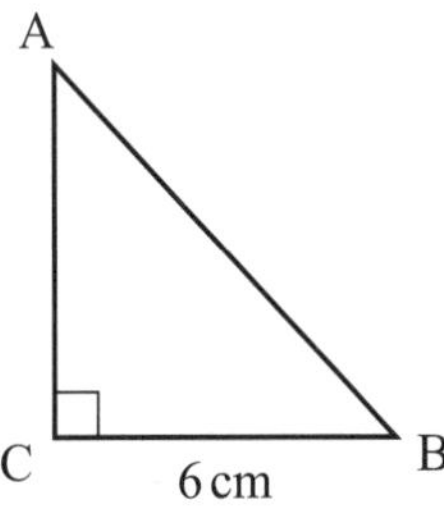

Work out the value of $B\hat{A}C$ if the area of the triangle is 60 cm^2.

14 Calculate the value of $B\hat{C}D$.

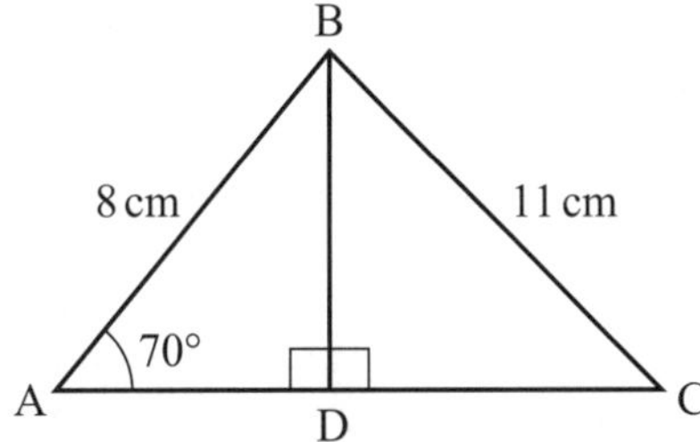

HWK 4M — **Main Book page 290**

For each triangle below, find the values of the letters marked, correct to 1 decimal place.

1

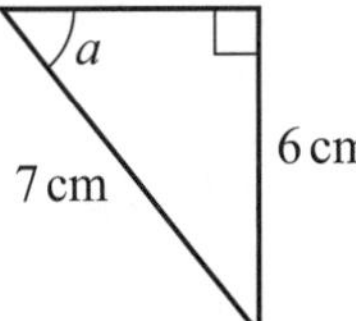

2

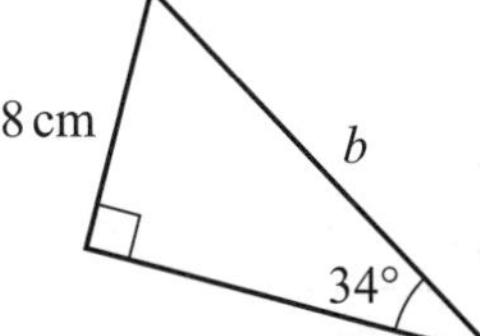

3

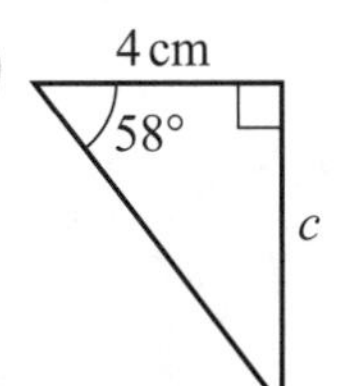

4

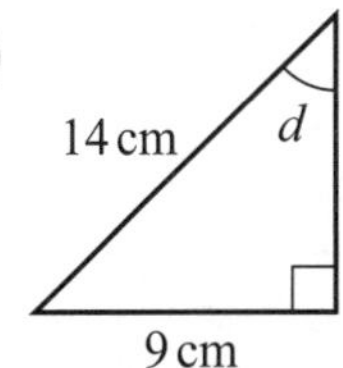

5 A ladder leans against a vertical wall so that it makes an angle of 29° with the wall. The base of the ladder is 1.6 m from the wall. A window is 3 m above the ground. Does the ladder reach the window? Give a reason for your answer.

6 The perimeter of triangle ABC is 30 cm. AB is 7 cm longer than AC. Work out the value of $A\hat{C}B$.

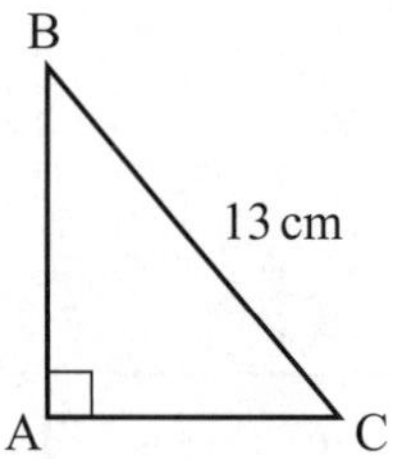

7 A ship sails due east for 7 km. It then sails on a bearing of 220° until it is due south of its starting position. How far has the ship sailed in total?

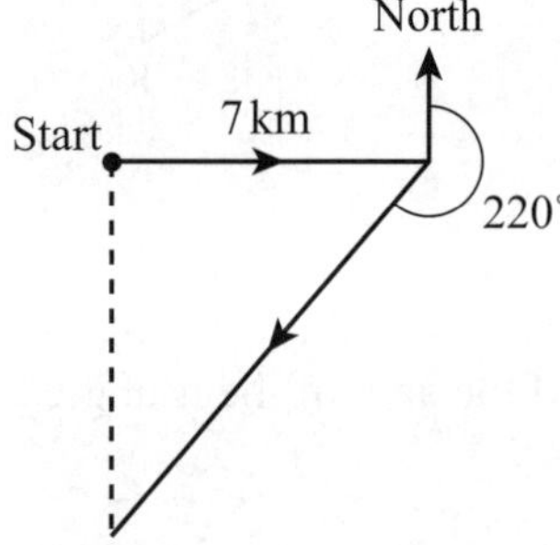

8 A ship sails due west for 11 km. It then sails on a bearing of 105° until it is due south of its starting position. How far has the ship sailed in total?

9

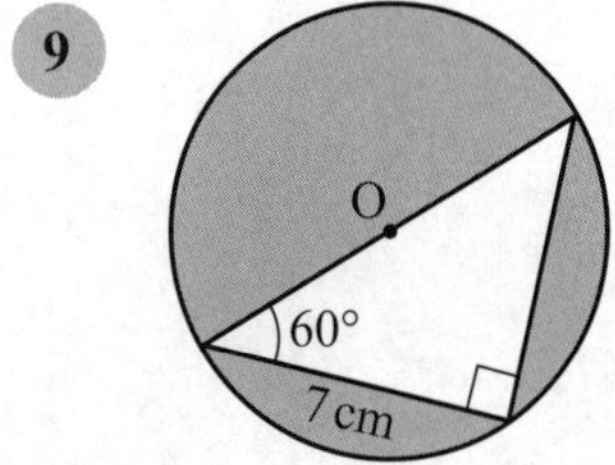

O is the centre of the circle. Work out the shaded area.

10 Work out the perimeter of the quadrilateral ABCD.

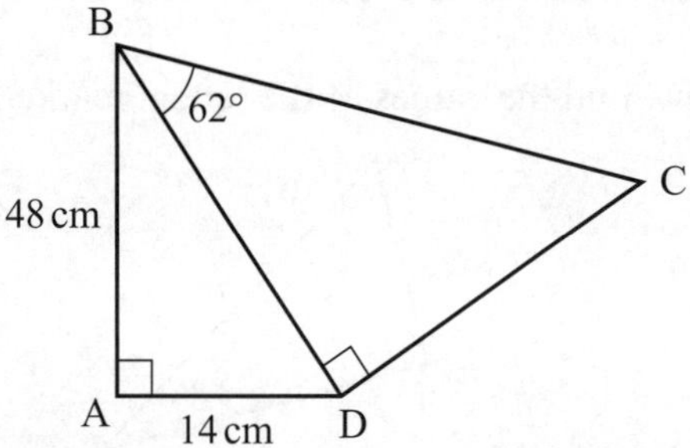

4.6 Negative numbers

HWK 1M/2M — **Main Book pages 295 and 296**

1 Work out

a 8 − (+3) **b** 6 + (−5) **c** 1 + (−3) **d** 5 − (−4)

e 4 − (−1) **f** 7 + (−6) **g** −3 − (−2) **h** −2 + (−4)

2 What is the difference between −19 and 17?

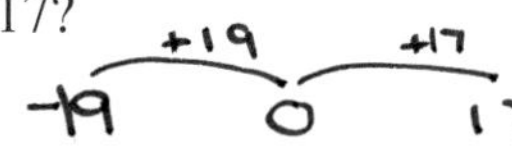

3 Write down the next three numbers in this sequence.

12, 5, −2, □, □, □

4 What is the sum of −6, 9, −8 and −15?

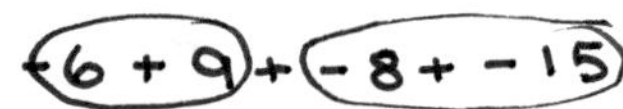

5 Copy and complete this number chain.

6 Work out

a 13 − (+18) **b** 27 + (−16) **c** −14 − (−30) **d** 43 − (+60)

e −32 + 24 **f** −29 + (−12) **g** 53 − (−19) **h** −16 − (+35)

7 Copy and fill in the missing numbers.

a −2 − □ = 1 **b** 5 − □ = 6 **c** −3 + □ = −7

8 Which calculation below gives the odd answer out?

A −4 + (−1) B −3 − (−1) C 3 + (−5)

9 Helen has four cards, as shown below.

−18	−14	23	−2

She needs to choose one more card which will make the total of all five cards equal to −15.
Draw the card she needs.

10 Copy and complete these magic squares. (You must get the same number when you add across each row, add down each column and add diagonally.)

a

−2	−3	
	−1	
	1	

b

	−3		−5
1		7	
		−7	
−8	3	−2	5

11 Work out $-6 - (-2) + 3 - 7 + (-2) - (-1)$

12 Copy and complete

$$7 + (-10) - 3 - (-5) - \square - 5 + (-2) = -6$$

HWK 3M

Main Book page 297

1 Work out

a $4 \times (-3)$ **b** $-2 \times (-6)$ **c** $8 \div (-2)$ **d** $-8 \times (-3)$

e $-20 \div (-5)$ **f** $-28 \div (-7)$ **g** -7×2 **h** $-5 \times (-2)$

i $2 \times (-9)$ **j** $40 \div (-5)$ **k** $-32 \div 8$ **l** $-45 \div (-9)$

m $6 \times (-6)$ **n** $56 \div (-8)$ **o** $-4 \times (-1)$ **p** $-16 \div 8$

2 Which question below gives the highest answer and by how much?

$-4 \times (-4)$ $5 \times (-4)$

3 -32 is divided by each number below. Write down which of these numbers will give an answer greater than zero.

4 −8 −2 16 32

4 Answer 'true' or 'false'.

a $-3 \times (-3) = -9$ **b** $(-3)^2 = 9$ **c** $-5 \times (-4) = 20$

d $2 \times (-3) \times (-4) = 24$ **e** $(-5)^2 = 10$ **f** $-1 \times (-1) \times (-1) = -1$

5 Copy and complete this number chain.

3 $\xrightarrow{\times (-3)}$ $\square$ $\xrightarrow{\times 2}$ $\square$ $\xrightarrow{\times (-5)^2}$ $\square$

6 Copy and complete these calculations.

a $-6 \times \square = -30$ **b** $9 \times \square = -36$ **c** $-10 \times \square = 70$

d $\square \times (-2) = -14$ **e** $-8 \times \square = 32$ **f** $\square \times (-8) = 48$

7 Find the values of x and y if

$\boxed{x + y = 2}$ and $\boxed{xy = -8}$

8 Find the values of p and q if

$\boxed{p + q = -2}$ and $\boxed{pq = -15}$

9 Copy and complete this multiplication table.

$\times$	-5		
		-9	6
4			-8
	35		

10 **a** Find two numbers whose sum is -3 and whose product is -18.
('Product' means multiplied together.)

b Find two numbers whose sum is -5 and whose product is 6

c Find two numbers whose sum is -9 and whose product is 20

11 Explain why n^3 must be negative if n is a negative number.

12 Work out

a $(-6)^2 \div (-3)$ **b** $0 \times (-4)$ **c** $(-2)^2 \times (-3)^2$

d $(-8) \times 4 \times (-5)$ **e** $(-4)^3 \times 2$ **f** $(-2)^3 \div (-4)$

UNIT 5

5.1 Sequences 2

HWK 1M — **Main Book page 318**

Remember: T(1) means 'the first term'
T(2) means 'the second term'
… and so on.

1 For the sequence 5, 8, 11, 14, 17, … write down

a T(3) **b** T(5) **c** T(10)

2 The *n*th term of a sequence is T(*n*) and T(*n*) $= 4n - 1$.

Write down the values of

a T(1) **b** T(4) **c** T(20)

3 The *n*th term of a sequence is T(*n*) and T(*n*) $= 3n + 5$.

Find **a** T(3) **b** T(7) **c** T(15)

4 Write the first five terms of the sequence where T(*n*) is

a $2n + 9$ **b** $3n - 6$ **c** $n^2 + 3$ **d** n^3

5 | $4n - 1$ | $n + 4$ | $2n$ | $n - 1$ | $3n + 2$ | $4n$ |

Write down each sequence below and match it to the correct expression for the *n*th term shown above.

a 4, 8, 12, 16, … **b** 3, 7, 11, 15, … **c** 0, 1, 2, 3, 4, … **d** 5, 8, 11, 14, 17, …

6 Callum is on the beach collecting shells.
After 1 hour he has collected 15 shells.
After 2 hours he has 25 shells.
After 3 hours he has 35 shells.
After 4 hours he has 45 shells.

a How many shells do you expect him to have after 5 hours?

b Answer *true* or *false*. 'After *n* hours, Callum will have $(15n + 10)$ shells.'

7 T(*n*) $= 3n + 5$ gives the sequence 8, 13, 18, 23, …
True or false? Give a reason for your answer.

8 $T(n) = 5n - 4$ gives the sequence 1, 6, 11, 16, …
True or false? Give a reason for your answer.

9 Find the value of n if

a $T(n) = 4n - 3$ and $T(n) = 21$

b $T(n) = 5n + 4$ and $T(n) = 39$

c $T(n) = 12 - 5n$ and $T(n) = -8$

10 Find the nth term $T(n)$ for the sequence

6, 10, 14, 18, …

HWK 2M

Main Book page 320

1 Look at the sequence 5, 8, 11, 14, …

The *difference* between terms is 3.

Copy the table which has a column for $3n$.

Copy and complete:

'The nth term of the sequence is $3n + \square$.'

n	$3n$	term
1	3	5
2	6	8
3	9	11
4	12	14

2 Look at each sequence and the table underneath. Find the nth term in each case.

a Sequence 8, 13, 18, 23, …

n	$5n$	term
1	5	8
2	10	13
3	$\square$	18
4	$\square$	23

nth term = $\square$

b Sequence 2, 6, 10, 14, …

n	$4n$	term
1	4	2
2	$\square$	6
3	$\square$	10
4	$\square$	14

nth term = $\square$

3 Look at the sequence 5, 7, 9, 11, …
Write down the *difference* between terms.
Make a table like those in question **2** and use it to find the nth term.

4 Write down each sequence in a table and then find the nth term.

a 2, 8, 14, 20, … **b** 10, 13, 16, 19, … **c** 13, 22, 31, 40, …

5 Now find the nth term of these sequences.

a $-19, -11, -3, 5, 13, \ldots$ **b** 49, 43, 37, 31, 25, … **c** $1\frac{2}{3}, 2\frac{1}{3}, 3, 3\frac{2}{3}, \ldots$

6 A pattern of sticks is made as shown below.

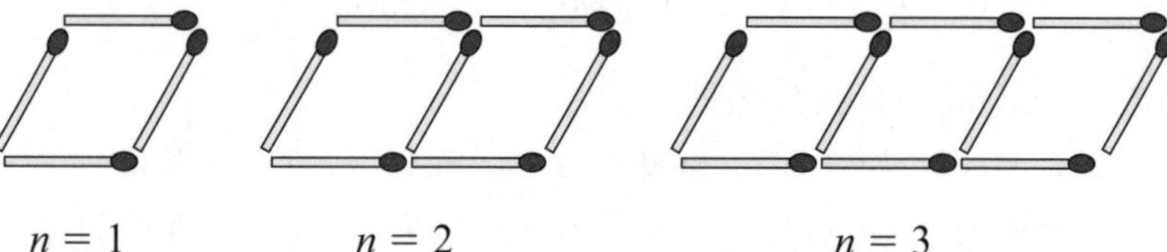

Shape number:	$n = 1$	$n = 2$	$n = 3$
Number of sticks:	4	7	10

Draw shape number 4 and shape number 5. How many sticks are there in the nth term?

7 Here is a pattern made with dots.

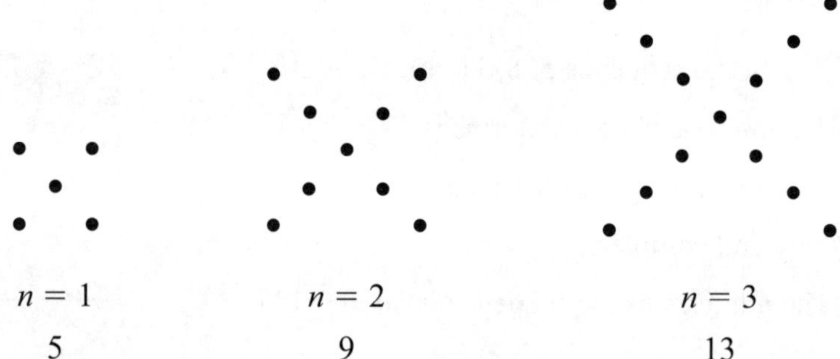

Shape number:	$n = 1$	$n = 2$	$n = 3$
Number of dots:	5	9	13

Draw the next diagram in the sequence. How many dots are there in the nth term?

8 Here is a sequence of hexagons made from sticks.

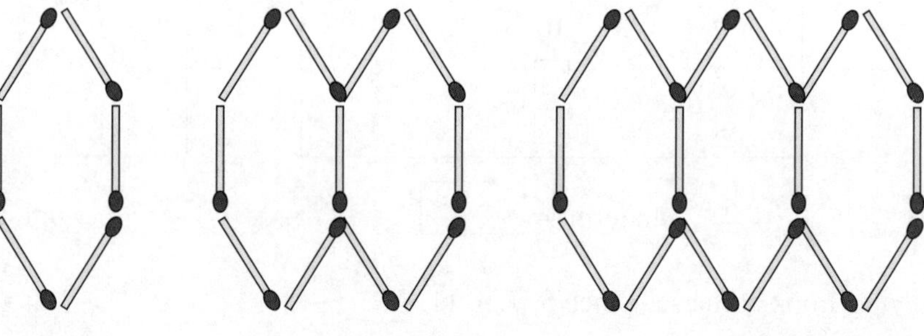

Shape number:	$n = 1$	$n = 2$	$n = 3$
Number of sticks:	6	11	16

Draw shape number 4. How many sticks are there in the nth term?

9 Here is a pattern made with dots.

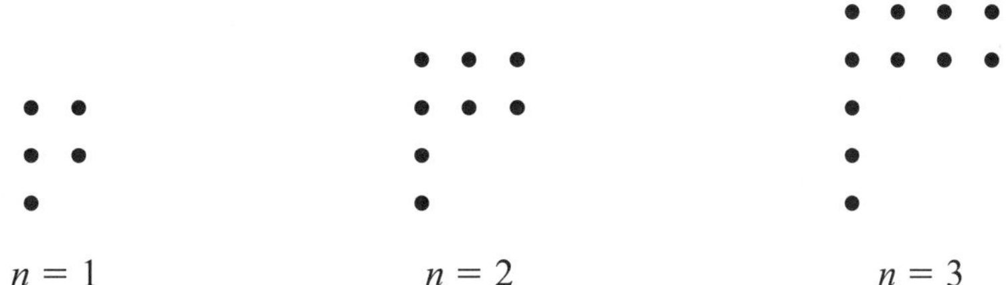

Shape number:	$n = 1$	$n = 2$	$n = 3$
Number of dots:	5	8	11

a Draw the next diagram in the sequence. How many dots are there in the nth term?

b How many dots are there in shape number 20?

c In which shape number are there 56 dots?

10 Here is another pattern made with dots.

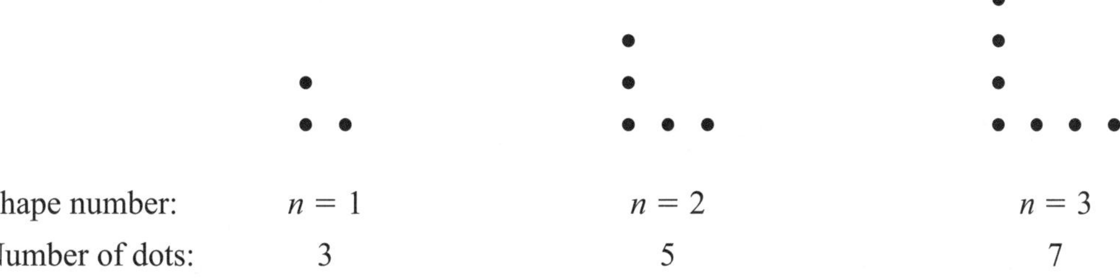

Shape number:	$n = 1$	$n = 2$	$n = 3$
Number of dots:	3	5	7

a Draw the next diagram in the sequence. How many dots are there in the nth term?

b How many dots are there in shape number 25?

c In which shape number are there 35 dots?

11 Design your own sequence of shapes using sticks or dots which has an nth term equal to $2n + 6$

5.2 Algebra – rearranging and factorising

HWK 1M — **Main Book page 327**

In questions **1** to **12**, make x the subject.

1 $x - w = m$

2 $x + a + b = y$

3 $p + q = x - y$

4 $ab^2 = x + mw$

5 $a = bx$

6 $mx - y = n$

7 $nx + p + cy = ab$

8 $m - n = cx$

9 $a + b^2 = n^2x$

10 $y + px = m$

11 $b^2 - a^2 = abx$

12 $m + nx - y = a$

13 Linda needs to make x the subject of the formula $a^2 + n^2x - w^2 = p + w^2$. Look at her working out below. Is she correct? If not, explain what mistake she has made.

$$a^2 + n^2x - w^2 = p + w^2$$
$$a^2 + n^2x = p + w^2 - w^2$$
$$a^2 + n^2x = p$$
$$n^2x = p - a^2$$
$$x = \frac{p - a^2}{n^2}$$

In questions **14** to **22**, make n the subject.

14 $myn - p^2 = q$

15 $mp^2 + pn = y + w$

16 $abn - my^2 = a^2$

17 $ab - ac^2 = abn$

18 $p^2 + w^2y = m^2n + q$

19 $ef^2n - wx = ac$

20 $bp + a^2b^2n = mw^2$

21 $ab^2cn - ab^2c = my$

22 $c - p^2 = w^2n - y^2$

HWK 2M

Main Book page 328

In questions **1** to **12**, make x the subject.

1 $m(x - y) = n$

2 $q(x + w) = p$

3 $p(ax - b) = w$

4 $a(x + w - n) = bc$

5 $ab(x - m - y) = w^2$

6 $p^2q^2 = m(ax - n)$

7 $p^2 = q^2(x + m)$

8 $m^2x + n^2y = a^2$

9 $mn - b^2 = a^2(y + bx)$

10 $m^2(a^2x + b^2y) = c - ap^2$

11 $a^2b^3 = p^2 + amx$

12 $m^2n^2(p^2x + q^2) = p^2$

13 If $p^2(mx + n) = a^2$

a make x the subject **b** make n the subject.

14 If $5bc^2 = 3m(2a + mx - p)$

a make x the subject **b** make a the subject.

15 If $acw(n^2p - wq) = a^2 + f^2m$

a make p the subject **b** make m the subject.

HWK 3M — Main Book page 329

In questions 1 to 15, make x the subject.

1. $\frac{x}{3} = m$
2. $\frac{x}{w} = m^2$
3. $\frac{m}{x} = y$
4. $\frac{w}{x} = p^2$
5. $\frac{a}{x} = 3mn$
6. $\frac{ax}{b} = m$
7. $\frac{x}{a} = a - b$
8. $7n^2 = \frac{m}{x}$
9. $\frac{ax}{by} = n^2$
10. $\frac{m}{x} = 5n^2$
11. $\frac{m}{n} = \frac{ax}{b}$
12. $\frac{m + n}{x} = y$
13. $\frac{ax}{m} = y + w$
14. $\frac{a}{b} = \frac{x}{a}$
15. $\frac{mn^2}{x} = ab^2$

16.

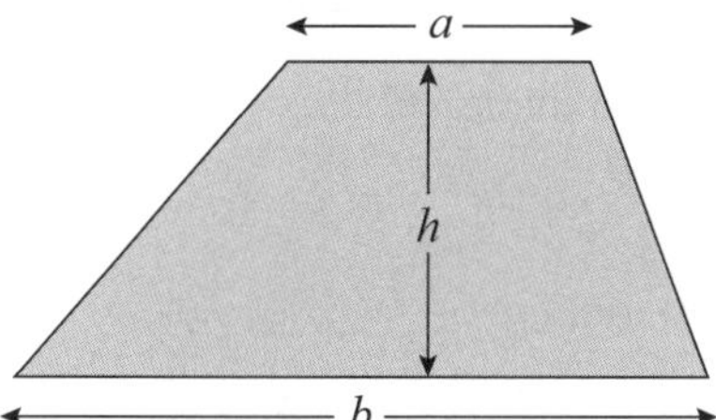

The area, A, of a trapezium is given by the formula

$$A = \frac{h(a + b)}{2}$$

Rearrange this formula to make a the subject.

17. If $P = \frac{F}{A}$, make A the subject.

18. If $s = \frac{d}{t}$, make d the subject.

19. If $\frac{v^2 - u^2}{2a} = s$, make a the subject.

20. **a** If $2s = 2ut - at^2$, make u the subject.
    b Work out the value of u when $s = 8$, $a = 10$ and $t = 4$

HWK 4M — Main Book page 330

1. Copy and complete
   a $m^2 + mn = \square(m + n)$
   b $10ab - 15a^2 = \square(2b - 3a)$
   c $6mp - 9mq = 3m(2p - \square)$
   d $21p^2 + 14pqr = 7p(\square + \square)$

Factorise each expression.

2. $6 + 20a$
3. $15p - 45$
4. $n^2 + np$
5. $8x^2 - 30$
6. $a^2 + 7ab$
7. $6y^2 - 14y$
8. $12mn + 8m^2$
9. $6a^2 - 12ab$

10 $8m^2 + 18mp$ **11** $11xy - 44y^2$ **12** $16mp - 12m^2$ **13** $35yn + 10y^2n$

14 $a^2b - ab^2$ **15** $3m^2n + 21mn^2$ **16** $12abc + 18bcd$ **17** $40a^2b^2 - ab$

18 $9m$ cm

?

The area of this rectangle is $(18m^2 + 27mn)$ cm^2
Write down an expression for the length of the rectangle if its width is $9m$ cm

19 Elsie writes that $20ab - 16a^2$ is equal to $2a(10b - 8a)$. This is not completely factorised. Write down the answer when the expression is completely factorised.

HWK 5M

Main Book page 331

1 **a** Find two numbers that multiply to make -18 and add to make -7
b Copy and complete $x^2 - 7x - 18 = (x + \square)(x + \square)$

2 **a** Find two numbers that multiply to make 8 and add to make -6
b Copy and complete $x^2 - 6x + 8 = (x + \square)(x + \square)$

3 Factorise

a $x^2 + 6x + 5$ **b** $x^2 + 8x - 20$ **c** $x^2 - 3x - 28$
d $x^2 - 10x + 25$ **e** $x^2 - 5x - 14$ **f** $x^2 + 8x + 12$
g $x^2 - 7x + 12$ **h** $x^2 + 11x - 26$ **i** $x^2 - 8x + 16$
j $x^2 - 3x - 54$ **k** $x^2 - 5x - 66$ **l** $x^2 + 4x - 21$

4

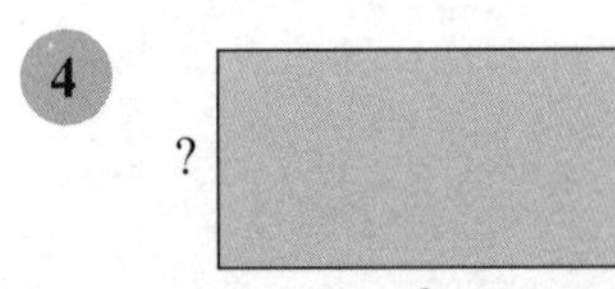

An expression for the area of this rectangle is $(x^2 + 9x + 14)$ cm^2

a Write down expressions for the length and width of the rectangle.
b Work out the area of the rectangle if the perimeter is 46 cm

5 **a** Expand $(x + 4)(x - 4)$
b Factorise $x^2 - 16$

6 **a** Expand $(x + 5)(x - 5)$
b Factorise $x^2 - 25$

7 Factorise

a $x^2 - 36$ **b** $x^2 - 81$ **c** $x^2 - 144$

8

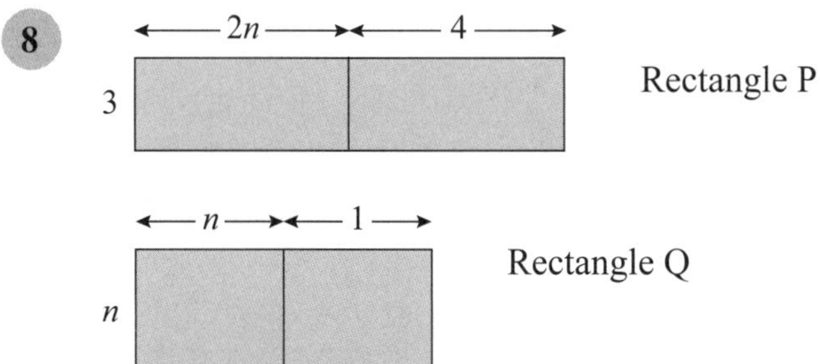

A rectangle has an area equal to the sum of the areas of rectangles P and Q.
Write down expressions for the length and width of this larger rectangle.

5.3 Interpreting and sketching real-life graphs

HWK 1M **Main Book page 335**

1

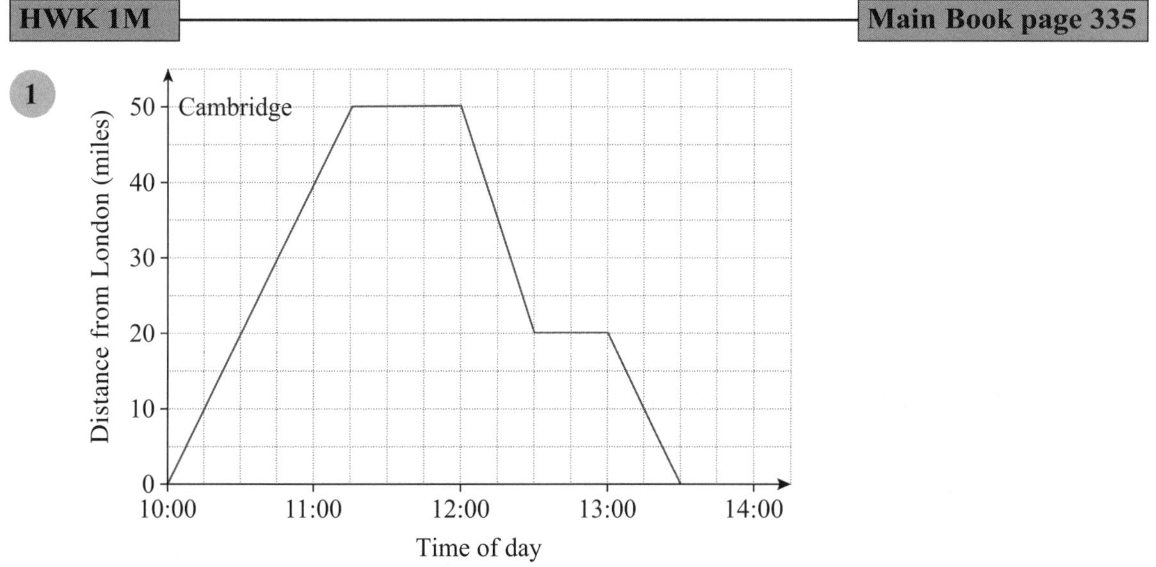

The graph above shows Alan's journey from London to Cambridge.

a When did he arrive at Cambridge?

b How long did he stop at Cambridge?

c When did he arrive back in London?

d Find Alan's speed on his journey from London to Cambridge.

e On his way back to London, Alan stops for half an hour. What is his speed for the final 20 miles of his journey?

2 A liquid is poured at a constant rate into this container until the container is completely full. Sketch a graph to show how the liquid level rises as the liquid is poured into the container.

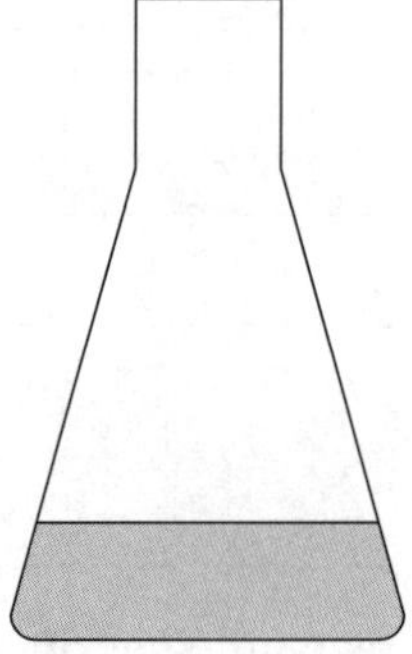

3

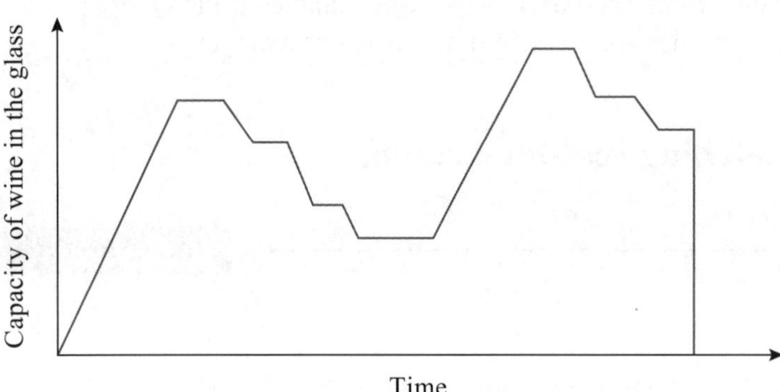

This graph shows the amount of wine in Claire's glass during one evening.

a How many times do you think the glass was filled up with wine?

b Explain the shape of the graph. What do the horizontal lines and sloping lines suggest?

c What do you think happened at the end?

4 Maggie has a peach tree. In the morning she picks a peach and places it on a window ledge in her kitchen. It is a very hot and sunny day.

In the evening she decides to put the peach in her freezer.

Sketch a graph to show the temperature of the peach during the day.

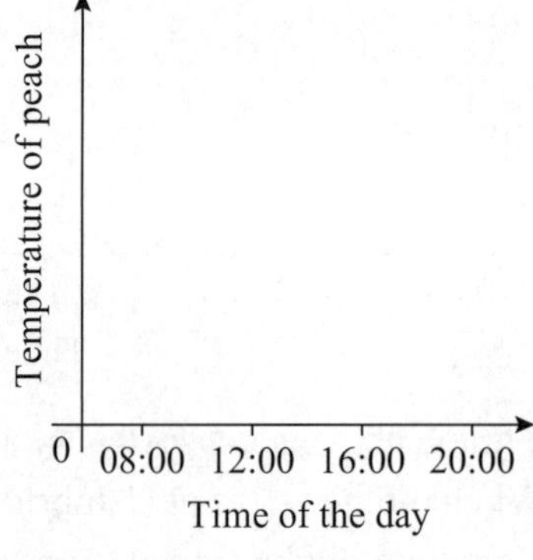

5 A person jumps out of an aeroplane and freefalls before opening a parachute. He then glides to the ground. Sketch a graph to show how quickly he heads towards the ground.

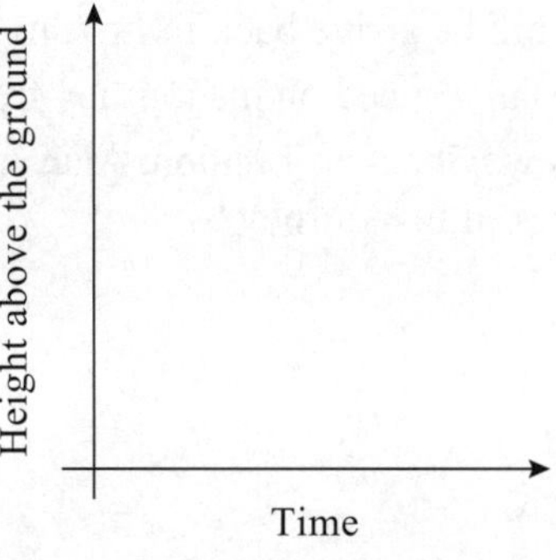

6 On squared paper, draw a vertical axis which goes up to 10 km. Draw a horizontal axis which goes up to 5 hours.

Lucy leaves her house and walks for 1 hour at 4 km/h. She then stops at a shop for $\frac{1}{2}$ hour. She then walks at 6 km/h for $\frac{1}{2}$ hour.

She now walks a further 1 km, which takes her another $\frac{1}{2}$ hour. At this point she walks directly home at a speed of 4 km/h.

Draw a travel graph to show Lucy's journey. When did she get back to her house?

5.4 Ratio

HWK 1M **Main Book page 342**

1 30:18 is the same as 5:3 because both numbers can be divided by 6

Write these ratios in a more simple form.

a 32:12 **b** 20:120 **c** 15:40 **d** 12:18:36

e 21:35 **f** 54:36 **g** 28:16:32 **h** 18:45:27

2 The Carlton family have three times as many rabbits as dogs. Write down the ratio of rabbits to dogs.

3 The ratio of men to women in a drama group is 5:3. If there are 20 men, how many women are there?

4

X	X	X	X	O	O
O	X	O	X	X	X
O	X	X	X	O	X
X	O	X	O	X	X

Write down the ratio of noughts to crosses in its simplest form.

5 Toni has some felt tip pens. The colours red to blue to green are in the ratio 5:2:3. If Toni has 12 green pens, how many red pens does she have and how many blue pens does she have?

6 If $\frac{3}{7}$ of the animals in a vet's surgery are cats and the rest are dogs, what is the ratio of cats to dogs?

7 The ratio of boys to girls in a class is 4:5. What fraction of the class are boys?

8 Some red and blue paint is mixed together in the ratio 7:2. If 27 litres of paint are used in total, how much of each colour paint is used?

9 The angles in a triangle are in the ratio 4:3:2.
Find the size of the largest angle.

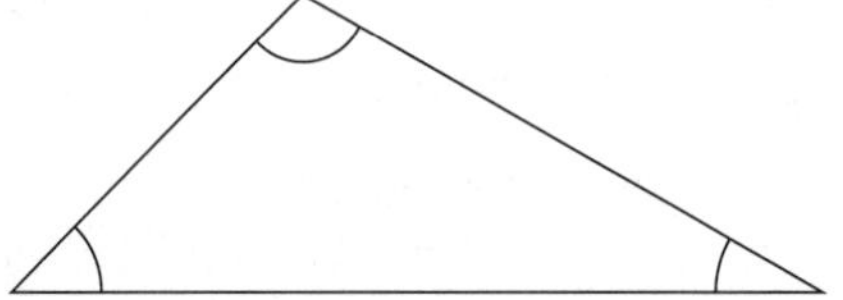

10 The marks in an exam are given for three different parts in the ratio 11:5:4.
The maximum mark for the exam is 100. Write down the maximum marks which can be awarded for each part of the exam.

11 Hugo and Ellie's mother gives them £80 in the ratio 7:9. Hugo gets the smallest share. Hugo owes Ellie £15 and so he gives her this money. Write down the ratio of Hugo's money to Ellie's money now. Write the ratio in its simplest form.

12

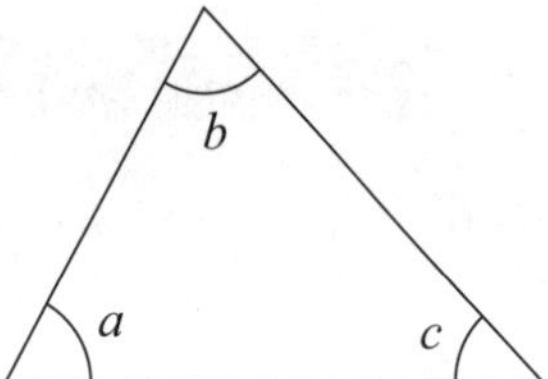

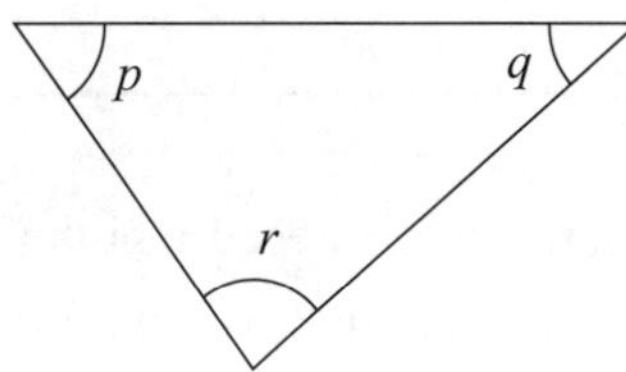

Angles in the triangle above are in the ratio 5:4:3. Angle b is the middle sized angle.

Angles in the triangle above are in the ratio 3:1:5. Angle p is the middle sized angle. Angle r is the largest angle.

Find the size of angle r if angle p is equal in size to angle b.

HWK 1E

Main Book page 343

1 The sides of a rectangle are in the ratio 7:3. The perimeter of the rectangle is 40 cm. Find the area of the rectangle.

2 The ratio of Wayne's weight to Caroline's weight is 3:2. How much does Wayne weigh if he weighs 20 kg more than Caroline?

3 The ratio of children to adults in a room is 2:5. Among the adults, the ratio of men to women is 3:4. Find the ratio of children to men.

4

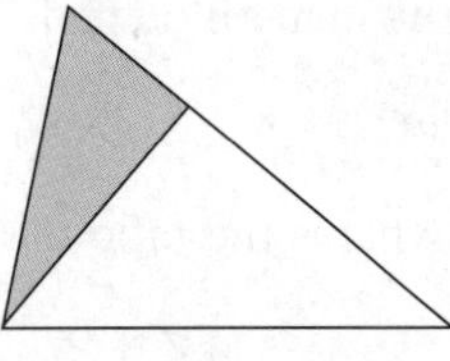

Area = 21 cm²

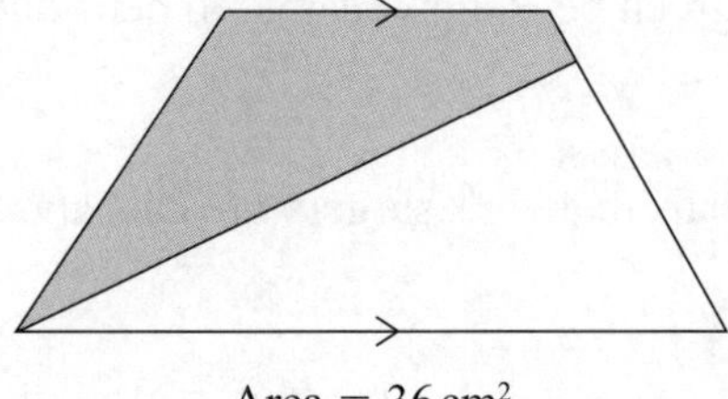

Area = 36 cm²

The shaded area to the unshaded area in the triangle is in the ratio 1:2. The shaded area to the unshaded area in the trapezium is in the ratio 4:5. Find the ratio of the total shaded area to the total unshaded area.

5 Find y if $y{:}20 = 5{:}y$ and y is positive.

6 A rectangular photo measures 18 cm by 7 cm. The lengths are enlarged in the ratio 2:3. What is the ratio of the area of the original photo to the area of the enlarged photo?

7 Beer and lemonade is mixed in the ratio 3:2 to make a shandy. 5% of the beer is alcohol. What percentage of the shandy is alcohol?

8 The ratio $m{:}n = 2{:}7$ and the ratio $n{:}p = 3{:}5$. Find the ratio $m{:}p$

9 Write the ratios in a more simple form.

a 3 cm : 2 mm **b** 6 kg : 250 g **c** 400 ml : 5 litres

d 0.4 km : 2 km : 600 m **e** 2 kg : 0.25 kg : 300 g **f** $0.6{:}\frac{7}{10}{:}\frac{1}{4}$

10 Two numbers p and q add up to 66. The ratio $p{:}q = 4{:}7$
What are the values of p and q?

11 The ratio of Martin's weight to Anna's weight is 8:9. How much does Martin weigh if he weighs 8 kg less than Anna?

12 Find the value of x if $(x + 4){:}6 = x{:}5$

13 $\frac{3}{7}$ of the chocolates in a box are dark chocolates. $\frac{5}{6}$ of the dark chocolates are soft-centred.
What is the ratio of soft-centred dark chocolates to the other types of chocolates in the box?

14 Find the two possible values for n if $(n + 6){:}n = n{:}3$

HWK 2M/3M — Main Book pages 345 and 346

1 The scale of a map is 1:100 000. The distance between two towns on the map is 8 cm. What is the actual distance in kilometres between the two towns?

2 Find the actual distance in metres between two pylons which are 2 cm apart on a map with the scale 1:10 000

3 The length of a field on a map is 1.5 cm. Find the actual length of the field in metres if the map scale is 1:40 000

4 Two cities are 6.5 cm apart on a map and the scale of the map is 1:2 000 000.
What is the actual distance in kilometres between the two cities?

5 A map has a scale of 1:50 000. On this map, the distance from Tom's house to the Red Bull pub is 3 cm and the distance from Tom's house to the White Horse pub is 5.5 cm. How many kilometres further from Tom's house is the White Horse than the Red Bull?

6 Colin and Adele are hiking. They fix their positions and are 12 km from each other. How far is this on a map with the scale 1:200 000?

7 Two ships are 30 km apart from each other. How far is this on a map with the scale 1:50 000?

8 Map A has a scale of 1:200 000. Map B has a scale of 1:50 000. Two villages are 8 cm apart on map A. How far apart will the two villages be on map B?

9 Bristol and Wells are 16 cm apart on map A with a scale of 1:200 000. How far apart would they be on map B with a scale of 1:500 000?

10 **a** The area of a lake on a map is 18 cm^2. Work out the actual area of the lake if the scale of the map is 1:40 000. (Be careful!)

b What is the area of the same lake on a map with a scale of 1:50 000?

11 A rectangular park measures 2 cm by 1 cm on a map with a scale of 1:80 000. Work out the actual area of the park.

12 The distance from Charlie's house to the Blue Bowl pub is 3 cm on a map with a scale of 1:200 000. The distance from his house to the Oyster restaurant is 5.5 cm on a map with a scale of 1:80 000. Which is closer to Charlie's house and by how much: the Blue Bowl or the Oyster?

5.5 Percentages 2

HWK 1M **Main Book page 350**

Remember: $$\text{percentage increase} = \left(\frac{\text{actual increase}}{\text{original value}}\right) \times 100$$

$$\text{percentage decrease} = \left(\frac{\text{actual decrease}}{\text{original value}}\right) \times 100$$

Give all answers to one decimal place.

1 A cereal manufacturer reduces the amount of sugar in a box of cereal from 170 g to 140 g. Work out the percentage decrease in the amount of sugar.

2 A farmer owns 530 hectares of land. The farmer sells off some of the land so the area of the farm is reduced to 360.4 hectares. What is the percentage reduction in the area of the farm?

3 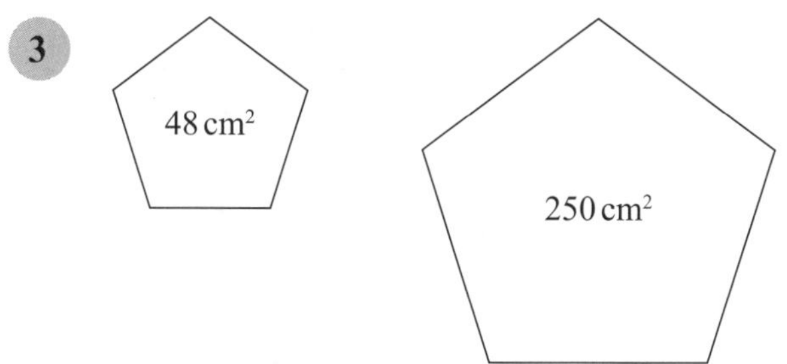

Work out the percentage increase in the area of this regular pentagon.

4 Use a percentage multiplier to increase 930 kg by 4%

930 × 1.04 = 967.2

5 A TV costs £580, including VAT. The price of the TV is increased by £90 then a further 6% of the new price. What is now the overall percentage increase in the cost of the TV from the original £580? 580 + 90 = 670 × 1.06 = £710.2

6 Josh sells camper vans. The table shows how many he sold in each of three months.

Month	March	April	May
Number of camper vans	7	9	11

Between which two months was the percentage increase in camper van sales the greatest? Give a reason for your answer.

7 A joiner pays £90 for the wood to make a window frame. The joiner sells the window frame for £148.50. Work out the percentage profit made by the joiner.

8 Three basketball players are shooting baskets. Their success rate is shown opposite.

	Successes	Total attempts
Jason	39	143
Cheryl	48	170
Mike	27	71

a Who had the highest percentage rate of success?

b What was the percentage difference in success rates between Cheryl and Mike?

9 The formula $v = u + at$ is used. An initial observation gives $u = 6$, $a = 14$ and $t = 3$. A second observation gives a 7% increase in the value of u, a 4% increase in the value of a and an 11% increase in the value of t. Work out the percentage increase in the value of v after the second observation.

10

Item	Cost price	Selling price
fish	£2	£5
chips	60p	£2
sausage	30p	£1.50
chicken	£1.50	£4
peas	20p	£1

The table shows the cost price and selling price of certain items in a fish and chip shop.

During one evening the fish and chip shop sells 70 fish, 120 portions of chips, 32 sausages, 25 pieces of chicken and 35 portions of peas. What percentage profit does the shop make on the sale of these items?

HWK 2M

Main Book page 352

Give answers to the nearest penny when needed.

1 £6000 is invested at 5% per annum (year) compound interest. How much money will there be after 2 years?

2 The population of a country is 3 200 000. Each year the population increases by 8% of the current population. What is the population of this country after 2 years?

3 The table shows money invested at the compound interest rate indicated. For each part, work out the amount of money after the number of years shown.

	Money	% rate	Time
a	£4000	7%	3 years
b	£12 000	3%	2 years
c	£6500	9%	5 years
d	£30 000	12%	10 years

4 A car costs £18 000. Each year its value reduces by 9% of its current value. How much is the car worth after 3 years?

5

RIGHT SAVE
4% per annum compound interest

BONUS SAVE
3% per annum compound interest plus an extra 1% after 3 years

Ashna has £7000 to invest for 3 years. Which of the above plans will give her more money? How much more money will this plan give?

6 Mr Abrahams invests £20 000 at 4% per annum compound interest. His sister invests £21 000 at 3% per annum compound interest. At the end of which year does Mr Abrahams first have more money than his sister?

7 Dougal can invest £18 000 at 6% per annum compound interest for 5 years or take a one-off bonus payment of £6000. How much more money will he have if he invests his money rather than taking the one-off bonus payment?

8 Milena invests £25 000 at 10% per annum compound interest. How much money will she have after 50 years?

5.6 Statistics review

HWK 1M Main Book page 357

1 M A J E S T I C

The word JET is removed from the cards above. Carys then removes one card at random. What is the probability that this card is a vowel?

2 Four people have a mean age of 30. Another six people have a mean age of 50. Work out the mean age of all ten people.

3 The stem and leaf diagram shows the weights of a group of people. Which is greater and by how much: the mean or the median?

Stem	Leaf
4	2 7
5	0 1 1 3 9
6	2 5 5 5 7
7	1 3 4 6 6 6
8	0 0 3 7
9	1 1 6

Key: 6|5 means 65 kg

4 Groups of people in Manchester and Bristol were asked if they prefer going to the cinema, to the theatre or to a restaurant. The results are recorded in the pie charts below.

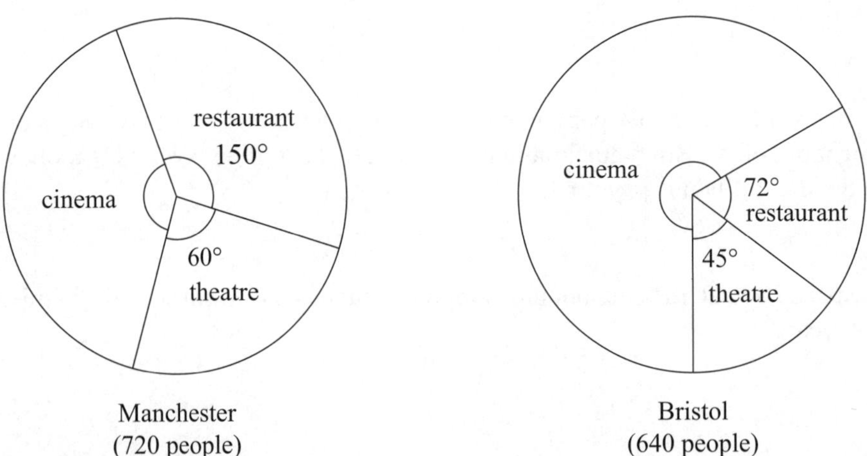

How many more people from Bristol prefer the cinema compared with the people from Manchester?

5 Two bags each contain red balls and blue balls. The probability of removing a red ball from bag A is $\frac{5}{12}$ and the probability of removing a red ball from bag B is $\frac{6}{13}$. Which bag has more red balls and by how many?

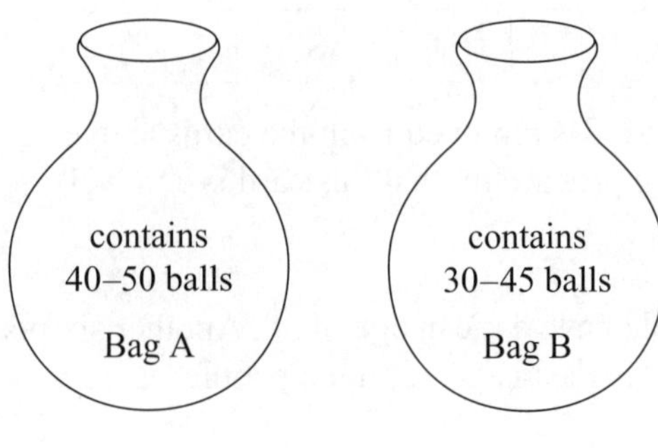

6 The number of bedrooms in 80 houses is recorded in the table below.

Number of bedrooms	1	2	3	4	5	6
Frequency	7	$n + 7$	28	25	n	3

a Work out the value of n.

b Work out the mean number of bedrooms per house.

c Is the mean higher or lower than the median? Give a reason for your answer.

7 The students in Year 8 at a local school study French, German or Spanish. The probability of a randomly chosen student doing each of these subjects is shown in the table below.

Subject	French	German	Spanish
Probability	?	0.2	?

a The probability of studying French is treble the probability of studying Spanish. What is the probability of a chosen student studying French?

b There are 215 students in Year 8. How many of these students study Spanish?

8 The scatter graph below shows the value of a certain type of car and the age of the car.

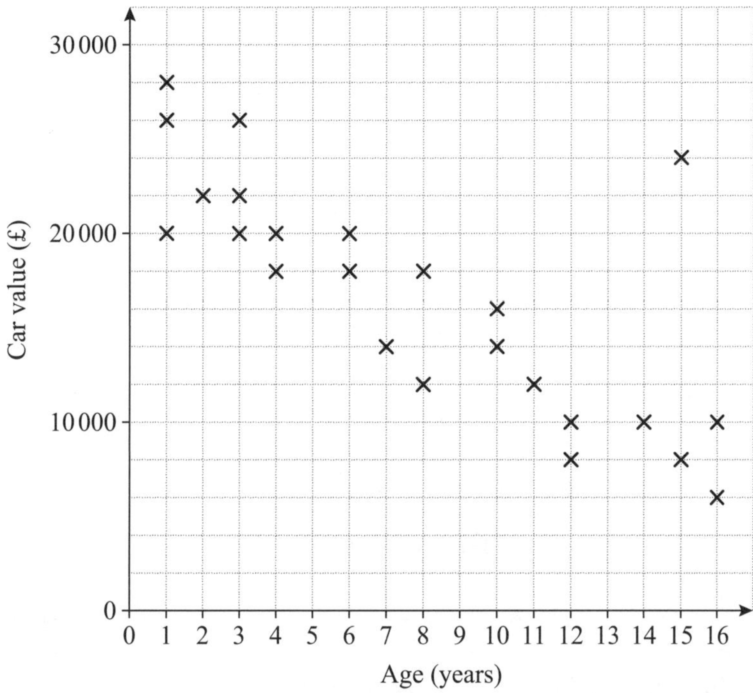

a Describe the correlation.

b How much would you expect a nine-year-old car to be worth?

c Write down the coordinates of an outlier.

UNIT 6

6.1 Algebra review

HWK 1M **Main Book page 379**

1

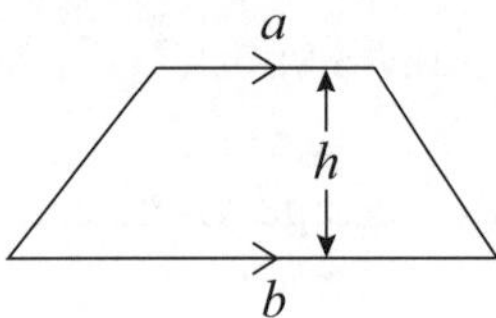

The area A of this trapezium is given by the formula

$$A = \frac{1}{2}h(a + b)$$

Find the value of A when $h = 10$, $a = 3$ and $b = 9$

2 The area A of this shape is given by the formula

$$A = n(m + p)$$

Find the value of A when $n = 20$, $m = 40$ and $p = 15$

3 $w = p^2 + 7p$

Find w when $p = 9$

4 $a = \frac{29 - 4n}{10}$

Find a when $n = 7$

5 $y = 4x(100 - x^2)$

Find y when $x = 5$

6 $m = p^3 + p^2 + p$

Find m when $p = 6$

7 Norman sells chocolates. Each month he buys n boxes of chocolates to sell at £9 for each box. He always gives one box to his partner and one box to each of his two children. Norman gets £m for selling the remaining boxes, given by the formula

$$m = 9(n - 3)$$

Find the value of m when

a $n = 43$ **b** $n = 60$ **c** $n = 100$

8 Find the value of y using the formulae and values given.

a $y = ab - 6$ when $a = 7$ and $b = -2$

b $y = (3x - 1)^2$ when $x = -4$

c $y = mn + n^2 - 8$ when $m = -3$ and $n = -4$

d $y = \frac{n^2 + 3n}{2n}$ when $n = -9$

9 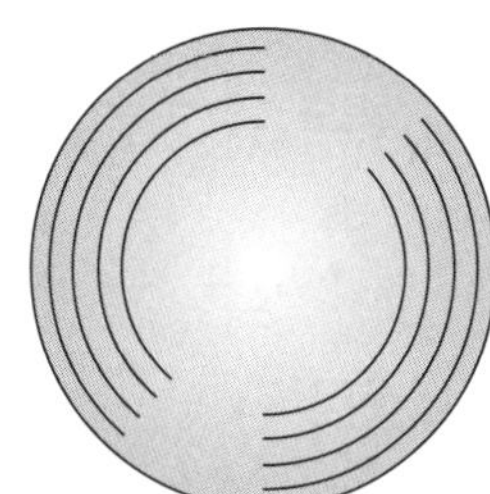

The surface area A of a sphere is approximately given by the formula

$$A = 12r^2$$

Find the surface area of a sphere with a radius of $\frac{3}{4}$ cm

10 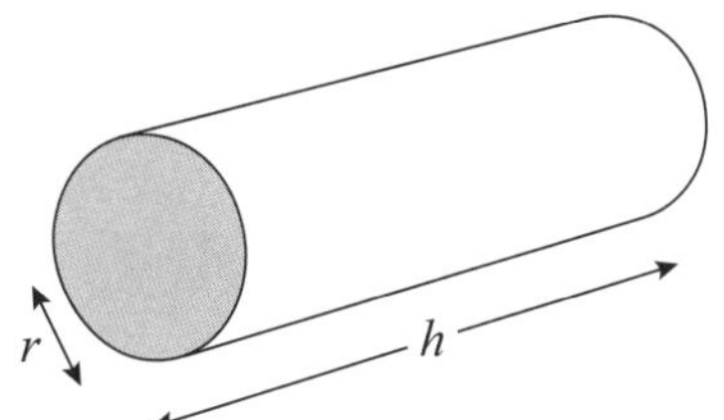

The total surface area A of a cylinder is approximately given by the formula

$$A = 6r(h + r)$$

Find the total surface area A of a cylinder with $r = \frac{2}{3}$ cm and $h = 1\frac{1}{2}$ cm

11 If you add the numbers $1 + m + m^2 + m^3 + \ldots m^n$, the sum is given by the formula

$$\text{Sum} = \frac{1 - m^{n+1}}{1 - m}$$

a Use the formula to work out $1 + 3 + 3^2 + \ldots + 3^{10}$

b Check your answer by adding the numbers in the normal way.

c Use the formula to work out $1 + 2 + 4 + 8 + \ldots + 8192$

12 This open box has no top.
The surface area A is given by the formula

$$A = 2np + mn + 2mp$$

Find the value of p if $n = 6$, $m = 7$ and $A = 146$

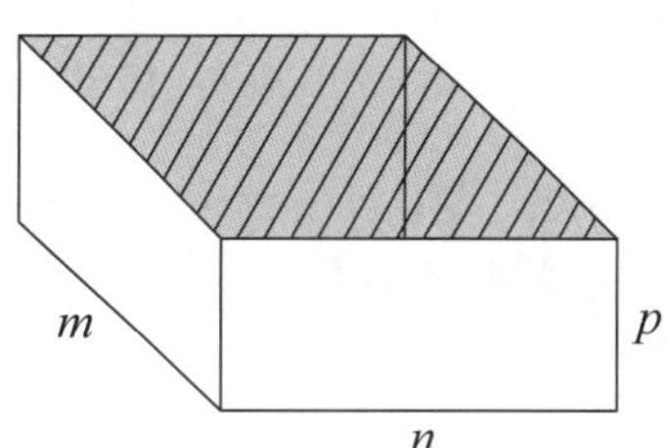

HWK 2M

Main Book page 382

Solve

1 $7x + 4 = 2 - 4x$

2 $8 - 3x = 3 + 3x$

3 $5 - 2x = 6x - 2$

4 $6 - 4x = 3 - 6x$

5 $7 = \frac{x}{5}$

6 $\frac{4x}{5} = 8$

7 $\frac{2}{x} = 9$

8 $\frac{6}{x} = \frac{3}{4}$

9 $\frac{x}{2} + 4 = 6$

10 $\frac{x}{7} - 3 = 3$

11 $\frac{5}{x} - 3 = 4$

12 $\frac{6}{x} + 5 = 4$

Solve

13 $5(x + 3) = 2(2x + 11)$

14 $7(x + 6) = 11(2x - 3)$

15 $4(2x - 3) = 3(2 + 2x)$

16 $3(4x + 1) = 9(2x - 1)$

17 $8(2x - 7) = 2x$

18 $6(x + 9) = 3(8 + 3x)$

19 $3(3x + 5) = 29(x - 5)$

20 $10(9 + 2x) = 33(x - 2)$

21 $4(2x + 1) - 2(x + 4) = 0$

22 $5(x - 4) - 2 = 3(3 - x)$

23 $6(2x + 3) - (3x + 2) = 0$

24 $5 + 2(4x + 3) = 6$

25 $3(2x + 5) + 2(3 - x) = 5x$

26 $8x - 3(x - 3) = 2x$

27 $3x - 4(2x + 5) = 2x$

HWK 3M/4M

Main Book page 384

1

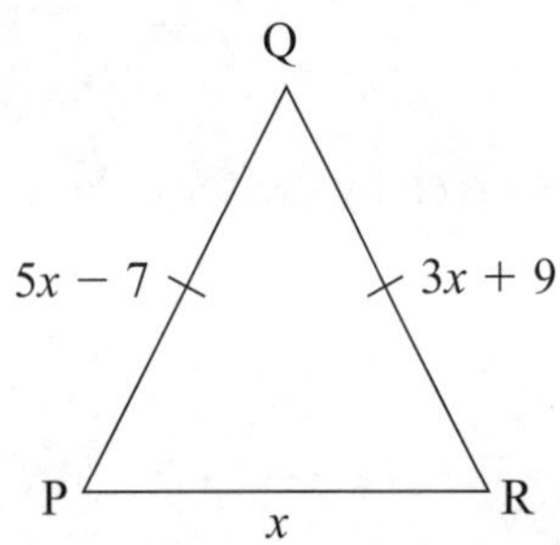

PQ = QR in this isosceles triangle.

All measurements are in cm.

a Find x.

b Find the perimeter of the triangle.

2 Football shorts cost £$2x$ and football shirts cost £$(3x + 2)$. Two pairs of shorts and three shirts cost £162 in total. Find the cost of one shirt.

3 Maurice is 40 years younger than his father. In 15 years' time his father will be three times as old as Maurice. How old is Maurice now?

4

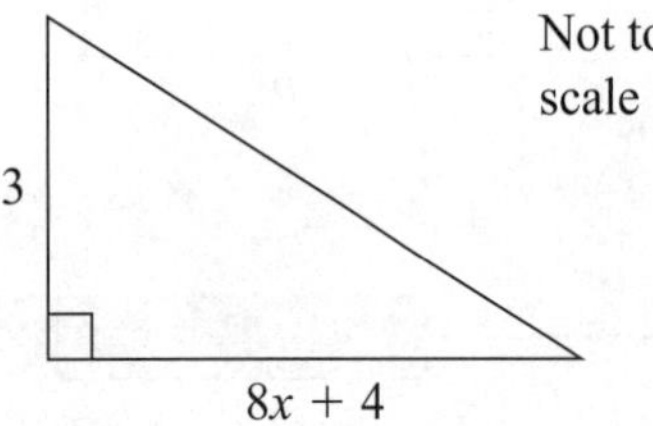

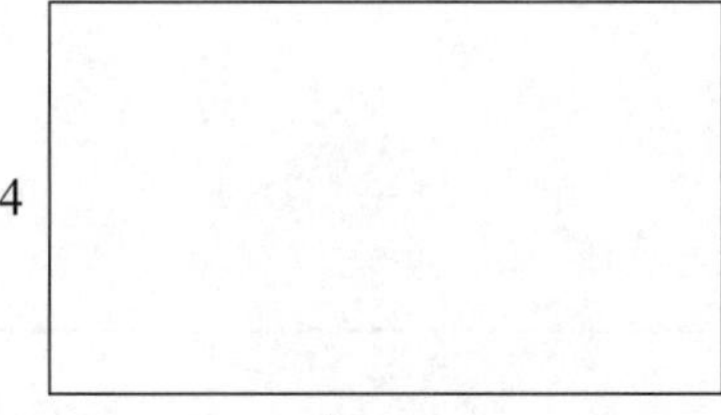

The area of the triangle is twice the area of the rectangle. Find the area of the triangle. All lengths are in cm.

5 The sum of five consecutive whole numbers is 355. Find the five numbers.

6 Rachel delivers newspapers each day. She starts with 81 newspapers. She delivers $2x$ newspapers on Stanley Street and $(x - 3)$ newspapers on Easton Way. She then has x newspapers remaining. How many newspapers did she deliver on Easton Way?

7

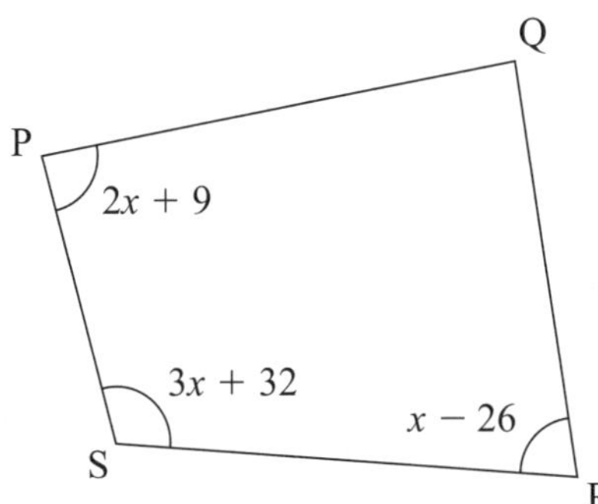

Angle Q is the difference between angles S and P. Find the values of the four angles in this quadrilateral.

8

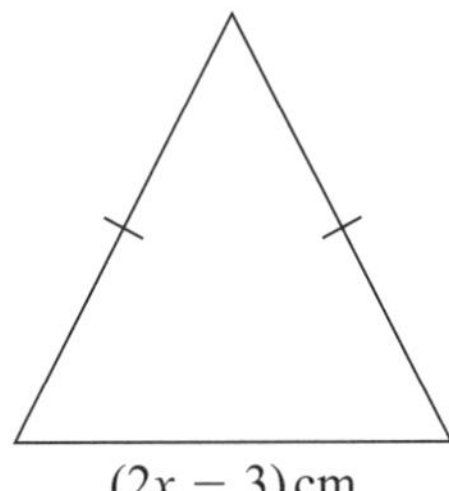

The perimeter of this isosceles triangle is $(8x + 5)$ cm.

Find the value of the perimeter if one of the equal sides is 25 cm long.

9 If $x = m^2 - 4n$, find the value of n when $x = 44$ and $m = -6$

10 In this number wall the number in each brick is found by adding the numbers in the two bricks below. Find the value of n.

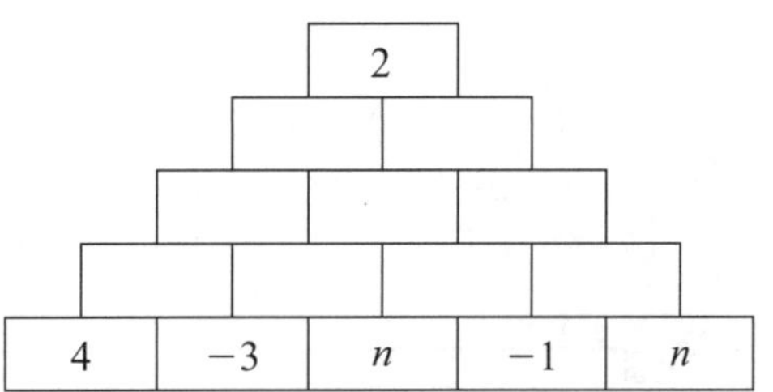

HWK 5M — **Main Book page 387**

Simplify and write each answer in index form.

1 $n^5 \times n^3$

2 $\dfrac{n^8}{n^4}$

3 $n^5 \times n^2 \times n^4 \times n^3$

4 $(n^6)^5$

5 $\dfrac{n^6 \times n^4}{n^7}$

6 $(n^4)^3 \times n^5$

7 $n^4 \times n$

8 $\dfrac{n^5 \times n^4}{n}$

9 $\dfrac{n^3 \times (n^2)^4}{n^6}$

10 $\dfrac{(n^5)^3}{n}$

11 $\dfrac{(n^3)^3 \times n^4}{(n^3)^2}$

12 $\dfrac{(m^5)^4}{(n^3)^2 \times (n^4)^2}$

13 Work out the area of this triangle, leaving the answer in index form.

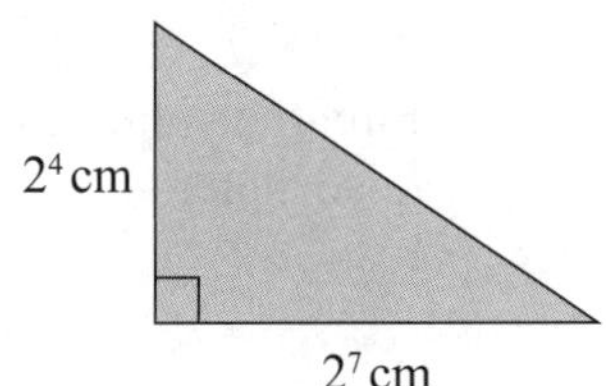

14 Work out $5^2 \times 2^3$

15 If $(n^2)^x \times n^5 = n^{13}$, write down the value of x.

16 If $\dfrac{n^7 \times (n^x)^5}{n^4 \times n^6} = n^7$, write down the value of x.

17 Copy and complete

a $n^{5x} \times n^{\square} = n^{8x}$ **b** $\dfrac{(n^{3x})^3}{n^{\square}} = n^{3x}$ **c** $n^2 \times n^{\square} = n^{5x+2}$

18 Does $\dfrac{w^2 \times w^{4x}}{w^4} = w^{2x}$? Give a reason for your answer.

19 Solve

a $2^{3x} = 64$ **b** $8^{2x} = 1$ **c** $3 \times 3^{2x} = 27$

20 Simplify $\dfrac{(m^3)^2 \times m^x \times (m^x)^2 \times m^5}{m^{2x} \times (m^2)^2 \times (m^2)^3}$

HWK 6M

Main Book page 388

Expand

1 $a(3a - b)$ **2** $5n(2m + 7n)$ **3** $(x + 6)(x + 3)$

4 $(m + 4)(m - 5)$ **5** $(a - 6)(a - 4)$ **6** $(p - 9)(p + 7)$

7 $(x - 3)(x - 10)$ **8** $(n + 6)^2$ **9** $(m - 4)^2$

Factorise

10 $m^2 - 6m$ **11** $8n^2 + 12np$ **12** $20xy - 12y^2$

13 $x^2 + 6x - 16$ **14** $m^2 - 11m + 30$ **15** $p^2 - 7p - 30$

16 $n^2 - 2n - 15$ **17** $a^2 + 5a + 4$ **18** $x^2 - 6x + 9$

19 **a** Expand $(x + 7)(x - 7)$ **b** Factorise $x^2 - 49$

20 **a** Expand $(x + 11)(x - 11)$ **b** Factorise $x^2 - 121$

21 Nadine buys $(n + 3)$ cartons of orange juice. The total cost of the cartons is £$(n^2 - 4n - 21)$. Write down an expression for the cost of one carton of orange juice.

22 The area of this rectangle is $(n^2 + 3n - 40)$ cm². Write down an expression for the perimeter of this rectangle.

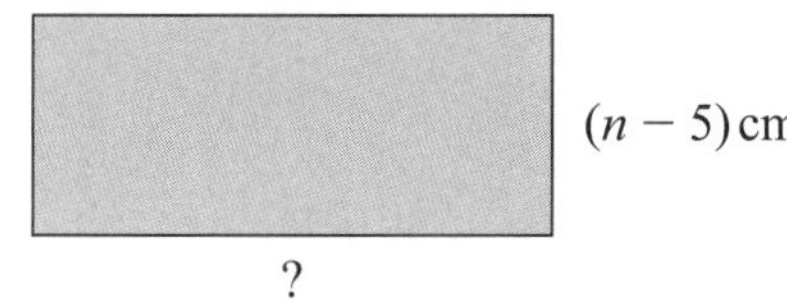

23 Expand and simplify

a $5(2x + 3) + 2(4x + 5)$ **b** $7(4x + 2) - 3(2x + 9)$

c $(x + 7)(x + 2) - x^2 - 14$ **d** $(x + 8)(x + 7) - x(x - 6)$

HWK 7M

Main Book page 389

In questions **1** to **9**, make x the subject.

1 $nx + w = y$ **2** $aw = p(x - q)$ **3** $b^2(mx - p) = w$

4 $\frac{cx}{m} = p$ **5** $\frac{w}{x} = y$ **6** $ac + b^2 = px + mn$

7 $\frac{x}{a} = \frac{b}{c}$ **8** $\frac{ax - b}{m} = w$ **9** $pq = \frac{a + b}{mx}$

10 **a** If $s = \frac{t(u + v)}{2}$, make u the subject of the formula.

b Find the value of u if $t = 6$, $v = 4$ and $s = 48$

11

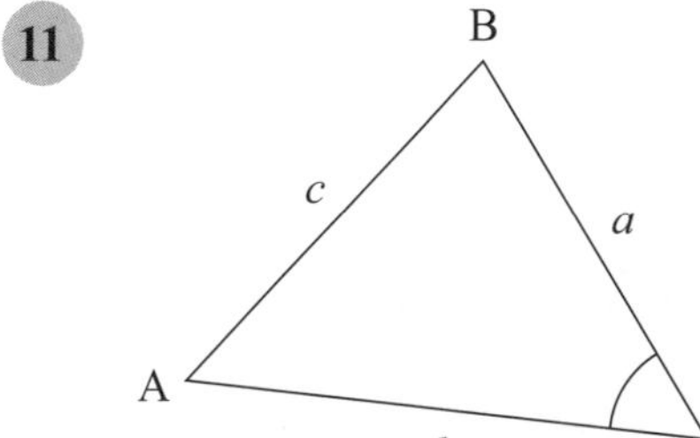

The area, A, of this triangle can be found by using the formula

$$A = \frac{ab \sin \widehat{C}}{2}$$

Make $\sin \widehat{C}$ the subject of the formula.

In questions 12 to 17, make n the subject.

12 $p(an + w) = 3c + f$

13 $\frac{2w}{3n} = 5p$

14 $\frac{wy + bn}{4ap} = 2c$

15 $c^2f - mw^2 = \frac{wn - a^2}{y}$

16 $5w^2 = \frac{m(2n + a)}{3wp}$

17 $\frac{5a}{3b} = \frac{2m}{7n}$

6.2 Volume of objects

HWK 1M Main Book page 395

1 Find the volume of this solid by splitting it into three cuboids. All lengths are in cm.

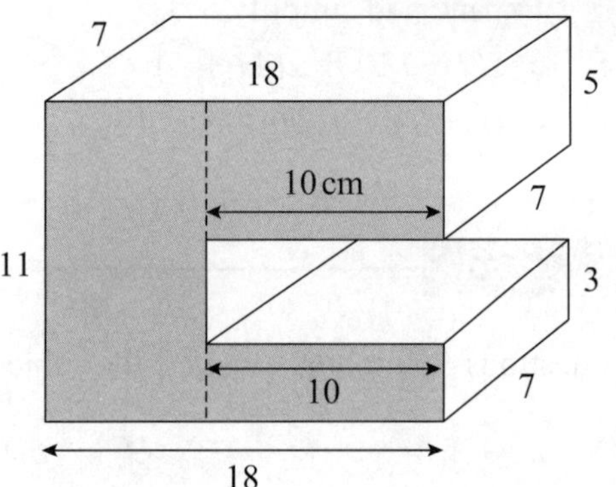

2 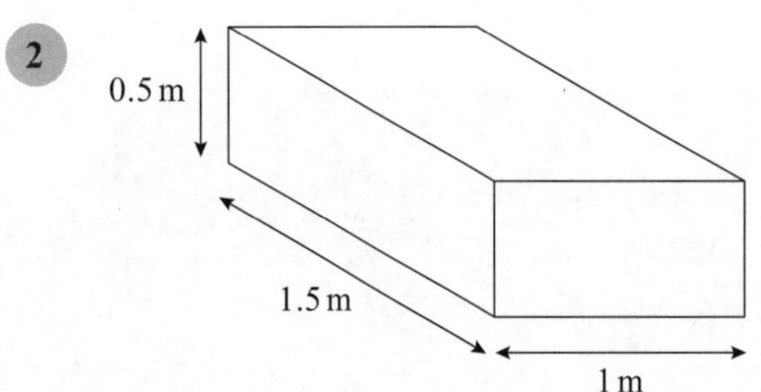

This water tank is full of water.
Hannah uses $0.32\ m^3$ of water.
What volume of water is left in the tank?

3 The entrance to a 300 m tunnel is shown opposite.
Work out the volume of the tunnel.

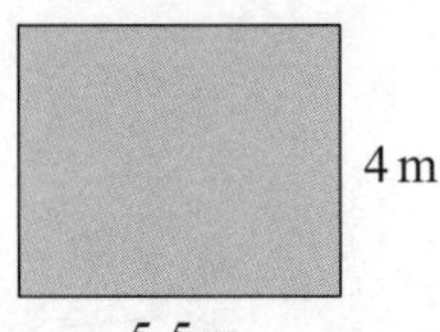

4

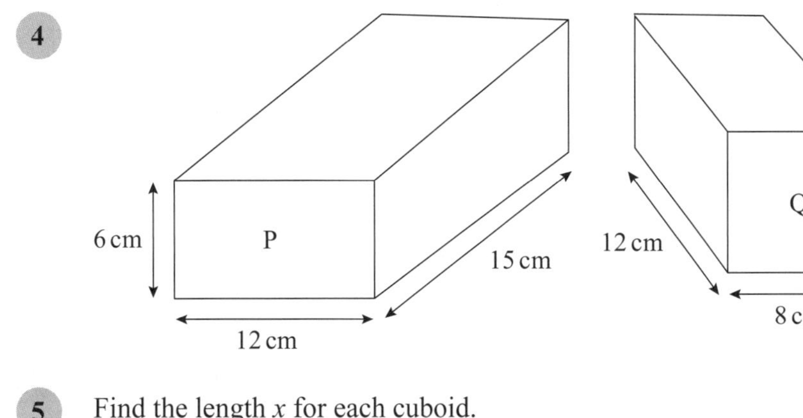

Work out the ratio of the volume of cuboid P to the volume of cuboid Q. Give the answer in its simplest form.

5 Find the length x for each cuboid.

a

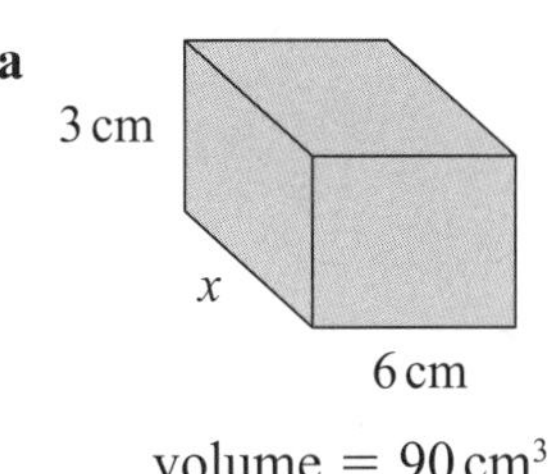

volume = $90\,\text{cm}^3$

b

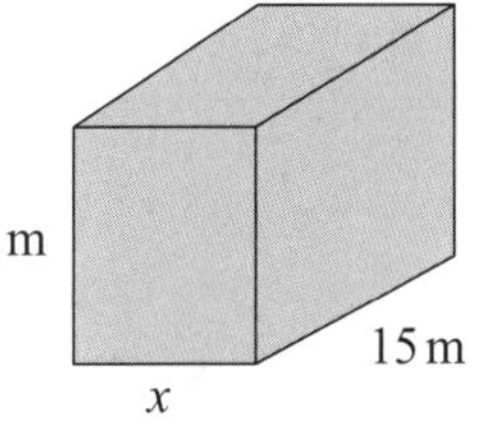

volume = $810\,\text{m}^3$

c

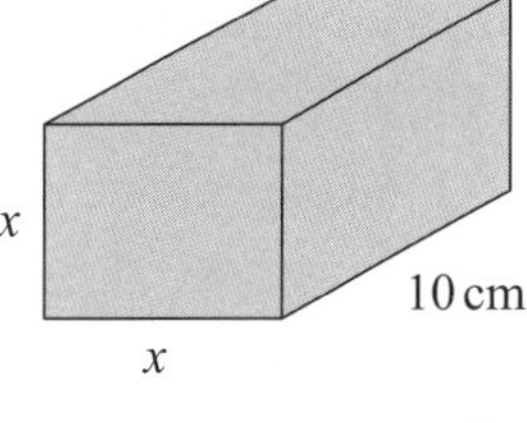

volume = $490\,\text{cm}^3$

6

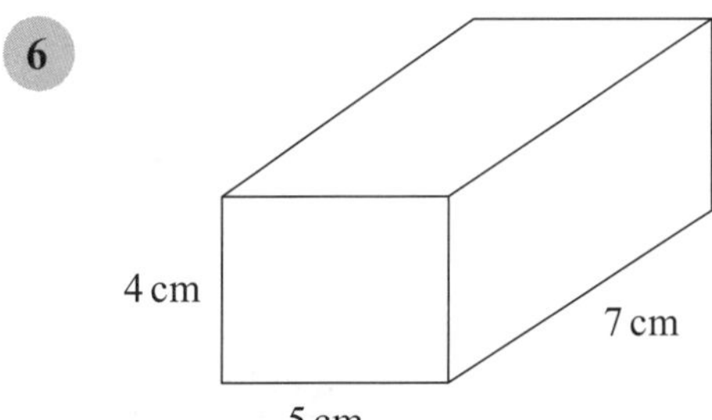

a Draw a *net* for this cuboid.

b Work out the volume of this cuboid.

c Work out the total surface area of this cuboid.

7

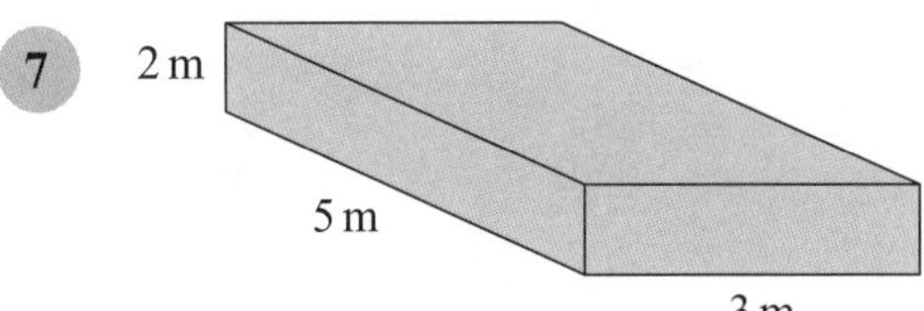

The container on a lorry is shown opposite. Sand is tipped into the lorry at a rate of $0.2\,\text{m}^3$ per minute. How long does it take to completely fill the container with sand?

8 How many small cubes of side 0.1 m will fit into a large cube of side 2.4 m?

9 **a** Write down an expression for the volume of this cuboid.

b Write down an expression for the total surface area of the cuboid.

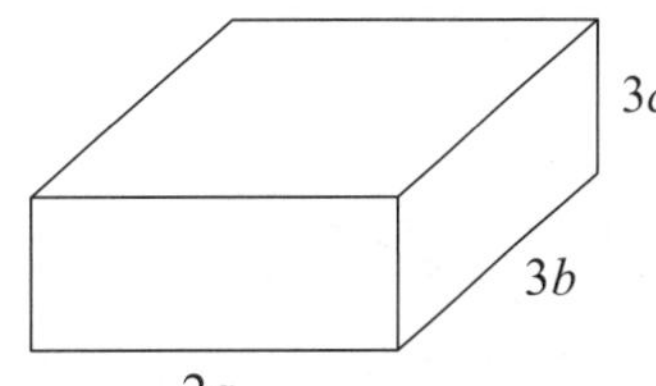

10 **a** Write down an expression for the difference in the volumes of these two cuboids.

b Write down an expression for the difference in the total surface areas of these two cuboids.

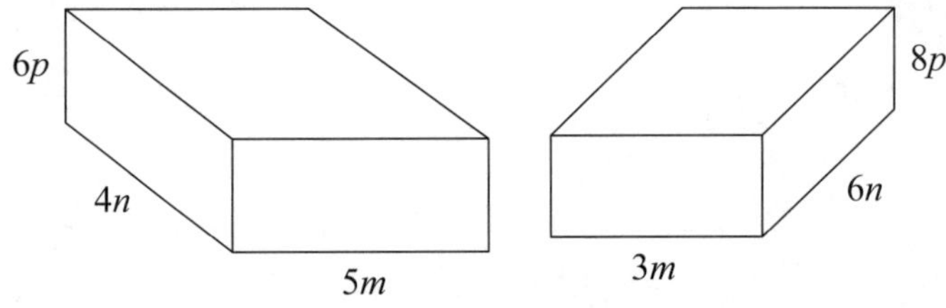

HWK 2M

Main Book page 398

Reminder: volume of prism = (area of cross section) × (length)

1 Find the volume of each prism.

a

12 cm
6 cm
15 cm
5 cm

b

16 cm
4 cm
5 cm
8 cm
11 cm

c

7 cm
14 cm
10 cm

2

prism A

18 cm
7 cm
9 cm
20 cm

Which prism has the larger volume and by how much?

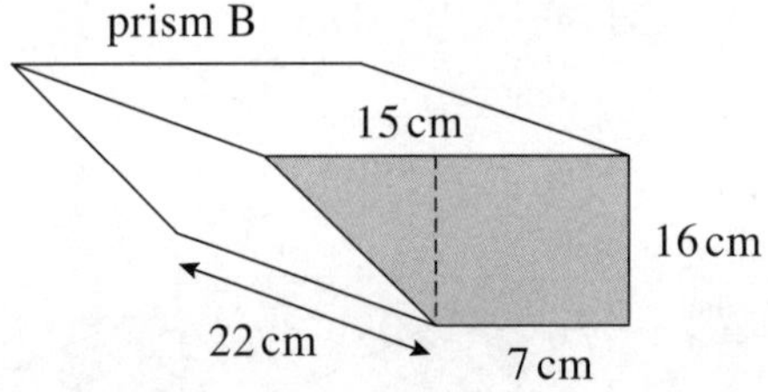

3

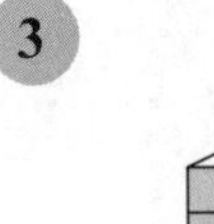

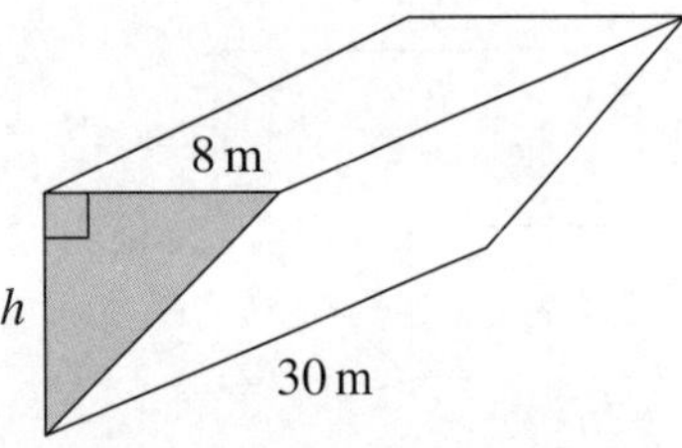

Find the height h of this triangular prism if the volume is $2160\,m^3$

4

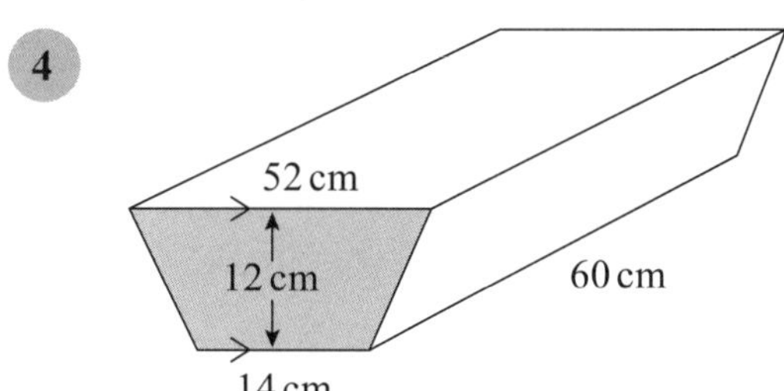

This container is full of water. The water leaks out of a hole in the bottom at a rate of 30 ml/sec. How long will it take for the container to become empty? (1 ml = 1 cm^3)

5 The front of this bridge is a semicircle cut from a rectangle. 1 m^3 of the stone used to make the bridge weighs 1150 kg. Calculate the weight of the stone used to make the complete bridge. (Give your answer to the nearest kg)

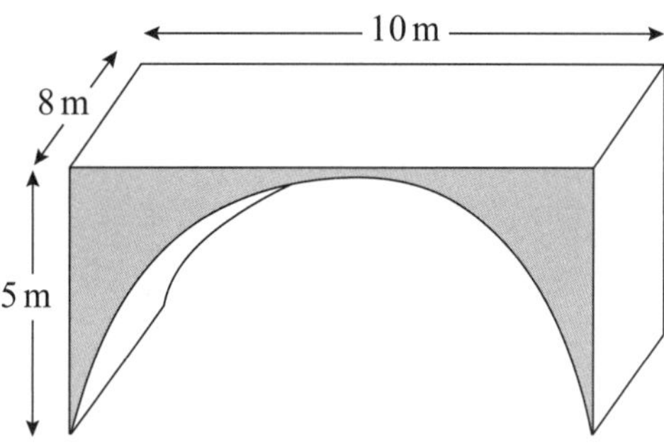

6

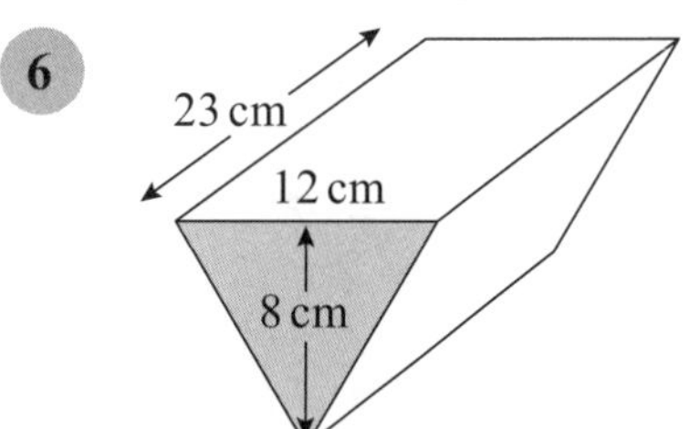

These two prisms have the same volumes. Find the value of x.

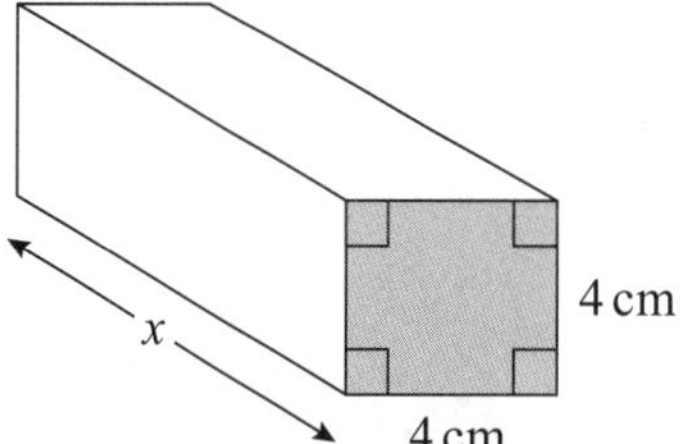

7

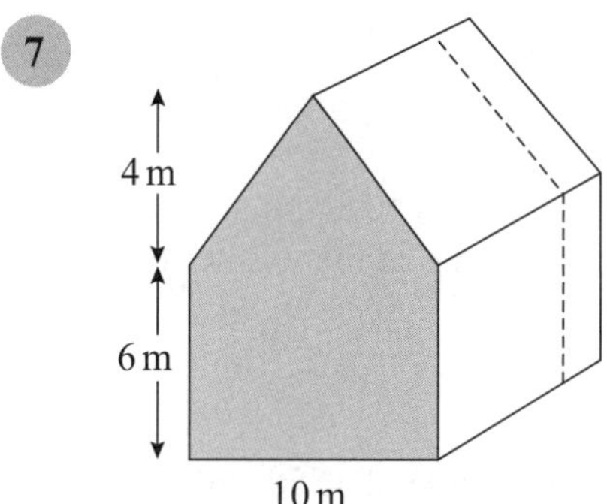

John owns a house with a volume of 1280 m^3. He wants to extend the house backwards using the entire cross section so that the volume of the house increases by 15%. How far will he extend the house backwards?

HWK 3M **Main Book page 400**

Give answers correct to 3 significant figures where necessary.

1 Find the volume of each prism.

a

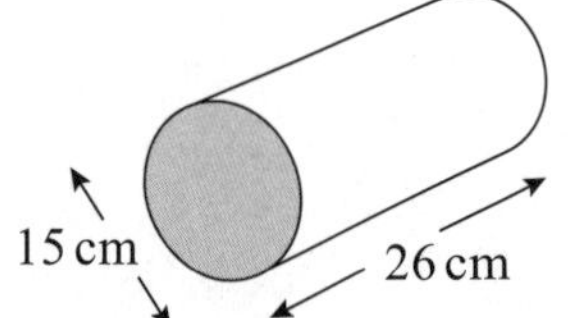

b

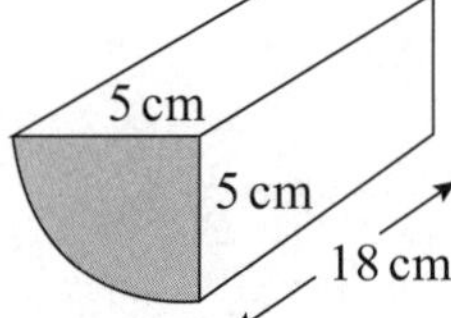

2 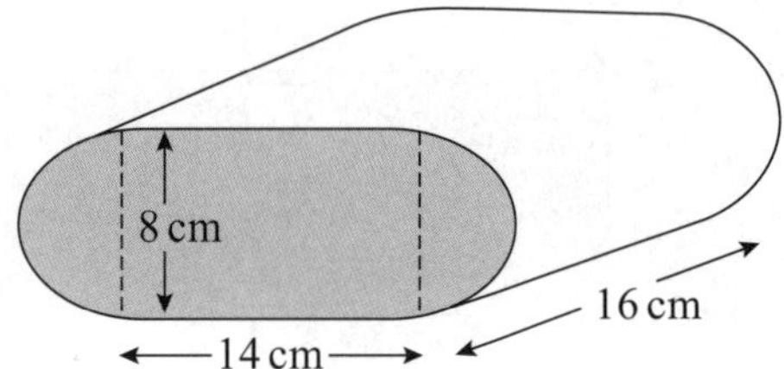

Calculate the volume of this prism.

3 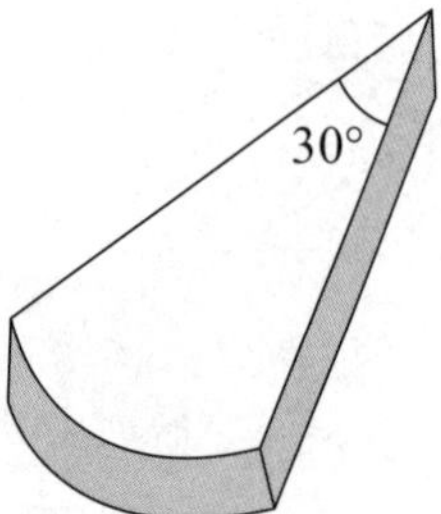

This slice of pie is cut from a circular pie of diameter 20 cm and thickness 5 cm. Calculate the volume of this slice.

4 A cylindrical glass has a diameter of 7.5 cm and a height of 10 cm. How many times can the glass be filled completely with juice from a rectangular carton measuring 21 cm × 13 cm × 8 cm?

5 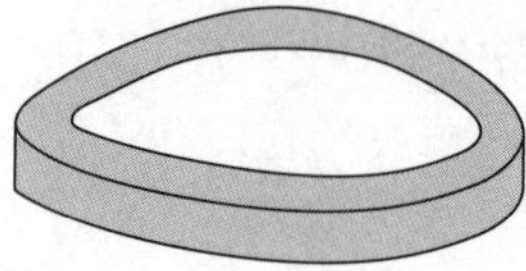

A rubber washer has an outside diameter of 18 mm and an inside diameter of 12 mm. Calculate the volume of the washer if its thickness is 3 mm.

6 Calculate the radius of a cylinder of height 12 cm which has a volume of 1550 cm^3

7 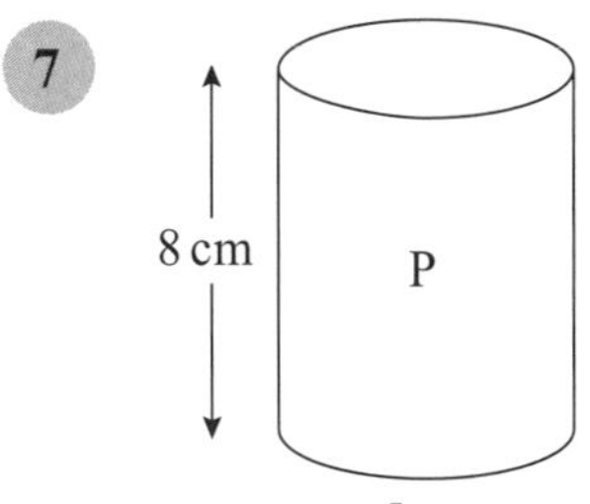

The cylinder is full of milk. All the milk is poured into the rectangular metal box. How far from the top of the box does the milk go up to?

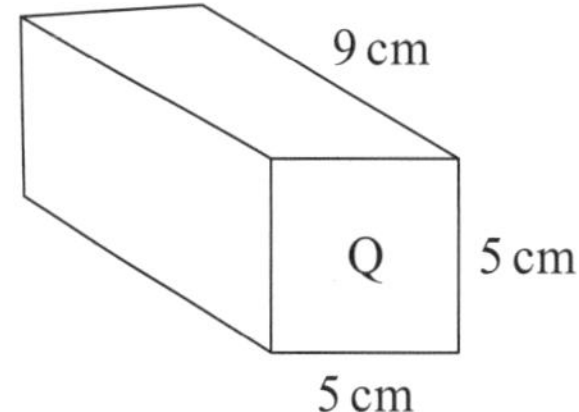

8 A 4 cm × 4 cm × 2 cm slab of chocolate is melted then made into twenty thin cylindrical chocolate sticks of diameter 4 mm. If 10% of the chocolate is wasted during the process, what is the length of one chocolate stick?

9 This rectangular piece of paper wraps perfectly around a tin can with no gaps at the top or bottom. Calculate the volume of the can.

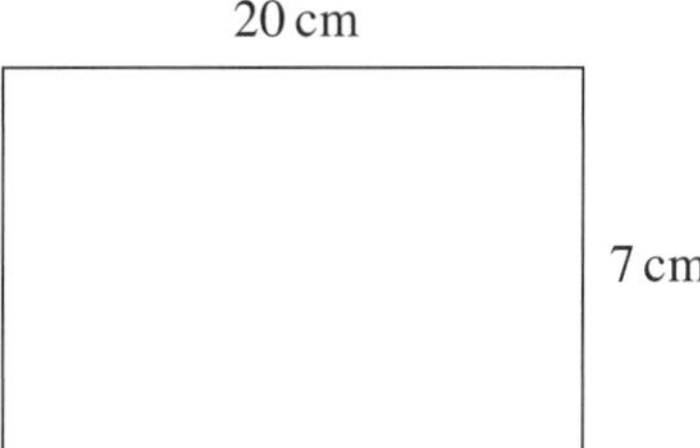

6.3 Drawing three-dimensional objects

HWK 1M **Main Book page 407**

A *plan view* is looking down on an object from above. In questions 1 to 4, draw the plan view, the front view and the side view of the object.

1 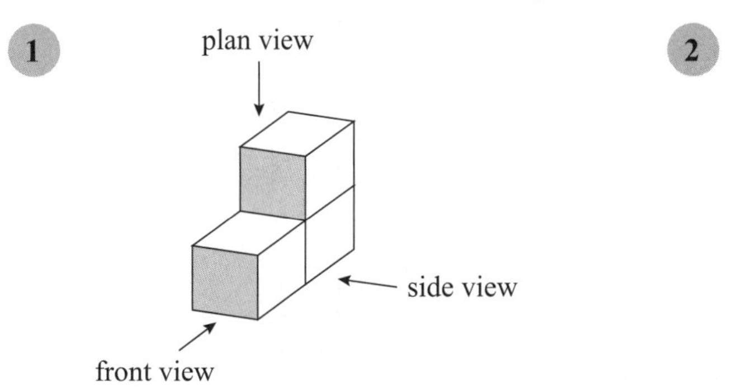

2 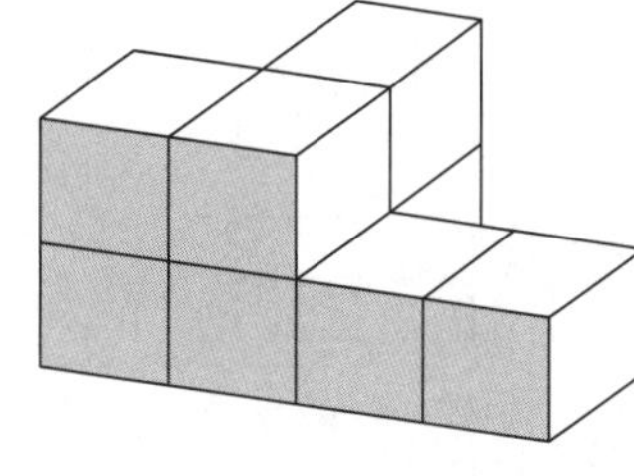

3

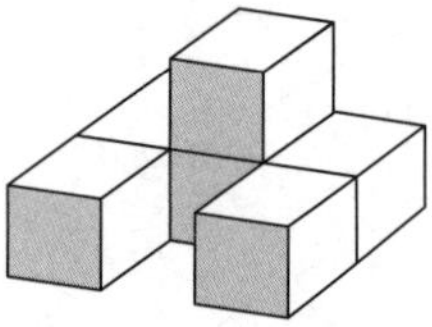

4

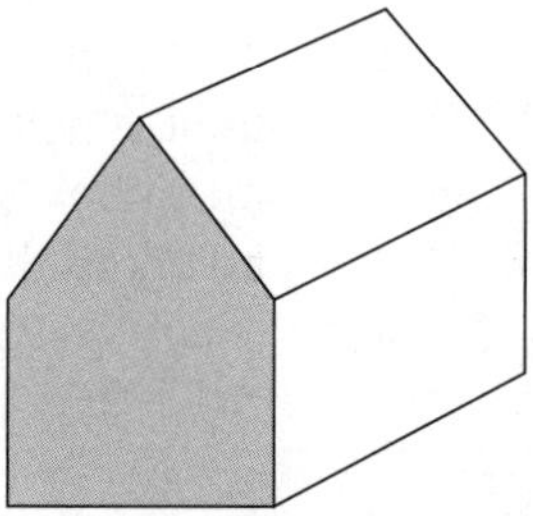

In questions **5** to **10** you are given three views of a shape. Draw each 3-D object (like those shown above).

5

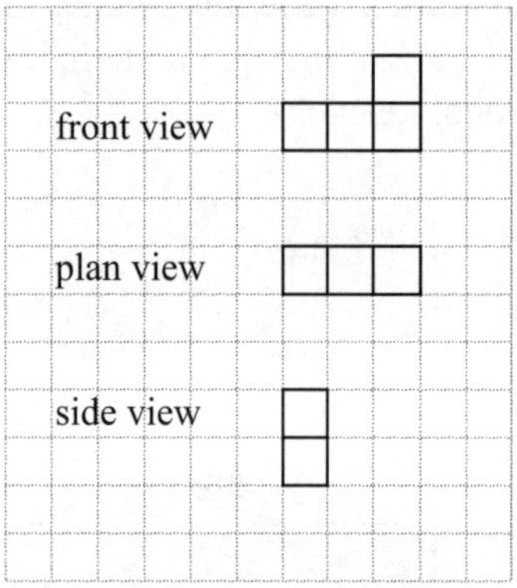

front view
plan view
side view

6

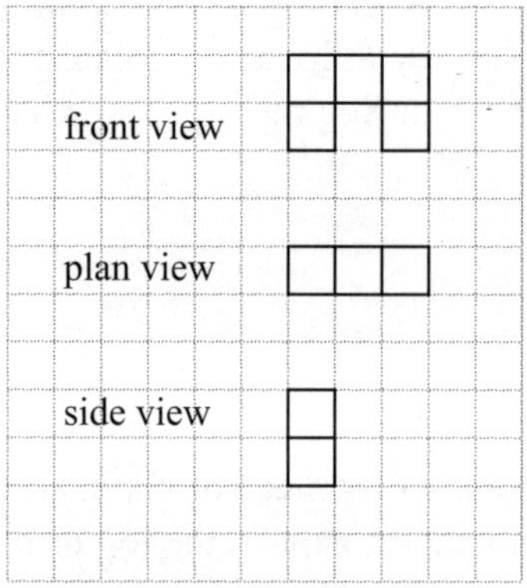

front view
plan view
side view

7

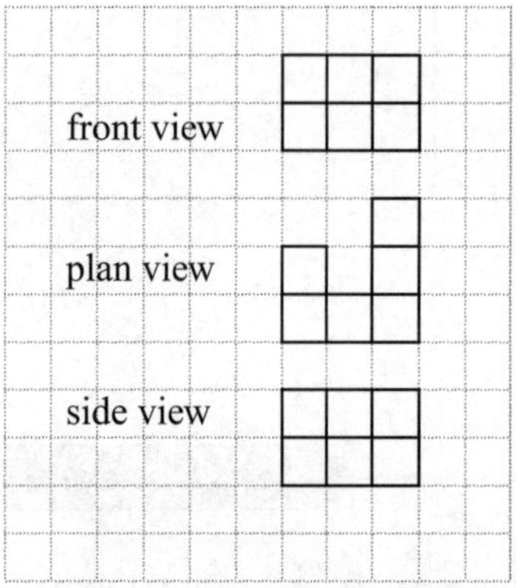

front view
plan view
side view

8

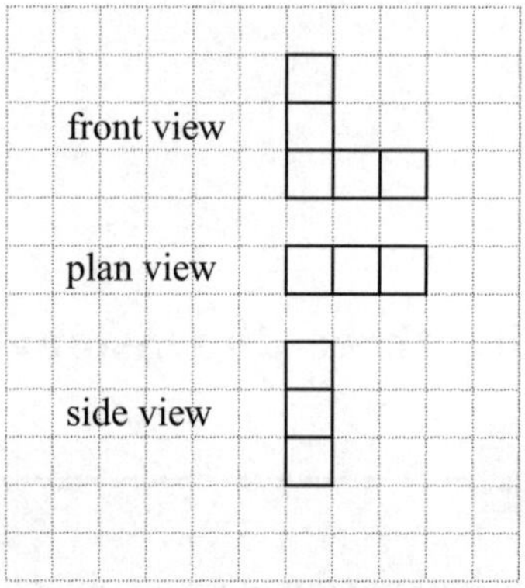

front view
plan view
side view

9

front view
plan view
side view

10

front view
plan view
side view

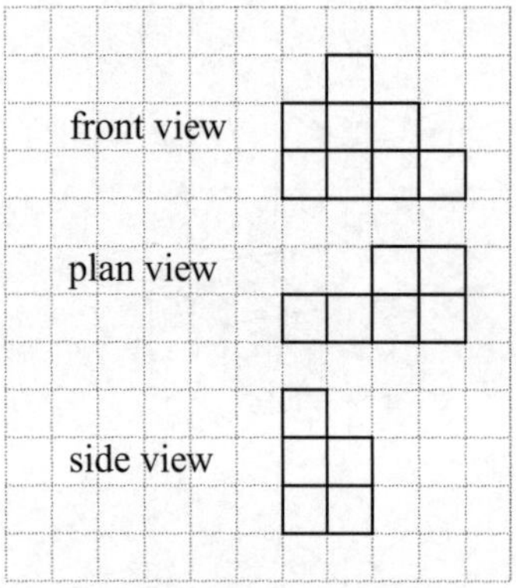

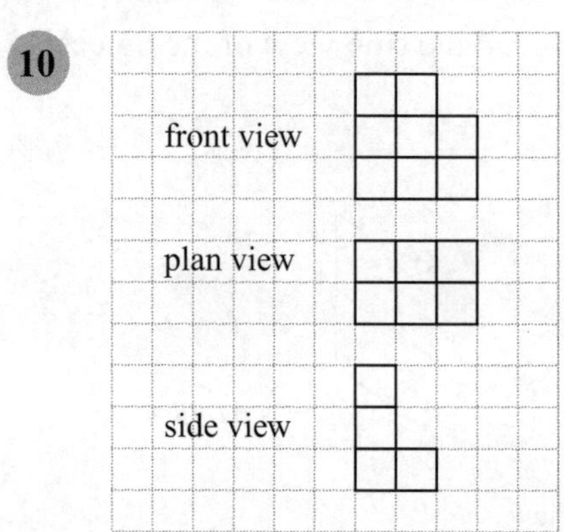

6.4 Simultaneous equations

HWK 1M — **Main Book page 415**

In questions 1 to 3, subtract the equations to eliminate the x terms.

1. $3x + 4y = 17$
   $3x + 2y = 13$
2. $2x + 3y = 14$
   $2x + y = 6$
3. $5x + 3y = 22$
   $5x - 2y = 2$

In questions 4 to 6, add the equations to eliminate the y terms.

4. $4x + 2y = 18$
   $3x - 2y = -4$
5. $2x - y = 5$
   $4x + y = 13$
6. $3x + 4y = 29$
   $7x - 4y = 1$

Solve

7. $2x + 3y = -1$
   $2x + y = -3$
8. $4x + 2y = -10$
   $x + 2y = 2$
9. $5x + 4y = 11$
   $2x - 4y = -18$
10. $3x - 5y = 19$
    $2x + 5y = -4$
11. $4x - 2y = 22$
    $4x - 3y = 23$
12. $2x + 3y = 1$
    $x + 3y = 5$
13. $2x + 3y = 13$
    $6x - 3y = -21$
14. $3x - 4y = 6$
    $4x - 4y = 4$
15. $5x - 2y = 3$
    $5x + 4y = -21$

HWK 2M — **Main Book page 416**

Multiply one equation first to solve each of the simultaneous equations below.

1. $2x + 3y = 14$
   $x + y = 6$
2. $2x + 2y = -2$
   $6x - 5y = -28$
3. $4x - 2y = 14$
   $3x + 4y = 5$

Multiply both equations first to solve each of the simultaneous equations below.

4. $3x + 2y = -6$
   $2x + 5y = 7$
5. $2x + 3y = 11$
   $5x + 2y = 0$
6. $3x + 4y = -13$
   $5x - 3y = 17$
7. $2x + 3y = 0$
   $7x - 5y = 31$
8. $4x - 6y = 14$
   $3x - 4y = 9$
9. $5x - 2y = -16$
   $3x - 3y = -6$

Solve

10. $5x + 3y = -7$
    $2x - 4y = -8$
11. $2x - 5y = 9$
    $3x + 4y = -21$
12. $3x - 2y = 10$
    $4x - 7y = 22$
13. $7x - 2y = -5$
    $3x + 5y = -8$
14. $4x - 3y = -27$
    $3x - 2y = -19$
15. $4x + 2y = 4$
    $5x - 7y = 24$

6.5 Probability trees

HWK 1M **Main Book page 419**

1. The probability of Julia getting homework on any day is 0.9. What is the probability of Julia getting homework on a Monday and a Tuesday?

2. The probability of Christian playing a computer game on any day is $\frac{3}{4}$. What is the probability that he will play a computer game on Saturday but not Sunday?

3. H O M E W O R K

   A card from above is chosen randomly. The card is then replaced and another card is taken. What is the probability that
   a both cards are the letter 'W'
   b the first card is the letter 'O' and the second card is not the letter 'O'?

4. The probability of a netball team winning a game is 0.6.
   What is the probability that the netball team will win the next 3 games?

5. There are 3 blue pencils, 2 red pencils and 4 green pencils in a pencil case. If I remove one pencil at random, replace it, then take another pencil, what is the probability that
   a both pencils are blue
   b both pencils are green
   c one pencil is blue and one pencil is red?

6. The probability of Molly hitting 'treble 20' with a dart is 0.2. What is the probability of Molly hitting 'treble 20' with
   a her next 2 darts
   b her next 3 darts?

7. A dice is thrown and the spinner is spun. What is the probability of getting two prime numbers?

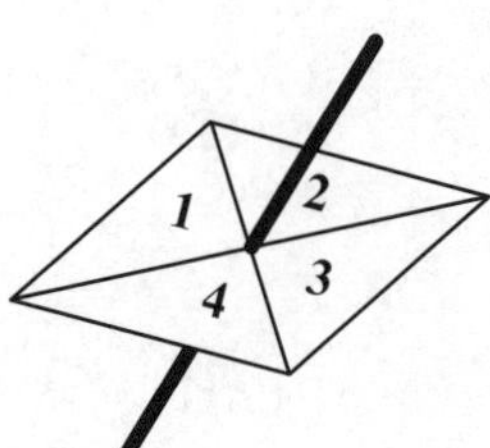

8. The probability of Gavin eating fruit on any day is 0.85. What is the probability that Gavin will eat fruit on one weekend day but not the other?

9 There are 52 cards in a pack. There are 13 clubs. A card is taken randomly, replaced, then another card is taken. What is the probability of choosing

a 2 clubs **b** 1 club and 1 card which is not a club?

10 A coin is thrown 6 times. What is the probability of getting 6 heads?

HWK 2M

Main Book page 420

1 On a Saturday morning, Alexa goes to a drama club, swims or visits her grandparents. The probability of going to the drama club is 0.6. The probability of swimming is 0.25

a Find the probability that Alexa goes to the drama club or visits her grandparents.

b Find the probability that Alexa visits her grandparents.

2 The table below shows the probability of Angus choosing particular toppings for a pizza.

ham	mushrooms	pepperoni	black olives	peppers
0.45	n	0.2	n	0.15

The probability of choosing mushrooms or black olives is the same for each. What is the probability of Angus choosing mushrooms?

3 In a Whitminster school, Years 7, 8 and 9 are allowed in the school canteen between 12:30 pm and 1 pm. The probability that the first student to walk through the canteen door is in Year 7 is $\frac{2}{5}$

The probability that the first student to walk through the canteen door is in Year 8 is $\frac{1}{4}$

What is the probability that the first student to walk through the canteen door

a is in Year 9

b is in Years 8 or 9?

4 The table below shows the probabilities of Will choosing certain fruits in a supermarket.

apple	pear	orange	peach	melon	banana
$\frac{1}{4}$	$\frac{1}{6}$	?	$\frac{1}{12}$	$\frac{1}{24}$	$\frac{1}{3}$

What is the probability of Will choosing

a an orange **b** a pear, melon or banana?

5 Zoe does jigsaws, plays board games or does puzzles. The probability of Zoe playing a board game is 0.35 and the probability of Zoe doing a puzzle is 0.2. What is the probability of Zoe doing

a a jigsaw **b** a jigsaw or a puzzle?

6 Some families have one pet only. A family is chosen at random. The table opposite shows the probabilities of the family having the pet indicated.

Dog	$\frac{2}{5}$
Rabbit	?
Cat	$\frac{1}{3}$
Guinea pig	$\frac{1}{15}$

a Which type of pet is the most popular?

b Find the probability of the family having a rabbit.

c Find the probability of the family having a dog or a cat.

HWK 3M **Main Book page 422**

1 The probability of Natalia going to work by train on any day is 0.9

a Copy and complete the tree diagram to show if Natalia goes to work by train on a Monday and Tuesday.

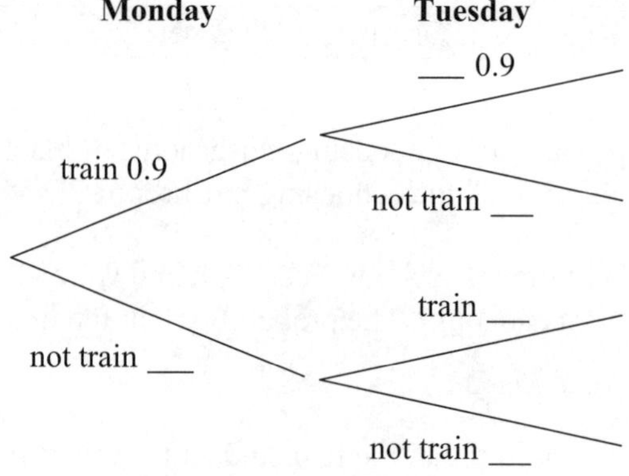

b Find the probability that

i Natalia goes to work by train on both days

ii Natalia goes to work by train on Monday but not by train on Tuesday.

2 There are 5 green tennis balls and 6 yellow tennis balls in a box. One tennis ball is removed at random then replaced. Another tennis ball is then removed.

a Copy and complete the tree diagram to show all the outcomes.

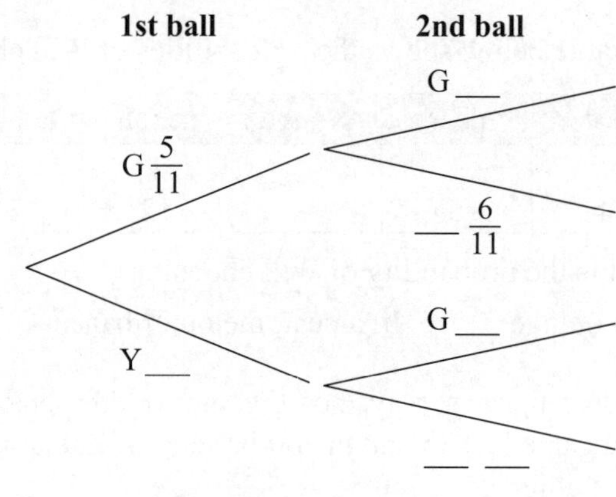

b Find the probability that

i both tennis balls are yellow

ii the first tennis ball is yellow and the second tennis ball is green

iii one tennis ball is yellow and one tennis ball is green.

3

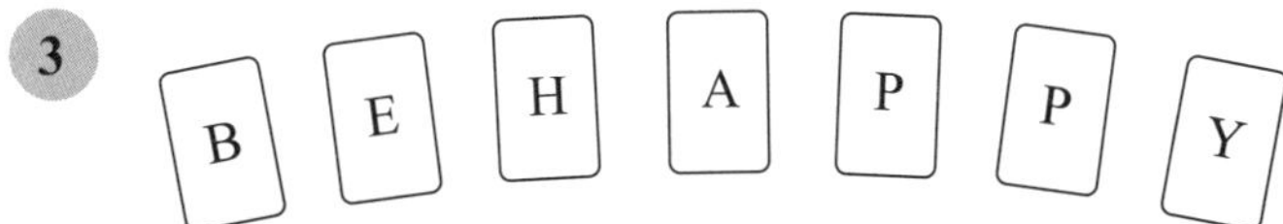

One of the above cards is removed at random then replaced. Another card is then removed.

a Draw a tree diagram to show if each card has a vowel on it or not.

b Find the probability that

- **i** no vowels are removed
- **ii** only one of the cards has a vowel on it.

4 Jiang tackles a crossword each week. The probability that he will complete the crossword is 0.7

a Draw a tree diagram to show if Jiang completes the crossword in each of 2 weeks.

b Find the probability that

- **i** Jiang completes the crossword each week
- **ii** Jiang completes the crossword during one week only
- **iii** Jiang completes the crossword during *at least* one week.

5 The probability that Sophie visits her cousin on 2 Sundays is $\frac{4}{9}$

a What is the probability that Sophie visits her cousin on any Sunday?

b Complete the tree diagram for whether Sophie visits her cousin on 2 Sundays.

c Work out the probability that Sophie will only visit her cousin on one Sunday.

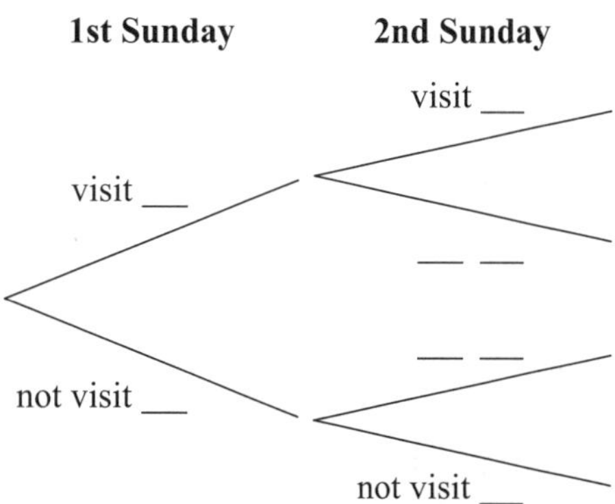

6 Every Tuesday evening Josh plays cricket, tennis or golf. The probability of Josh playing cricket is $\frac{1}{4}$ and the probability of Josh playing golf is $\frac{1}{6}$

a Copy and complete the tree diagram for 2 Tuesdays, showing what Josh does.

b Find the probability that

- **i** Josh plays tennis on both Tuesdays
- **ii** Josh plays the same sport on each of the Tuesdays.

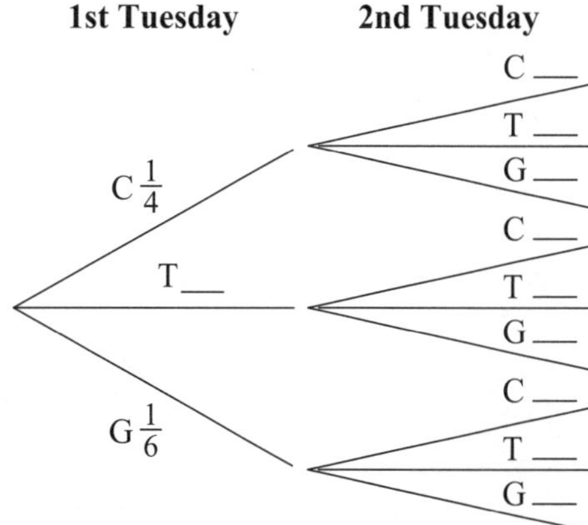

6.6 Geometry review

HWK 1M Main Book page 428

1 Work out the area of this trapezium.

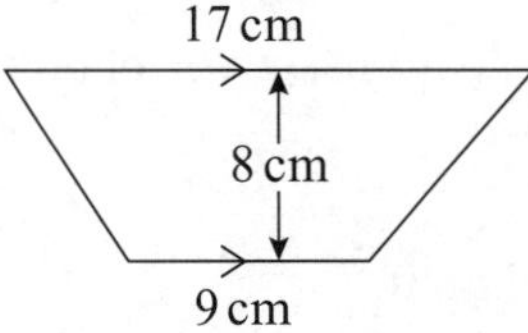

2 Work out the value of x.

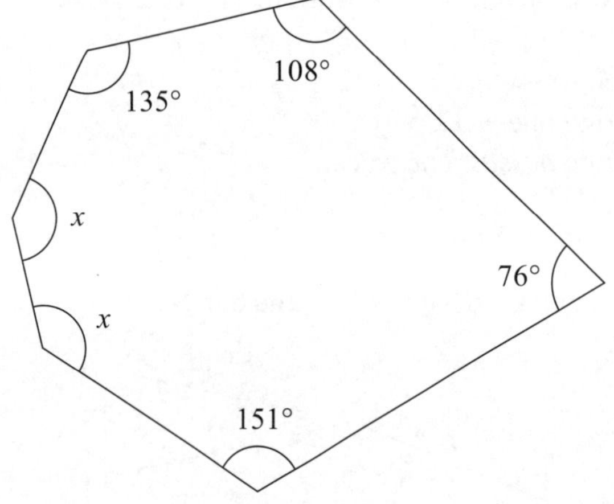

3 Work out the value of angle n.

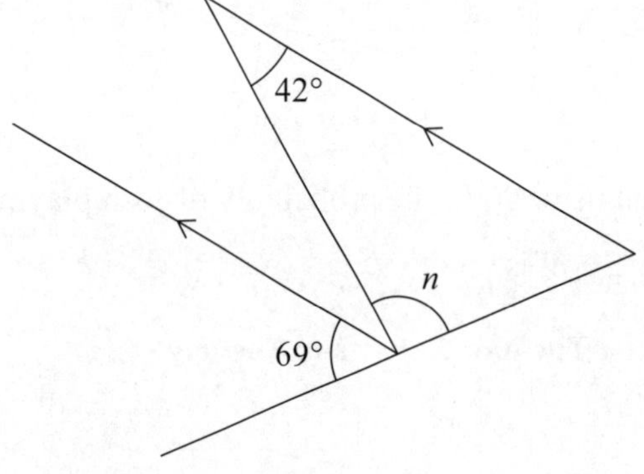

4 Which shape has the greater area and by how much: A or B?

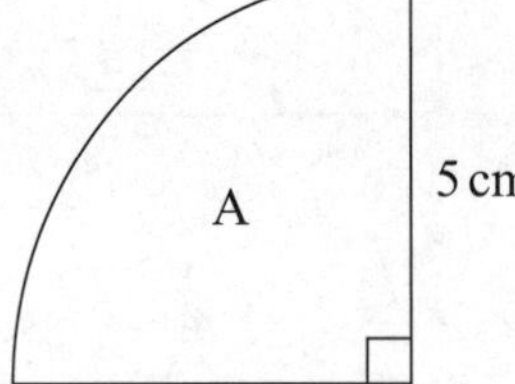

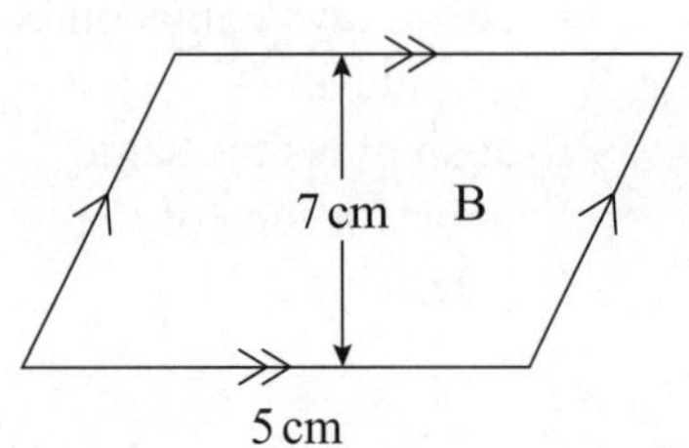

5 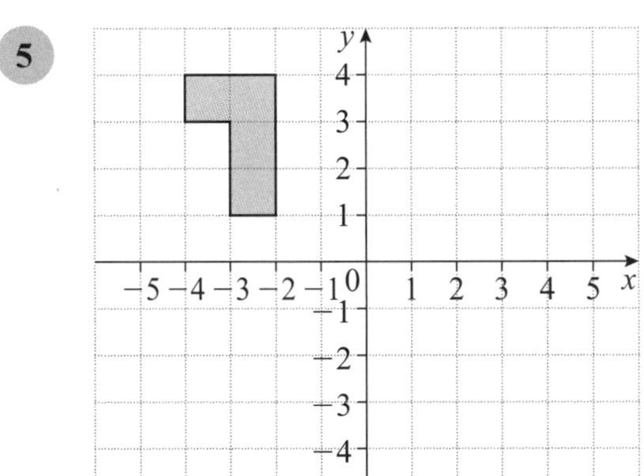

a Copy the diagram opposite.

b Rotate the shape 90° clockwise about (0, 0).

6 A 3.5 m ladder rests against a vertical wall, 2.3 m above the ground. How far is the bottom of the ladder from the wall?

7 What is the length of this prism if its volume is 336 cm^3?

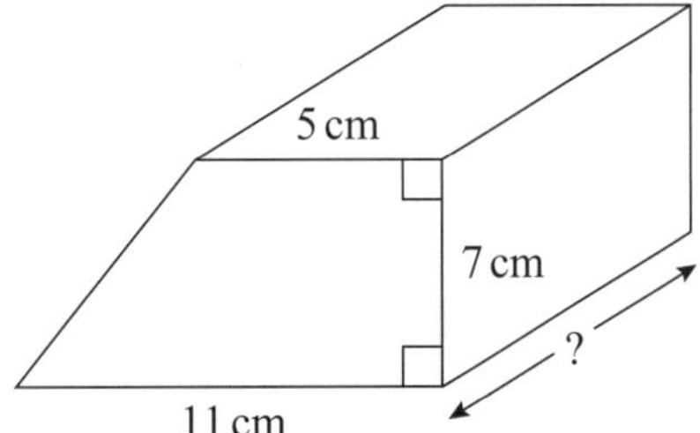

8 A circle fits inside an 18 cm square. Work out the shaded area.

18 cm

9 Work out the bearing of R from P.

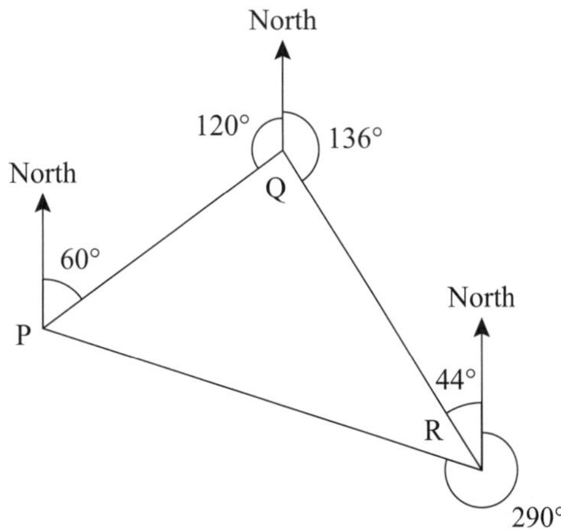

10

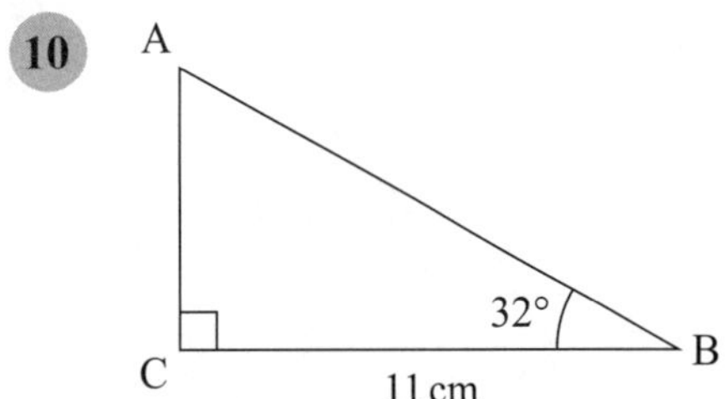

Work out the length AB.

HWK 2M Main Book page 430

1 A regular polygon, P, has exterior angles each equal to 15°. How many more sides does a regular polygon, Q, have if each of its exterior angles is 3° less than an exterior angle for polygon P?

2 Work out the difference between the perimeters of the triangle and the semicircle. Give the answer to 1 decimal place.

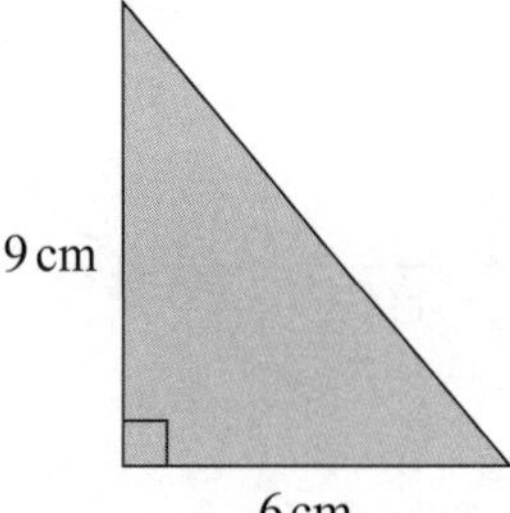

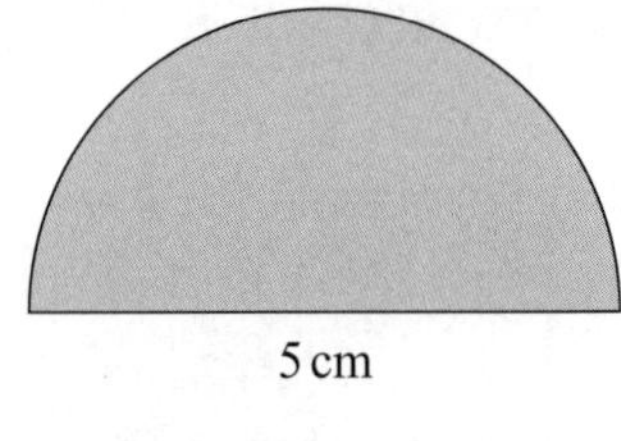

3 A shape is translated by $\begin{pmatrix} 2 \\ -4 \end{pmatrix}$. The shape is then translated back to its original position. Write down the translation vector which sends the shape back to its original position.

4

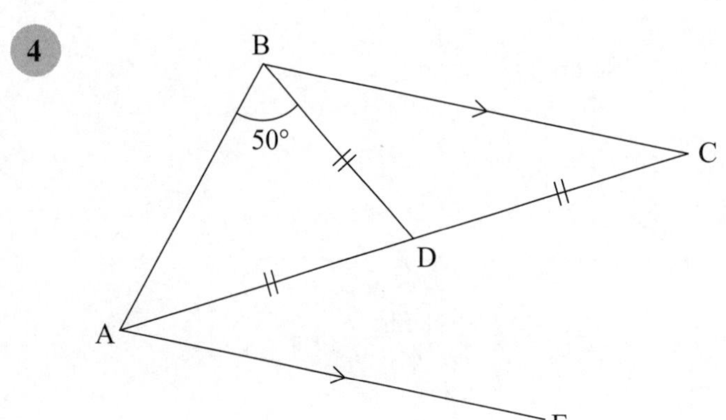

Work out the value of $B\hat{A}E$, giving full reasons for your answer.

5 Work out the area of this parallelogram.

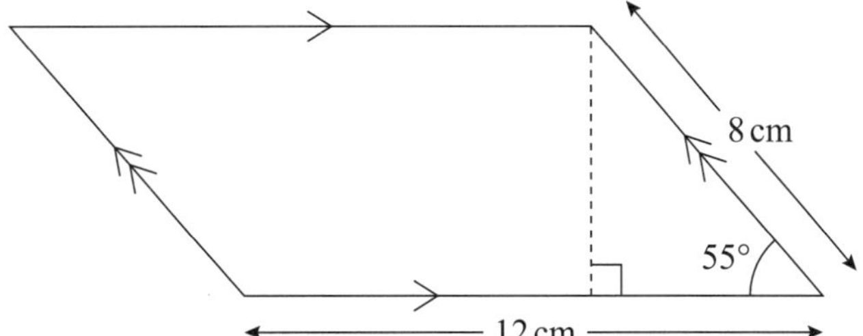

6

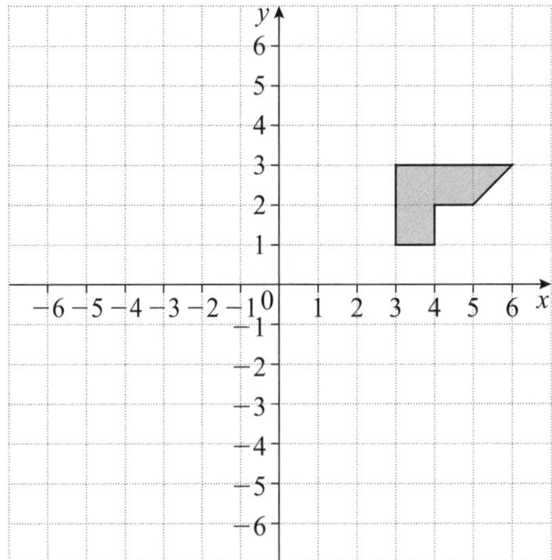

a Copy the diagram opposite.

b Reflect the shape in the line $y = x$.

7 P is 15 km due west of Q and R is 10 km due south of Q.
Calculate the bearing of R from P.

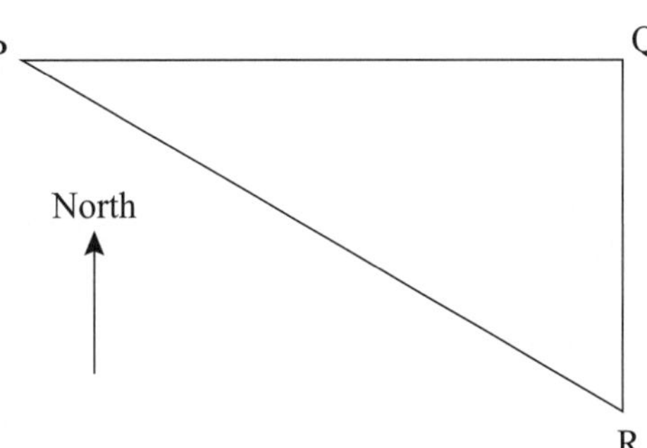

8 Write down the ratio of an interior angle of a regular pentagon to an interior angle of a regular decagon. Give the answer in its simplest form.

9 Work out the volume of this triangular prism.

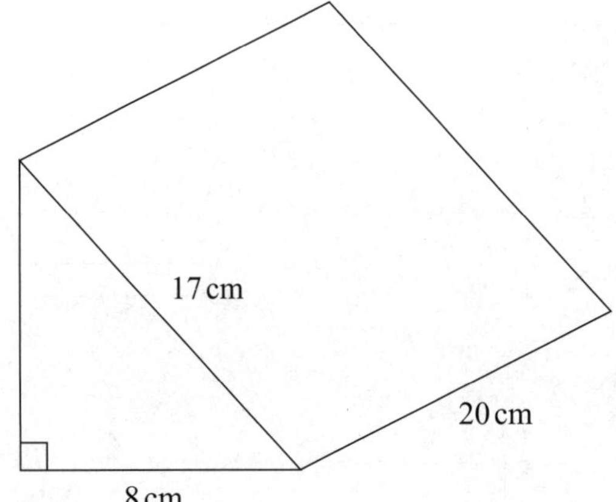

10

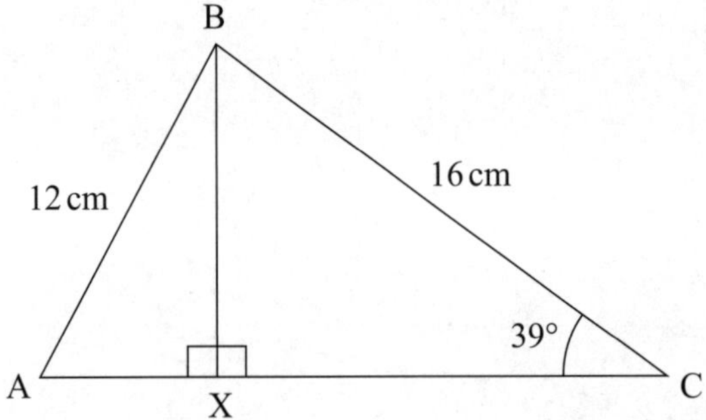

Calculate the area of triangle ABC.